Please Return to:

Eric Hoffman

With Love, From Dad

With Love, From Dad

by

Malcolm E. Smith

SUFFOLK HOUSE
155 East Main St.
Smithtown, N.Y. 11787

ISBN 0-936066-00-8

Printed in the United States of America

Library of Congress Catalog Card Number 78-70650

A FATHER'S PROJECT

It was almost 10 years ago that I first became alarmed that marijuana could be harming my children. Like all parents, I had little to go on. My warnings to my children were answered with the usual, "marijuana is no worse than tobacco or alcohol." I could not give them the facts necessary to convince them otherwise.

I determined to assemble those facts. This book is the result of that decision and an endless amount of time and effort spent in reading, researching and assembling what I believe is the most overwhelmingly convincing argument ever put together that marijuana is not only more dangerous than cigarettes and more dangerous than alcohol, but that it can cause irrevocable brain damage and adversely affect almost every part of the human body.

The source of every bit of information in this book is listed. The sources include eminent doctors in America and throughout the world, Nobel Prize winners, famous universities, leading hospitals, state and federal bureaus and agencies, medical associations, pharmacologists, toxicologists, medical journals, foreign governments, the United Nations, etc. etc.

There is no 'preaching' on my part . . . no 'sales talk' . . . no 'lecturing.' After all, nobody cares what I think about it any more than my children did when I warned them that marijuana is harmful. But there is no arguing against the endless array of medical findings, scientific research and evidence presented by all the experts and world famous institutions whose patient work has made this book possible.

Malcolm E. Smith

PREFACE

There exists in this country, as well as in countries throughout the world, an immense body of research on the harmful effects of marijuana, almost all of it unknown to the American people.

As early as 1970 there were 936 articles in English, 386 in French, 206 in German, 106 in Portugese, 74 in Spanish, 45 in the Slavic languages, and many more in Italian, Dutch, Turkish, Russian and other languages, and virtually none of them had anything favorable to say about marijuana.

Recently, a doctor at one university was reviewing 1800 published papers, the overwhelming majority of which dealt with its harmful effects.

Today an ever increasing body of material is being printed showing how marijuana can damage the brain, the glands, the body's organs, the lungs. There is extensive material on how it alters depth perception, which could cause fatal automobile accidents. Doctors warn that it may disrupt normal sexual differentiation during fetal development, can impair the body's hormone balance, cause birth defects, affect DNA, RNA and the immune response system, and, in the words of one well known writer, can be "permanently harmful to the human body."

Yet in spite of all that is known about marijuana's harmful effects, the common view of most Americans remains that marijuana can be used without concern.

This book is designed to correct that view. It presents the bad side of marijuana in the most compelling and convincing way imaginable. You can open it at any page you wish and find 3 or 4 short digests of, and excerpts from, the massive amount of material that has been printed. You will find 758 such short presentations, all adding up to the most devastating critique of marijuana ever assembled.

Some will point to marijuana's beneficial use in the treatment of cancer and glaucoma as a way to disparage the thrust of this book. But such use requires medical supervision, just as it is necessary in the use of chemotherapy and other drugs which are damaging to the body and are dispensed only with a prescription.

Not the least of marijuana's damaging effects is the manner in which it affects the minds of young people. On the following pages there is documentation of how marijuana undermines a person's drive, dissipates energy, leaves users without ambition, without the will to succeed—passive, lazy, disoriented, unable to make decisions. The head of one state's treatment foundation estimated that marijuana has probably damaged 20,000,000 people in this way. Other experts warn that such damage may be permanent.

Surely these facts should be known by all Americans.

TABLE OF CONTENTS

With Love, From Dad

Chapter I

HARMFUL EFFECTS ON THE BODY

1.
"MOUNTAIN OF SCIENTIFIC EVIDENCE IS BEGINNING TO ACCUMULATE"

A "mountain of scientific evidence is beginning to accumulate that marijuana use results in massive damage to the cellular process, to the reproductive system, and to the respiratory system.

"The principal ingredient in marijuana tends to accumulate in the brain and creates the serious possibility of brain damage, distortion of perception and reality, chronic passivity, and lack of motivation. These effects are all the more dangerous because its early use is deceptive: the marijuana user is not aware that an irreversible deterioration of mental functioning has begun.

"Other scientific data show that marijuana causes genetic damage and mutation, weakens immunity to disease, has a 'precancerous' effect on lung tissues, and severely damages the process by which cells are restored and replaced in a healthy body," reports Phyllis Schlafly.

2.
DOCTOR REPORTS ON FUNDAMENTAL BIOLOGICAL PROBLEMS FROM MARIJUANA USE

Dr. Robert L. DuPont stated that research done from 1973-1975, in both the U.S. and Switzerland, "all pointed toward possible fundamental

1

biological problems resulting from marijuana use. These new areas of concern include the effects of cannabis on DNA, the fundamental repository of genetic information; and on sex hormone (testosterone) levels. Other sources of concern included interference with the body's immune response, effects on fundamental cell metabolism and acute effects of marijuana intoxication including the effects on driving and work performance."

3.
NATIONAL INSTITUTE ON DRUG ABUSE REPORTS POSSIBLE BIOLOGICAL EFFECTS OF MARIJUANA USE

"Several areas of marijuana research findings which were highlighted in previous years have created considerable concern over the possible biological implications of cannabis use."

The possible effects involved, as reported by the National Institute on Drug Abuse, are:

"a. Impairment of the body's natural defense system against disease—i.e. interference with or depression of the immune response;

"b. Chromosomal alterations—i.e., increases in the number of abnormal chromosomes and a reduction in the number of chromosomes in some body cells;

"c. Basic alterations in cell metabolism;

"d. Impairment of endocrine functioning; specifically, a reduction in the male hormone testosterone and in growth hormone levels;

"e. Brain damage."

4.
"MOST POTENTIALLY DANGEROUS"

"Particularly impressive—and perhaps surprising—is the evidence on marijuana . . . facts show that of all drug users take for a strong sense of pleasure, marijuana is 'the most potentially dangerous'. Its impact on the brain, sexual function, and other body systems is accumulative. . . . It may also have an impact on the next generation. Marijuana smokers are likely to have more broken chromosomes in cultures of their white blood cells."

5.
HAZARDS OF LONG-TERM SMOKING

"Recent medical evidence indicates that long-term marijuana smoking in amounts currently used in the U.S. is associated with the following hazards: "Hormonal imbalance, inhibition of spermatogenesis, lung damage, impairment of immunity, increased formation of chromosome deficient cells with possible damage to offspring, interference with memory and speech and impairment of driving performance."

6.
DANGER SIGNALS

"Many of the damaging effects of marijuana are due to the accumulations of its active ingredients in the fatty tissues of the body, most notably the brain and sex glands. In anyone other than the occasional smoker, this continuous accumulation raises the possibility that damage may be done to the mental and reproductive functions. No one disputes the reality of these danger signals," reported several prominent physicians.

In their joint letter to the *New York Times*, Drs. W. Blanc, H. Clay Frick, W. M. Manger, and G. G. Nahas, as members of Columbia University's College of Physicians and Surgeons, stress that medical evidence shows marijuana has adverse long-term effects. These include "hormonal imbalance, impairment of spermatogenesis, lung damage, impairment of immunity, increased formation of chromosome-deficient cells with possible damage to the offspring, interference with DNA formation, decreased cell division, apathy and lack of motivation, interference with memory and speech and impairment of driving performance." They ask, "Why should the U.S. be the only country in the world where the harmful effects of marijuana, observed for centuries, are ignored?"

7.
SERIOUS EFFECTS NOT MENTIONED IN NEWS STORIES

"Usually popular reporting only mentions the relatively superficial physical effects such as, a slight rise in pulse rate and blood pressure. A more serious effect is that marijuana use can produce cancerous alterations in tissues faster and more thoroughly than tobacco smoke. Another serious effect is that THC interferes with the body's production of DNA which weakens the immunity system, making the user more susceptible to disease."

8.
LONG TERM SMOKERS FAR WORSE OFF THAN NONSMOKERS

Tharp, Paul, "Cannabis Conference: The Latest Word From Science," *The Village Voice*, February 9, 1976.

University of Florida Medical School physicians compared a sample of Costa Rican males who had smoked marijuana for ten years or more with nonsmokers. "Results showed that smokers experienced more weight loss, more gastrointestinal complaints, and jaundice—as well as atrophy of the testes. Additional tests showed smokers were more vulnerable to syphilis, and experienced eye aches and faulty color perception," reported Paul Tharp. All subjects in the study were matched for occupation, educational level, marital status, and tobacco and alcohol use.

9.
SCORES OF SCIENTISTS HAVE SHOWN EFFECT OF CANNABINOIDS IN BODY

"Scores of scientists," reported Gabriel G. Nahas, "have shown that cannabinoids decrease the incorporation of leucine into protein, uridine into RNA, thymidine into DNA, and choline into phospholipids, in brain, testis slice, or cell culture." These effects are evident at higher concentrations, but occasionally are seen at lower concentrations as well.

10.
THC CHANGED BY BODY'S ENZYMES INTO ACTIVE METABOLITES

The variation in the intoxicating effect of marijuana is related to the chemical compouition of THC. THC has been found by three scientists to be changed by enzymes. Enzymes change the molecular composition of chemicals so that they become inactive substances, or metabolites. After a drug, such as penicillin, performs its designated function, enzymes render it inactive. The body's handling of THC is quite different. THC is transformed by enzymes into *active* metabolites that have an even greater biological activity. The three scientists involved in this discovery are Dr. Monroe Wall of the Research Triangle Institute, Dr. Erminio Costa of the National Institute of Mental Health and Dr. Sumner Burstein of the Worcester Foundation.

11.
OVERUSE CAN SHORTEN LIFE EXPECTANCY

Dr. William Paton told the United States Senate Subcommittee on Internal Security that: "The price for overuse is paid in later life—cannabis reduces life expectancy from about seventy-five years to seventy."

12.
SUBTLE AND INSIDIOUS

"In general the effects of the drug (marijuana) continue to be noted as subtle and insidious. I would like to emphasize one way to describe the effect of cannabis: it is subtle and insidious, but harmful reactions in the heart and circulatory system are suspected, and there are indications of adverse reaction in the body's anti-infection chemistry."

This was part of Dr. Henry Brill's opening statement to the United States Senate Internal Security Subcommittee in 1974 as Regional Director of the New York State Department of Mental Hygiene. Commenting on a report by M. Beaubrum, in the Jamaica Psychiatric News, he also said, "I may add that in my own view marijuana must still be classed as a dangerous drug, dangerous to enough people to warrant full control."

13.
MARIJUANA AFFECTS MANY BODY SYSTEMS

Dr. Hardin B. Jones and Helen C. Jones wrote that "In addition to the brain, marijuana has been observed to affect the liver and the respiratory, reproductive, and blood cell systems.

14.
AMA ADVISES PHYSICIANS THAT MARIJUANA IS A MEDICAL PROBLEM

Excerpt from THE SEEKERS by Jess Stearn. Copyright © 1968, 1969 by Jess Stern. Used by permission of Doubleday & Company, Inc.

Based on evidence accumulated all over the country, the American Medical Association reported that marijuana is definitely a medical problem: "It is important . . . for the physician to remember that a person who has a psychological dependence on marijuana is sick and deserving of understanding and treatment, even though he may have been involved in unlawful activity." A chronic user, the AMA warns, may be symptomizing "serious underlying personality problems, severe conflicts or psychotic reactions."

15.
BIOCHEMICAL ACTIONS IN LIVER, KIDNEYS, ETC.

Some of the biochemical actions of marijuana are "uncoupling of oxidative phosphorylation in liver, activation or inhibition of ATPase (according to conditions in liver, cell culture or red cells); stimulation of adenyl cyclase; inhibition of liver microsomal enzymes; inhibition of prostaglandin synthesis in seminal vesicle, kidney and synaptosomes," according to Dr. Gabriel G. Nahas.

16.
HARMFUL EFFECTS CITED IN 1894 REPORT NOW BEING SUBSTANTIATED SCIENTIFICALLY

"It is interesting to note that the damage to the lungs, brain, and liver; suppressed semen production; intestinal disturbances; and general debilitation of health from cannabis use reported by witnesses in the 1894 Indian Hemp Drugs Commission Report are now being substantiated scientifically."

17.
LOW POTENCY MARIJUANA INCREASED HEARTBEAT AND CAUSED MUCOUS MEMBRANE CONGESTION

Essentially all of the prisoner-volunteers in the La Guardia Report exhibited signs of increased heartbeat (tachycardia) and congestion of the mucous membranes of the eye (conjunctivae) after smoking marijuana. This startled many people because the potency of the marijuana used in the study was below the strength of the marijuana smoked by many people today.

18.
PRACTICING PHYSICIANS FIND 16 PHYSICAL EFFECTS

Excerpt from THE SEEKERS by Jess Stearn. Copyright © 1968, 1969 by Jess Stearn. Used by permission of Doubleday & Company, Inc.

Some of the physical effects of marijuana are: Disturbance of the normal blood pressure reflexes, bloodshot eyes, an affinity for light, muscular incoordination, spasms, increase in appetite, vomiting, urinary frequency, diarrhea, cold extremities and white fingertips (a Raynaud-like syndrome), lowered temperatures, excessive dilating of pupils, dryness of mouth, nausea and respiratory depression, stated one issue of *Medical Letter on Drugs and Therapeutics* prepared by a distinguished group of practicing physicians.

19.
DIFFERING EFFECTS OF MARIJUANA

Researchers for the Western Electric Company noted that "the effects of smoking marijuana are often similar in many respects to those of alcohol. The marijuana user will speak freely, daydream and appear in a state of semisedation. However, the overall effect of the drug is predicted largely by the user's personality and the presence of others in the room who are having similar sensations. After five or ten minutes, many users have a feeling of restlessness and anxiety. Speech becomes rapid, time appears to pass slowly, distances may appear shortened, memory deteriorates and concentration becomes difficult. Large amounts of marijuana may produce hallucinations after 20 to 25 minutes. The total effects of a marijuana "trip" can last from three to five hours."

20.
FORMER BUREAU OF NARCOTICS FOUND MANY ADVERSE EFFECTS

"During the early years of increasing use of marijuana, Donald E. Miller of the Bureau of Narcotics (now the Drug Enforcement Administration) opposed acceptance of the concept that marijuana was harmless. In 1967 he said . . . "marijuana use affects coordination of the limbs, causes the pulse rate to rise, lowers body temperature, increases appetite, inflames the mucous membranes and bronchial tubes.

"Other effects include fantasia, exhilaration of mood; the feeling of being above reality; there is a loss of timing, minutes seem like hours; and there is often uncontrollable hilarity over something which is not particularly amusing to a normal person."

When larger doses are used, "extremely vivid hallucinations often occur; there may be panic and fear of death; illusions; periods of paranoia; and a high enough dose can result in a condition resembling toxic psychosis."

21.
MAJOR GENERAL TESTIFIES ON HARMFUL EFFECTS

"As to the physical impact of cannabis used in small amounts by the casual or recreational user, it may interfere to a degree with physical performance which depends upon visual function. In relatively high doses which are common to the daily user of hashish or oil of hashish, cannabis regularly produces hallucinogenic effects, abnormal sensations such as numbness, difficulty with thinking, concentration or speaking, and altered perceptions.

"Cannabis use may be associated with certain less severe psychological reactions, such as depressive and panic reactions, particularly in inexperienced users . . . Other research shows that it is also probable that cannabis is a factor in some cases of chronic psychosis and lack of motivation. . . ." explained Major General Frank B. Clay, Deputy Assistant Secretary of Defense, Drug and Alcohol Abuse, in testimony before the Internal Security Subcommittee in 1974.

22.
BIOLOGICAL REACTIONS TO POT

"Pulse rate is regularly increased, the mechanism not yet being worked out," reported Dr. L.E. Hollister. "Effects on blood pressure are variable, with reports of an increase, no change, or a decrease. The latter certainly occurs with high doses of THC, where orthostatic hypotension may be of such a degree as to cause fainting. Respiratory rate is said to be increased, as well as the amplitude of thoracic excursions; other evidence, such as the sensitivity of the respiratory center to accumulated carbon dioxide, also suggests a stimulant effect."

23.
CLINICAL STUDY DESCRIBES RESULTS OF INTOXICATION

Reese T. Jones and Neal Benowitz, "The 30 Day Trip—Clinical Studies of Cannabis Tolerance and Dependence," in *Pharmacology of Marihuana*, vol. 2., eds. M.C. Braude and S. Szara (New York: Raven Press, 1976), pp. 631-632.

On the first few days of a study conducted by Reese T. Jones, the subjects experienced a pleasant and moderate degree of intoxication due to 70-mg. doses of THC. Nevertheless, when the dosage was increased to 140 to 210 mg., a lethargic, sluggish and sedated state followed. This state was described as unpleasant.

Some of the symptoms reported during the maximum-dose period were sleepiness, impaired coordination, brief feelings of internal arousal, lethargy, muscle tension and soreness, impaired concentration, dry throat and mouth, and abdominal discomfort.

The clinical signs exhibited included slow speech, conjunctival injection, ataxia, pallor, lethargy, eyelid ptosis, postural dizziness and nystagmus.

24.
CANNABIS PRODUCES MANY UNPLEASANT EFFECTS

"For a drug supposedly taken for pleasure, dysphoria and anxiety are surprisingly common results of taking cannabis. Malaise, nausea, vomiting, giddiness, visceral feelings of panic, muscle discomfort, headache, palpitations, uneasiness and 'feeling tight inside' are reported symptoms, and it appears in general that onset of action, even in the experienced, commonly has unpleasant somatic effects," reported Drs. Paton and Pertwee.

25.
NATIONAL EDUCATIONAL ASSOCIATION STUDY FINDS MANY ADVERSE EFFECTS

According to a study prepared by the National Educational Association, in conjunction with Smith Kline and French Laboratories, "the mental effects (of marijuana) include a feeling of euphoria, exaltation and a dreamy sensation accompanied by a free flow of ideas. Senses of time, distance, vision and hearing are distorted. Sometimes panic and fear are experienced. Hallucinations may develop with large doses. The initial period of stimulation is frequently followed by a moody reverie and drowsiness. The user's ability to perform many tasks normally or safely—particularly automobile driving—is seriously impaired.

"Other effects of marijuana include dizziness, dry mouth, dilated pupils and burning eyes, urinary frequency, diarrhea, nausea and vomiting, and hunger, particularly for sweets."

26.
BIOCHEMICAL AND PSYCHOLOGICAL ASPECTS TO MARIJUANA

Dr. Gabriel G. Nahas reports that marijuana has a biochemical as well as a psychological aspect to it: ". . . When one smokes marijuana there is a change of biochemistry which is triggered and which will occur each time one smokes marijuana."

27.
A REPORT FROM THE NEW YORK STATE NARCOTIC CONTROL COMMISSION

"The immediate effects experienced by a marijuana smoker vary with the quality, amount and frequency of the marijuana smoked and with his own personality. They also depend on his attitude and the setting and circumstances under which it is smoked. When smoking marijuana, the individual first experiences euphoria and exaltation—he feels that all is well with the world.

"As the drug's effects become more pronounced, his senses of time, distance, vision, and hearing may become distorted. A minute may seem like an hour; his eyes may focus on one object—to the exclusion of all others; hearing may be confined to a single sound or tone; he believes that some disjointed ramblings are profound statements; he finds that his concentration is weakened and that he has difficulty recalling recent events.

"Physically, the smoker experiences a slight increase in pulse rate, slight tremors, congestion of the eyes, some muscle incoordination and a subtle retardation of speech."

These passages are taken from a pamphlet on marijuana distributed by the New York State Narcotic Addiction Control Commission.

28.
GREEK BIOCHEMIST REPORTS: MARIJUANA HAS SAME DAMAGING ABILITY AS HASHISH

Excerpt from THE SEEKERS by Jess Stearn. Copyright © 1968, 1969 by Jess Stearn. Used by permission of Doubleday & Company, Inc.

Constandinos Miras, a Greek biochemist reported that marijuana is another form of hashish and although it is a weaker form it has the same ability for damaging eyes, liver, brain and the respiratory system. "There are those . . . who have tried to tell me the two are different, but I have seen no evidence of this," he stated.

29
ADVERSE REACTION IN MONKEYS SIMILAR TO THOSE IN HUMANS

Dr. Raphael Mechoulam of Israel injected monkeys with THC. The symptoms shown by these animals were loss of muscle strength, decline of aggression, impairment of motor skills, drooping eyelids, increased heartbeat and indifference to environment. These symptoms are all similar to those of humans who are stoned on pot.

30.
ADVERSE EFFECTS FOUND FROM THC AND CRUDE MARIJUANA ADMINISTERED TO RATS

Harris Rosenkrantz, "Cellular, Immunological, and Hormonal Effects," in *Pharmacology of Marihuana*, vol. 1., eds. M.C. Braude and S. Szara (New York: Raven Press, 1976), p. 141.

Large doses of THC and crude marijuana extract were administered orally for 28 days to Fisher rats. The marijuana extract and the THC induced a decrease in the total nucleated cell counts (29%) and initiated a bone marrow hypocellularity in some of these rats. Furthermore, pituitary, testicular, and prostatic weights were depressed and adrenal weights increased.

31.
HARMFUL EFFECTS ON YOUNG RATS

Dr. Peter A. Fried of Carlton University in Canada conducted experiments in which rats were exposed to marijuana smoke. The young rats suffered a decrease in body weight, and had smaller brains and hearts in relation to their total body weight.

32.
REACTION TO POT IS NOT ALWAYS THE SAME

In discussing the effect of marijuana on the user, the American Medical Association stated that ". . . neither potency of the drug, regularity of use, or combined use with alcohol or other substances is an absolute factor. As with other psychoactive drugs, size of dose and frequency of ingestion are variables interacting with the route of administration, the setting in which the drug is taken, and, most important of all, the complex physiological and psychological makeup of the user."

33.
OVER 50% OF HASHISH USERS REPORTED SPECIFIC HASHISH-RELATED AILMENTS

Dr. Forest S. Tennant, Jr., former Chief of the Special Action Office for Drug Abuse, U.S. Army in Europe, outlined the results of a study conducted in 1971 in which 1,018 U.S. Army soldiers were surveyed by anonymous questionnaires. They were asked if using cannabis adversely affects them. 492 of the group (48%) responded that they had used hashish in West Germany. "This group of hashish smokers stated that the drug caused the following problems:

"1. Bronchitis, 30 out of 492 smokers, 6.1 percent.
"2. Sore throat, 122 out of 492 smokers, 24.8 percent.
"3. Running nose, 43 out of 492 smokers, 8.7 percent.
"4. Diarrhea, 23 out of 492 smokers, 4.7 percent.
"5. Headache, 70 out of 492 smokers, 14.2 percent.
"6. Emotional problems, 42 out of 492 smokers, 8.5 percent.
"7. No bad effects, 205 out of 492 smokers, 41.7 percent."

Over 50 percent of the hashish users, therefore, reported physical ailments after use of the drug.

34.
EFFECTS OF MARIJUANA ON EXPERIENCED USERS SEEN IN 20 MINUTES

Edward F. Domino et al., "Short-Term Neuropsychopharmacological Effects of Marihuana Smoking in Experienced Male Users," in *Pharmacology of Marihuana*, vol. 1., eds. M.C. Braude and S. Szara (New York: Raven Press, 1976), p. 411.

Domino, Rennick, and Pearl studied the effects of various doses of marijuana cigarettes (containing either 0%, 1.5%, or 2.9% delta-9-THC) on experienced marijuana users. The twelve subjects of this study were physically and mentally healthy with the exception of having smoked marijuana for at least the previous year.

These investigators observed dose-related changes within 20 minutes after smoking. Some of the alterations observed after some of the subjects had smoked the 2.9% delta-9-THC marijuana were decreased palpebral fissures, slightly elevated diastolic and systolic blood pressure, decreased clear thinking, increased heart rat, and increased dizziness.

35.
VERY HEAVY USERS RUN RISK OF HYPOXIA

In a test of 30 chronic users and 30 nonusers, "chronic, heavy smokers (more than 20 tobacco cigarettes per day, plus chronic ganja (marijuana) smoking by spliff and/or pipe) are at greater risk of functional hypoxia, i.e., deficiency of oxygen in body tissues," reported Rubin and Comitas.

36.
IMPAIRMENT OF BODY FUNCTIONS

L.E. Hollister notes that some of the changes resulting from the use of cannabis are a drooping of the eyelids (ptosis), an impairment of hand and body steadiness, and an increase in muscle weakness.

37.
PULSE RATE INCREASES . . . BLOOD SUGAR DECREASES

After smoking marijuana, the user experiences an increase in pulse rate and a rise in blood pressure. In addition the user's rate of metabolism increases. Then the level of blood sugar decreases and the user becomes very hungry, especially for sweets. There is also a need to urinate.

38.
SURGEON GENERAL DESCRIBES PHYSICAL EFFECTS

Dr. Jesse L. Steinfeld, Surgeon General of the United States Public Health Service, described some of the physical effects of marijuana use:
"The most frequent physical effect of marijuana is a conjunctival hyperemia (red eye). This is not due to an irritative smoke effect, because it also occurs when THC is swallowed . . .
"While an increase in heart rate is regularly noted, blood pressure, respiratory rate, blood sugar level, and body temperature do not change significantly. Nausea, a dry mouth from decreased salivation, and a cough from the irritant effects of the smoke are often mentioned."

39.
AFFECTS NEARLY EVERY BODY FUNCTION

"Marijuana is a drug with multifaceted action on nearly every body function: brain, heart, lung and endocrine. No scientist can refer to it as a 'mild intoxicant'." This is the consensus of a three-day international meeting organized by the National Institute on Drug Abuse held in December of 1974. Participants heard no less than 67 papers.

40.
SMOKING MARIJUANA CAUSES GREATER EFFECTS THAN INJECTING THE SAME QUANTITY

"An early study suggested that the route of administration did not matter much, with effects being about equal regardless of whether the drugs were injected, ingested, or smoked, only that the rapidity of onset of clinical effects was faster with smoking. A subsequent study with THC of known composition indicated an almost three-fold potentiation of action when the material was smoked. That such is the case seems to be confirmed by users who prefer to smoke, rather than ingest, the same amount of marijuana in order to attain greater effects," reported Dr. L. E. Hollister.

41.
9 WITHDRAWAL SYMPTOMS NOTED IN GERMANY

One research report from Germany notes that some of the physical symptoms that occurred following the discontinuance of marijuana use included: nausea, vomiting, diarrhea, sweating, irritability, restlessness, lack of appetite, inability to sleep, and tremors.

42.
ALLERGIC REACTION TO MARIJUANA

In the May 1978 issue of *Science Digest,* Dr. I.R. Rosengard reported one of the more unusual reactions to marijuana: "Recently, a single case report describes an extreme allergic response in a 29-year-old woman after smoking a marijuana cigarette for the first time. Skin tests gave positive evidence of allergy to marijuana constituents. Researchers reported the case felt that, in view of the large number of people reported to have used marijuana and the paucity of reports of allergic reactions, the alergenic potential of marijuana may be quite low. It was noted, however, that other factors might prevent reporting of similar cases and, if this were the case, marijuana allergy might be more common than supposed."

43.
MORE HARMFUL EFFECTS OF MARIJUANA

In his *Manual of Pharmacology*, Torald Sollman states that it takes about two grains of marijuana extract in solid form to produce the effects of loss of appetite and dryness of the mouth followed by intense thirst. Sollman indicates that the drug's effects vary in kind and degree with respect to the individual, his personality, disposition, and environment.

44.
POSSIBLE RESULTS OF CHAIN SMOKING HIGH POTENCY MARIJUANA

"The chain smoking of high-potency marijuana, although it is not common in the U.S., results in a prolonged coma."

45.
ADVERSE REACTIONS TO POT REPORTED IN 1944 SIMILAR TO THOSE REPORTED NOW

In 1944 Dr. S. Allentuck administered marijuana to 78 subjects. He noted that the subjects experienced difficulties in concentration and euphoria frequently; with anxiety, excitement and dysphoric reactions occurring in only some of the subjects.

46.
MARIJUANA USERS TEND TO BE THIN AND UNDERDEVELOPED

In reference to body composition, Dr. Hardin B. Jones says that ". . . the young marijuana user tends to remain thin and to be underdeveloped for his age. The trend is more pronounced with heavy use. The daily marijuana user of several years duration is likely to appear emaciated. The buttocks are thin; the facial muscles are atrophied."

47.
STUDY TEAM FINDS THREE EFFECTS ON BODY FUNCTIONS

A study team led by Dr. I.R. Rosengard reported the effects of marijuana on hearing as affecting "the awareness of the subtle qualities of sound." Another common reaction is "the subjective enhancement of the non-dominant senses, such as touch, taste, and smell . . ." Thirdly, marijuana intoxication radically changes perception of space and time.

48.
EFFECTS OF LARGE DOSES ADMINISTERED TO MONKEYS

Harris Rosenkrantz, "Cellular, Immunological, and Hormonal Effects," in
Pharmacology of Marihuana, vol. 1, eds. M.C. Braude and S. Szara (New York:
Raven Press, 1976), p. 141.

In the laboratory of Harris Rosenkrantz and his associates, large doses of
THC and marijuana extracts were given orally to monkeys. Some of the
results of this study: decrease in testicular weight, occurrence of thymus
atrophy and elevation of adrenal weight. In conjunction with diminished
total nucleated counts, bone marrow hyperplasia was observed.

49.
DIABETIC COMA RESULTS FROM EATING LARGE AMOUNT OF MARIJUANA

A young male with no previous history of any diabetic symptoms and no
family history of adult onset diabetes, ate a large amount of marijuana over a
three-day period. The result was a severe diabetic coma and ketoacidosis.

50.
EASTERN AND WESTERN RESEARCH REPORTS PHYSICAL EFFECTS OF CANNABIS USE

"A number of minor physical effects associated with use of cannabis are
reported by Eastern and Western writers. Such things as weight loss,
gastrointestinal complaints, congestion of the ciliary vessels of the eye, and
sleep disturbance are among the reports."

51.
CANNABIS-RELATED HOSPITAL ADMISSIONS

In the May 1978 issue of Science Digest, Dr. I.R. Rosengard stated that
"recent researchers report, in a 12-month period at a state hospital, 0.9 per
thousand of admissions directly attributable to cannabis use. In 1.9 per
thousand it was a contributary factor. . . . Although these figures suggest
that serious adverse reactions to marijuana are relatively infrequent, a more
definitive answer awaits further epidemiological study."

52.
STATE OF INTOXICATION IS FREQUENTLY VIVID

A report prepared by the Department of Health, Education, and Welfare
contains the following passage: "Although the state of intoxication is
frequently vivid as described by the user, an observer may see little change
from a normal state. Mild states of intoxication often go completely

undetected. The user's mood may be quite variable from being happy and gregarious to quiet and detached. At higher doses, speech may be slowed or slurred. Physiological changes are notably minimal. Increase in pulse rate and bloodshot eyes are the most obvious. Dry mouth and throat along with an increase in appetite are common. Other physiological effects often are inconsistent or not reproducible."

Chapter II
FAR MORE HARMFUL THAN ALCOHOL OR TOBACCO

53.
DOCTOR FINDS MARIJUANA MORE DANGEROUS

"The effects of marijuana are different from alcohol in many ways. THC damages chromosomes; alcohol does not. THC affects DNA, RNA, and the immune response; alcohol does not. Irreversible brain changes are apparent after only three years of daily marijuana use; it takes decades for irreversible brain changes to appear in the heavy drinker. Three people in six who use marijuana are likely to become addicted; one person in six who uses alcohol is likely to become addicted," stated Dr. Hardin B. Jones.

54.
POT DOES DAMAGE MUCH FASTER

There is evidence that marijuana "damages the brain, that it damages your ability to think, it damages your chromosomes, it damages your immunity system—all of this at a rate of something in the neighborhood of 20 times as rapidly as alcohol."

55.
"MUCH MORE DANGEROUS . . ."

"Marijuana is a much more dangerous drug than alcohol or tobacco. One can have one or two drinks a day for 20 or 30 years and never suffer ill effects from it. Alcohol is water soluble. One ounce is completely metabolized and broken down to water and carbon dioxide in 12 hours," reported Dr. Nicholas A. Pace. Marijuana, however, is not water soluble. The active psychotropic ingredient, delta-9-tetrahydrocannibinol, accumulates in the fat laden tissues of the body. Places where these tissues are located are the nervous system including brain and sex organs.

56.
EFFECT ON THE BRAIN IS MUCH MORE RAPID THAN ALCOHOL

While discussing why he feels that marijuana is more dangerous than alcohol, University of California's Dr. Harvey Powelson explains that "the concentration (of marijuana) in the brain is cumulative—it stays in the brain, so that people who are using marijuana are sub-clinically stoned all the time." He also notes that "alcohol leaves (the body) within 24 hours, marijuana is in for days to months. Its effect on the brain is much more rapid than alcohol. The mental effect that I have been describing from marijuana takes in the neighborhood of three years. That much has been demonstrated. Alcohol takes ten times that time. It is also very probable that it causes lung cancer."

57.
1978 CONFERENCE FINDS MARIJUANA "FAR MORE DANGEROUS THAN ALCOHOL"

On January 12, 1978, a conference at New York University School of Medicine was attended by over 300 doctors, medical students, social workers and high school teachers. Although press reports disagreed, one of the doctors who presented research at the conference stated that every speaker agreed that marijuana is far more dangerous than alcohol.

58.
POT'S HARMFUL EFFECTS DEVELOP FASTER

The "chronic disabling effect of alcohol tends to become fully apparent after 10 to 20 or more years after excessive alcohol abuse, whereas in the case of cannabis, this slides in insidiously, and within two or three years an individual has problems, and it takes some technical and professional experience to realize where this came from. . . ." reported Dr. Henry Brill, senior psychiatric member of the Shafer Commission on Marijuana and Drug Abuse.

59.
MORE PROFOUND EFFECTS ON THE MIND

In comparing marijuana to alcohol, Dr. D. Harvey Powelson states that: "Overall, marijuana affects the mind much more than alcohol, much sooner, and in a much more profound way."

60.
MARIJUANA IS A MAJOR PROBLEM DRUG

"Marijuana is becoming one of the major problem drugs. Out of 41,873 admissions to federally financed treatment clinics, marijuana was given as the reason for admission two and one-half times more often than was alcohol."

61.
MORE HARMFUL THAN ALCOHOL

Research by scientists at Stanford University "showed that marijuana ingestion caused more harmful effects than a similar dosage of alcohol . . . doses of tetrahydrocannabinol (THC), especially when smoked rapidly, induced greater temporal disorganization, amplification, depersonalization and delusional-like ideation than than the administration of doses of alcohol that are comparably intoxicating."

62.
PUBLIC GENERALLY UNAWARE OF EMERGING HARMFUL EVIDENCE

The New York State Conservative Party is on record to the effect that there is substantial medical evidence that marijuana has considerably more harmful effects than alcohol or tobacco . . . and that the fashionable rush to decriminalize is likely to foster increased use by a public (especially the young) generally unaware of the emerging evidence that marijuana is harmful.

63.
EFFECTS OF ALCOHOL MINIMAL COMPARED WITH MARIJUANA

"An illness does not become more attractive by the statement that another one is just as bad," stated Dr. Franz Winkler in response to the argument that alcohol use is just as harmful as marijuana use. He says that the "lasting effects of moderate amounts of alcohol are minimal in contrast to the harmful effects of even a couple of reefers a week." Dr. Winkler added that many marijuana users become alcohol users when the drug "no longer suffices to mask the growing despair of inner emptiness."

64.
MARIJUANA IS MORE HALLUCINOGENIC

A prominent physician has clearly pointed out the hallucinogenic character of marijuana is worse than that of alcohol.

"In order to hallucinate," reported Dr. Nicholas A. Pace, "an alcoholic would have to develop far advanced disease, with brain damage and/or the withdrawal syndrome.

"On the other hand, the psychotropic effect of marijuana causes hallucinations in small doses and in some cases—every time the drug is used."

65.
AMA WARNS AGAINST COMBINING MARIJUANA AND ALCOHOL

". . . The practice of combining the use of marijuana and alcoholic beverages is becoming more common and, as such, poses a hazard of more widespread and severe acute reactions resulting from their combined effects," reported the American Medical Association Council on Scientific Affairs.

66.
MARIJUANA IS UNPREDICTABLE

"Marijuana is unpredictable in its reaction. You can predict with certainty what one ounce of booze is going to do, but you cannot predict what one joint of marijuana is going to do, what one reefer, or one stick of hashish is going to do," commented Dr. Robert W. Baird of the Haven Clinic in New York.

67.
MARIJUANA AND ALCOHOL TOGETHER ARE FAR MORE POTENT

It should be pointed out that smoking marijuana has not replaced alcohol use, and in fact the two are being used together with increasing frequency. Scientists who testified before the United States Internal Security Subcommittee agreed that a "combination of the two intoxicants produces a far more potent and dangerous form of intoxication, whose short and long term consequences we still know very little about."

68.
DISTINCTION BETWEEN ALCOHOL AND MARIJUANA USERS

Excerpt from THE SEEKERS by Jess Stearn. Copyright © 1968, 1969 by Jess Stearn. Used by permission of Doubleday & Company, Inc.

"Whereas the alcoholic is sufficiently in tune with society to be defensive about his habit, the pothead has so lost a sense of perspective that he feels that there must be something radically wrong with anybody who doesn't smoke pot." This distinction between alcohol and marijuana was observed by Dr. Edward R. Pinckney. He feels that the reason for continuing use of drugs is that "most people who use drugs do so mainly to avoid having to think. . . ."

69.
EFFECT ON PERFORMANCE

"When alcohol and marijuana are consumed together," wrote Dr. Stanley F. Yolles, "the detriment on performance is greater than when either is used alone."

70.
ACTS MORE QUICKLY AND STRONGLY THAN ALCOHOL

From MARIJUANA AND YOUR CHILD by Jules Saltman. Copyright © 1970 by Jules Saltman. Used by permission of Grosset & Dunlap, Inc.

In the development of a craving for marijuana, Dr. Benjamin Kissin of the State University of New York Downstate Medical Center, stated that "marijuana acts more quickly and more strongly than does alcohol. Consequently, young people who develop psychogenic dependency on marijuana usually find themselves more compelled in their need for the drug than do the average young persons who use alcohol."

71.
A WARNING ON LEGALIZING MARIJUANA

From MARIJUANA AND YOUR CHILD by Jules Saltman. Copyright © 1970 by Jules Saltman. Used by permission of Grosset & Dunlap, Inc.

Author Jules Saltman questions whether marijuana is better or worse than alcohol. "Should the use of pot be freely permitted because liquor is permitted?" This is the "two-wrongs-make-a-right argument" and not sensible at all, answered Dr. Dale Cameron an official of the World Health Organization. "We have enough on our hands with alcohol without taking in another problem until we know more about it."

72.
ONE YEAR OF MARIJUANA EQUALS TWENTY YEARS OF TOBACCO IN HARMFUL EFFECTS

According to Dr. Nicholas A. Pace, "It takes 20 years of heavy tobacco smoking to produce the same type of severe sinusitis, pharyngitis, bronchitis, emphysema that less than one year of daily marijuana smoking produces proving that marijuana smoke is far more irritating to the respiratory tract than tobacco."

73.
MORE DAMAGING TO LUNG TISSUES THAN TOBACCO

Marijuana smoke, either by itself or mixed with tobacco smoke, "is far more damaging to lung tissues than tobacco smoke alone." This is one of the many scientific findings presented at the United States Senate Internal Security Subcommittee hearings in 1974 by world-renown Drs. Tennant and Leuchtenberger.

74.
COMPARISON WITH TOBACCO SMOKE ON LUNGS

"The lungs of the marijuana user are more blackened by smoke than those of the tobacco smoker because, to get an effect, marijuana smoke must be inhaled deeper and held longer in the lungs. Indeed, the concentration of THC in the lungs is very much greater than in the body as a whole. Autopsy examination of the lungs of heavy marijuana smokers show extreme breakdown in the lung structure," according to Dr. Hardin B. Jones.

75.
MARIJUANA SMOKE VS. TOBACCO SMOKE

Cecile Leuchtenberger and Rudolf Leuchtenberger, "Cytological and Cytochemical Studies of the Effects of Fresh Marijuana Cigarette Smoke on Growth and DNA Metabolism of Animal and Human Lung Cultures," in *Pharmacology of Marihuana*, vol. 2., eds. M.C. Braude and S. Szara (New York: Raven Press, 1976), p. 609.

Atypical growth similar to the growth evoked by tobacco smoke in lung cultures, is also evoked in lung cultures by marijuana cigarette smoke, reported Cecile Leuchtenberger and Rudolf Leuchtenberger. Furthermore, the smoke from marijuana cigarettes produces more serious alterations in number of chromosomes and DNA content than did tobacco cigarettes, according to their studies.

76.
MORE HARSH AND IRRITATING THAN TOBACCO

"There is an awful lot of 'junk' in marijuana that is bound to be extremely harsh and irritating. Marijuana is much more harsh and irritating than tobacco and produces considerable irritation in the respiratory tract. . . ." said Dr. Robert Heath of the Tulane University School of Medicine in commenting on the effects of marijuana on monkeys in 1974.

77.
EARLIER ADVERSE ACTION FROM POT THAN FROM ALCOHOL OR TOBACCO

". . . It seems to me that cannabis shares the disadvantages of alcohol and tobacco, together with its own psychotogenic and biochemical actions, its chronic effects being accentuated by its cumulative tendency, giving it much earlier adverse action," reported Dr. W.D.M. Paton, Professor of Pharmacology at Oxford University.

78
ADDING MARIJUANA TO TOBACCO CAUSES ADVERSE EFFECTS

Cecile Leuchtenberger and Rudolf Leuchtenberger, "Cytological and Cytochemical Studies of the Effects of Fresh Marijuana Cigarette Smoke on Growth and DNA Metabolism of Animal and Human Lung Cultures," in *Pharmacology of Marihuana*, vol. 2., eds. M.C. Braude and S. Szara (New York: Raven Press, 1976), p. 598.

The addition of marijuana to tobacco cigarettes, according to Cecile Leuchtenberger and Rudolf Leuchtenberger, produces a smoke that evokes cytochemical and morphological alterations in cells of lung explants. The alterations produced are of a higher degree than the alterations produced by smoke from tobacco cigarettes alone.

79.
MARIJUANA MAKES TOBACCO MORE DAMAGING

"Scientific studies," stated Dr. Nicholas A. Pace, "have shown that marijuana smoke mixed with tobacco smoke is far more damaging to lung tissue than tobacco smoke alone."

80.
CONTAINS MORE TAR THAN TOBACCO

According to *National Review Magazine:* "Marijuana cigarettes have 50 per cent more tar than regular cigarettes, and it is this component in tobacco that is supposed to be carcinogenic."

81.
MARIJUANA SMOKE CAUSES GREATER DAMAGE TO LUNG CELLS THAN TOBACCO SMOKE

Recent work on lung tissue cultures by Dr. Leuchtenberger has "clearly established that marijuana smoke causes a greater range and degree of damage to the lung cells than tobacco smoke."

82.
HIGHER CONCENTRATIONS OF SEVERAL CANCER-CAUSING AGENTS THAN IN TOBACCO

Marijuana cigarettes contain higher concentrations of several cancer-causing agents than tobacco cigarettes, according to a study carried out by members of the Department of Chemistry at Indiana University. The study compared the smoke of 2,000 Mexican marijuana cigarettes with that of 2,000 tobacco cigarettes smoked by a machine.

Although the research is not yet fully conclusive, ". . . the presence of larger amounts of polynuclear aromatic hydrocarbons in marijuana is highly suggestive," stated Dr. Milos Novotny, Indiana University scientist.

"A marijuana smoker takes longer puffs (than a cigarette smoker), therefore, there is more combustion. My guess is that this produces more carcinogenic hydrocarbons. Marijuana smokers also hold the smoke in their lungs for a longer period and this will also have its effect," he added.

Chapter III
STAYS IN THE BODY

83.
STAYS IN BODY FROM 6 WEEKS TO 6 MONTHS

In comparing the effects of marijuana with the effects of other drugs, Dr. D. Harvey Powelson states that "marijuana is the most dangerous drug we have to contend with . . . it stays in the body for a very long period of time. It stays in the brain and keeps operating long after people are high from six weeks to six months. . . . If you drink alcohol . . . it goes into the bloodstream and continues to circulate, and then it is burned and leaves the body. Marijuana just stays there."

84.
THERE IS NO OTHER DRUG THAT LINGERS IN THE BODY SO LONG

"We know by careful chemical measurements taken in the bodies of marijuana users that the drug actually accumulates in a linear way. . . . A week after a person smokes marijuana, 30 percent is still in the body in the active form. There is no other drug or medication that lingers in the body so long. . . . I can see some effects in all marijuana users any time I examine them, even though they haven't used marijuana for hours, days or weeks."

85.
ANYONE WHO USES MARIJUANA MORE THAN ONCE A WEEK CANNOT BE DRUG FREE

According to Dr. Nicholas A. Pace, "marijuana produces a half life of 7 days. This means that after one week only 50 percent of the substance is eliminated, therefore, anyone who uses marijuana more than once a week cannot be truly drug free and has a build up of the drug in his tissues.

"One might remember the recent headlines of the engineer involved in the train crash in Chicago. Although he had not used marijuana for the previous 24 hours, evidence of the substance was still detected in his system."

86
REMAINS IN BODY FOR UP TO 8 DAYS

As early as 1970, scientific researchers Drs. Louis Lemberger, Julius Axelrod, and Irwin J. Kopin of the National Institute of Mental Health, discovered that marijuana's metabolites remain in the body for up to eight days. This was made possible by using radioactively tagged delta-9-THC.

87.
MARIJUANA IS STORED IN BODY

"One reason why marijuana is harmful when taken over a long period of time is that unlike other drugs, such as alcohol, marijuana is stored in the body for a long time. It takes a week before a single dose is completely eliminated from the body. By contrast, alcohol is eliminated after only a few hours. Thus it is the cumulative effect of marijuana which has the potential for harming the cells."

88.
ONE WEEK AFTER SMOKING 30% OF THE THC IS STILL IN BODY

"A study conducted by Louis Lemberger of the Indiana University School of Medicine indicates that 30 percent of the THC (the active ingredient in marijuana) is retained in the body at the end of the week, and this 30 percent is then eliminated more slowly than the first 70 percent."

89.
LONG DURATION OF CANNABIS IN BODY

Dr. Conrad Schwarz, chairman of the Drug Habituation Committee of the British Columbia Medical Association, stated "probably because of the long duration of active cannabis ingredients in the body, regular users . . .

show clinical evidence of continuing low-grade intoxication, characterized by memory impairment, mood swings, sleep disturbances, and generally lessened functioning." He also pointed out that evidence exists indicating that regular cannabis users build up a tolerance to it and require an increase in dosage.

Chapter IV

DAMAGES THE BRAIN

90.
"THE FACTS SHOULD BE OUT—MARIJUANA DAMAGES THE BRAIN"

"The active ingredient in marijuana impairs the brain circuitry. We seem to be playing with dangerous, dangerous stuff," reported Dr. Robert Heath of the Tulane Medical School.

"It appears that the active ingredient in marijuana, called Delta-9-THC, goes directly to the cell membranes of the emotional center. Temporarily it stimulates pleasure symptoms, but after repeated use it exhausts the pleasure chemicals of the brain . . . Marijuana is complex with a persisting effect."

"I personally don't give a damn if people drink whiskey or smoke pot . . . but the facts should be out. Marijuana damages the brain," concluded Heath.

91.
MARIJUANA APPEARS TO DAMAGE "MECHANISMS OF THE MIND"

Dr. Hardin B. Jones, senior scientist at the world-famous Donner Laboratory of Medical Research, explains that "marijuana appears to injure the fine, hairlike extensions of the brain cell membranes that communicate with the other brain cells. Such damage is critical, for although each cell has tens of thousands of these connectors, the brain needs them all. They are the mechanisms of the mind."

92.
FREQUENT ADOLESCENT INTOXICATION MIGHT INDUCE PERMANENT CHANGES IN THINKING AND BEHAVIOR

Although cannabis has not been shown to cause structural changes in the brain, ". . . alterations in sensitivity of brain cells, or distortions in their functions occur, which result in changes in performance or mental functioning. One cannot exclude the possibility that repetitive impairment of these processes by frequent and long-term cannabis intoxication in adolescent years might induce permanent changes in thinking patterns or behavior. Such permanent changes would be related to permanent organic alterations."

93.
CHANGES IN THE CHEMICAL PROCESSES OF BRAIN CELLS

Dr. Keith Yonge, while President of the Canadian Psychiatric Association, warned of lasting changes in the chemical processes of brain cells and of damage to the cellular structure of the brain as a result of using marijuana. He says the most significant fact about the drug is that marijuana causes lasting alterations in the personality of the user, which are pathological.

94.
CAN CAUSE BRAIN DAMAGE AFTER HEAVY USE

Evidence shows that marijuana when used daily over a long period of time, may actually cause irreversible damage to the brain. There are many cases on the records of brilliant young people who had gone on a marijuana binge and then found that they could no longer perform at their previous level of efficiency.

95.
ACTIVE SUBSTANCE STORED IN BRAIN CELLS

"It is now known that the active substance in cannabis is stored in certain brain cells, and this may be an important explanation of the chronic effects of cannabis smoking," reported Dr. Nils Bejerot.

96.
AFFECTS REGULATIVE CENTERS OF THE BRAIN

"Nearly all the effects of marijuana, which are extensive, are physiological. With heavy marijuana use there is often atrophy of the body musculature. It's very discernible because there is corresponding atrophy in the brain. . . . The primary damage is in the brain. Marijuana is a powerful drug, and it has a wide sweep of effects throughout the regulative centers of the brain. We call this the autonomic nervous system because it automatically controls the body. The entire autonomic nervous system is affected by a drug like marijuana, and all the control centers are altered. In addition, the control centers that affect the thinking process are altered. There is personality change in marijuana users."

97.
MAY PRODUCE CEREBRAL ATROPHY

In reviewing the findings of the 1971 Campbell studies on cannabis use and the brain, Dr. M. Evans (one of the researchers of that study) observed that our work calls "for urgent investigation of the possibility that regular smoking of cannabis resin may produce cerebral atrophy."

98.
EVIDENCE OF BRAIN ATROPHY AFTER 3 YEARS' USE

"The majority of young marijuana users show remarkable, complete recoveries after they stop using the drug. However, in the heavily affected marijuana user—the one who is already showing atrophy of the muscles— evidence of his recovery (after giving up marijuana) is less marked. There's a residue that doesn't come back. We believe that this is due to the destruction of parts of the brain.

"There is good evidence that brain atrophy may occur in people who use marijuana within the ordinary range. . . . Brain atrophy begins to occur after three to ten years of use, and it occurs without daily use."

99.
CEREBRAL ATROPHY IN YOUNG ADULTS

According to Dr. A.M.G. Campbell of the Royal United Hospital in England, "regular use of cannabis produces cerebral atrophy in young adults."

100.

MONKEYS SHOW "IRREVERSIBLE ALTERATIONS" AFTER HEAVY USE FOR 3 MONTHS

Dr. Robert Heath, Chairman of the Department of Psychiatry and Neurology at Tulane University School of Medicine, testified before a United States Senate Subcommittee that monkeys exposed regularly to active marijuana heavily smoked began to show evidence of "irreversible alterations" in brain function about 3 months after onset of the experiment. He said that the chronic effects lasted as long as five days. "Our previous experience with similar situations would lead us to assume that this chronic smoking of marijuana has probably produced irreversible changes in brain function."

101.

RESULTS OF ANIMAL STUDIES IN THE SOVIET

Many investigators are taking a special interest in the Soviet studies on dogs exposed to marijuana. One scientist, Dr. Nicholas A. Pace, reported: "These dogs showed signs of organic brain damage of the central nervous system; disturbances of various reflexes, motor coordination, muscle movements, and states of depression followed by periods of excitement, aggressive behavior and fears.

"Autopsies on the brains of these dogs showed large areas of destruction in the cortex (thinking and learning centers) of the brain as well as in the cerebellum (balance section of the brain)."

102.

CAUSES CHANGES IN BRAINS OF MONKEYS

"Brains of monkeys which received active material in the form of smoke or by intravenous injection showed distinct changes in the synaptic cleft and in those regions—septal region, hippocampus and amygdala—where EEG changes had occurred," reported Dr. Heath. "Changes were (1) a widening of the cleft, (2) deposition of a dark opaque material in the cleft, and (3) a beginning clefting of the synaptic vesicles at the terminus of the axone. These changes all suggest incipient damage to the neurones."

103.

HUMAN-LEVEL DOSES OF MARIJUANA HAVE CAUSED BRAIN CELL CHANGES IN MONKEYS

". . . Profound changes that occur in the surface membranes of brain cells in animals exposed to doses of marijuana (are) within the range of human doses. Changes have been found to occur in the membrane of brain cells, red and white blood cells, liver and lung cells, and sperm," reported Dr. Hardin B. Jones, summarizing the work of his colleagues Dr. W.D.M. Paton and Dr. Robert Heath.

104.
RESULTS OF RESEARCH INVOLVING 37,000 USERS

Dr. Rosengard and his associates recently completed a two year study of the effects of marijuana on the human body and its ability to perform. The study involved 37,000 individuals. On the basis of their studies, Dr. Rosengard concluded that "their findings suggest that regular use of cannabis produces cerebral atrophy in young adults, and emphasize the need for future studies of the neurological consequences of drug abuse. . . . Cerebral atrophy is a finding of such seriousness that the report requires careful consideration and emphasizes the need for study."

105.
MOST OF DOCTOR'S COLLEAGUES BECOME MORE AND MORE CONCERNED AS STUDENTS SHOW EFFECTS

In 1974 Dr. Robert Heath, Chairman of the Department of Psychiatry and Neurology at Tulane University School of Medicine, told the United States Senate Internal Security Subcommittee that he believes marijuana "is a very harmful drug." It "seems to produce real and significant damage," and he believes that his data show marijuana "has strongly deleterious effects with probable destructive effects on the brain in heavy users." Dr. Heath noted that most of his colleagues at Tulane "have become more and more concerned with the marijuana problem, as students using it are showing distinct, often severe and lasting effects."

106.
CHEMICAL CHANGES IN THE BRAIN

"Those who push for the unrestricted use of marijuana insist there is no proof the drug has a lasting or harmful effect. But that line of argumentation was undermined recently. Biochemists Harris Rosenkrantz and Yugal Luthra reported the first evidence of dangerous chemical changes in the brains of animals exposed to marijuana over a long period of time."

They report finding chemical changes in the brains of rats injected with THC (tetrahydrocannabinol). In a three-month period, 12 of the 40 rats died, and about half of the animals experienced tremors during the testing. The autopsies performed on the rats showed a deficiency in brain protein and RNA in the animals' brains.

107.
ALTERATIONS IN LOCOMOTOR ACTIVITY FOUND IN MONKEYS BORN TO THC TREATED PARENTS

A preliminary report by E.N. Sassenrath and Golub stated that alterations in locomotor activity and responsiveness have been found in monkeys born to THC treated parents. This could be an indication of an alteration of their brains.

108.
CHANGES IN BRAIN DEMONSTRATED IN TESTS WITH PRIMATES

"Many investigators, employing electrodes attached to the scalps of primates, have found a variety of inconsistent changes in electroencephalograms obtained during the subject's use of cannabis," reported Thomas H. Maugh, II.

109.
POTENTIAL IRREVERSIBLE BRAIN DAMAGE

There is "the possibility that long-term, heavy use of marijuana may produce sharp personality changes that lead to a marked deterioration in what is normally considered good mental health and may cause potentially irreversible brain injury," stated Thomas H. Maugh, II.

110.
LOSS OF BRAIN FUNCTION

". . . Disorder of thinking characterized by a general lack of coherence and an exacerbation of pathological thinking processes," are the long-range effects of smoking marijuana, according to Dr. D. Harvey Powelson.

111.
NATIONAL INSTITUTE ON DRUG ABUSE REPORTS ON DOSE-RELATED ACUTE BRAIN SYNDROME

"An acute brain syndrome associated with cannabis intoxication including such features as clouding of mental processes, disorientation, confusion and marked memory impairment has been reported. It is thought to be dose-related (much more likely at unusually high doses) and to be determined more by the size of the dose than by pre-existing personality. . . . Acute brain syndrome also diminishes as the toxic effects of the drug wear off."

112.
CHRONIC USE FOR SEVERAL YEARS INFLICTS IRREVERSIBLE DAMAGE OF THE BRAIN

Along with the fact that THC accumulates in the tissues of the body, there is evidence that marijuana "inflicts irreversible damage on the brain, including actual brain atrophy, when used in a chronic manner for several years," stated United States Senator, James O. Eastland.

113.
TESTS PROVE EFFECT ON BRAIN FUNCTION LONG AFTER USE

"Marijuana stays active in the brain long after the user feels high. It's very deceptive. . . . Your brain isn't functioning right. And this can be proved. You can give a person mental tests before he takes a joint and then you can show that he can't do the same test as well for as long as 72 hours after the equivalent of one to three joints. It depends on the concentration."

114.
CAN IMPAIR BRAIN'S NORMAL DEVELOPMENT

Dr. Sidney Cohen, Director of the Division of Drug Addiction and Drug Abuse at the National Institute of Mental Health, stated that marijuana use by young people can impair normal development of the brain. Dr. Cohen told the Select Committee on Crime that regular use of the drug may "retard their mental growth and emotional maturation. . . ."

115.
MARIJUANA AFFECTS THOUGHT FORMATION

Dr. Hardin B. Jones has found that "thought formation in the marijuana user tends to be less powerful: conclusions are relatively impetuous, and expressed ideas are often *non sequiturs*. It is as though some of the reference checking in thinking has gone astray. The user has the illusion that his chronic state is simply a mature mellowing."

116.
STIMULATORY AND DEPRESSANT ACTION ON BRAIN

"The overall actions of marijuana on the brain are a mixture of apparent stimulatory sensory effects with superimposed depressant elements. Temporally, the activation is followed by sedation, but there is considerable overlap," stated Braude et al.

117.
SPECIFIC SHORT TERM EFFECTS

Cannabis is a psychoactive drug and has a number of short-term effects on the brain. Included in these are: "alterations in the concentrations of biogenic amines, such as serotonin and norepinephrine; changes in the activity of enzymes, such as acetylcholinesterase; and variations in electrical activity as measured by an electroencephalograph," reported Thomas H. Maugh, II.

118.
HARMFUL EFFECTS ON THE MIND

A 1965 report of the Committee on Drug Dependence of the World Health Organization, provided the following ways in which cannabis can affect the mind: "Release of inhibitions, distortion of perception and judgment, increased response to suggestion, production in susceptible people of illusions and delusions that predispose to antisocial behavior, impairment of memory, distortion of emotional responsiveness, irritability and confusion and a predisposition to anxiety and aggressiveness as a possible result of various intellectual and sensory derangements."

119.
DOCTOR SEES PATIENTS' ABILITY TO THINK AFFECTED

"One patient whom I knew quite well . . . took up marijuana and hashish. . . . It became clear that there was something changing about his ability to think, to remember, to judge, to understand. The things happening to his brain were things we would expect from somebody who was having brain damage from alcohol or a tumor or organic brain damage . . . then I began to see the same connection in other patients."

120.
AFFECTS "SWITCHING CENTERS" OF BRAIN

"The effect of marijuana is not at the outer levels of consciousness in the zone of here and now, but at the switching centers that have to do with the mix of sensory information coming into the brain."

121.
HALLUCINOGENIC EFFECT

"Smoking marijuana with its 'high' has in reality, a hallucinogenic effect on the brain with distortion of time, space and sound," stated Dr. Nicholas A. Pace.

122.
POSSIBLE EVIDENCE OF BRAIN DAMAGE SUGGESTS CAUTION IS NEEDED

The link between heavy long-term cannabis use and brain damage has been the subject of considerable study and controversy. Thomas H. Maugh, II stated, "there seems to be enough evidence suggesting the possibility of brain damage that discretion would require avoiding the risk."

123.
BRAIN ATROPHY OF YOUNG USERS RESEMBLES ATROPHY FOUND IN 70-90 YEAR OLDS

Brain atrophy has been detected in a number of young smokers in a controversial English study, reported Dr. William Paton. The brain atrophy found is equivalent to the amount usually found in people of ages 70 to 90.

124.
BEHAVIORAL EFFECTS AFTER RELATIVELY SHORT USE

"But with marijuana, as the facts are beginning to accumulate, it seems as though you have to use it only for a relatively short time in moderate to heavy use before persistent behavioral effects along with other evidence of brain damage begins to develop," said Dr. Robert Heath, Chairman of the department of Psychiatry and Neurology at Tulane University School of Medicine in 1974.

125.
INDICATIONS THAT BRAIN IS IMPAIRED

In 1974 it was the finding of Dr. Heath of the Tulane School of Medicine, that, "with the acute smoking of marijuana you do get a pleasure response in humans and you find this reflected in their recordings. In contrast and most significant, however, is the finding that with chronic usage you begin to get recording changes indicating that the area is impaired in its function and that is associated with a reduction in pleasure responsivity, a lessening of motivation and a reduction in awareness. That, then, is the acute effect of smoking marijuana."

126.
TETRAHYDROCANNABINOL ACTS ON BRAIN AND OTHER TISSUES

The principal psychoactive constituent of cannabis, tetrahydrocannabinol, "has a very high affinity for brain and other lipophilic tissues, that is, tissues with a very high proportion of hydrocarbonlike components," reported Thomas H. Maugh, II, commenting on brain damage arising from the use of marijuana.

127.
MAY HAVE PERSISTING EFFECTS ON BRAIN METABOLISM

Dr. Victor Zarcone expresses his concern that marijuana may have persisting effects on brain metabolism as a result of the distortion in normal sleep patterns brought on by marijuana.

128.
CHRONIC USE SLOWLY ERODES BRAIN "RESERVES"

Gabriel G. Nahas, *Marihuana: Deceptive Weed* (New York: Raven Press, 1973), p. 249.

"The brain is the organ of the mind. Can one repetitively disturb the mental function without impairing the brain? The brain, like all other organs of the human body, has very large functional reserves which allow it to resist and adapt to stressful abnormal demands. It seems that chronic use of the psychotropic drugs, including *Cannabis* derivatives, slowly erodes these reserves," concluded Dr. Gabriel G. Nahas.

129.
MAY CHANGE BRAIN WAVES

Volavka, et al., reported that marijuana smokers experience a slight increase in the amount of alpha waves and also a decrease in the amount of beta and theta brain waves. More work needs to be done, however, to be sure of these effects.

130.
IRREVERSIBLE BRAIN CHANGES AFTER HEAVY USE

"For some persons, smoking the weed once or twice a week may constitute heavy use as judged by its effects," reported Dr. Hardin B. Jones. "It depends on the individual sensitivity to the drug and the strength of the marijuana used. Certainly all daily smoking of marijuana is heavy use and there are many signs of chronic debilitation.

"It appears that irreversible brain changes may be encountered as marijuana ese extends beyond three years."

131.
DANGERS OF THC

THC (delta-9-tetrahydrocannabinol) "has been reported to inhibit brain RNA (ribonucleic acid) synthesis in rats." Secondly, THC has been reported to remain in the brain for at least a week. Thirdly, it has been discovered that THC or its metabolite(s) accumulate in an area of the brain, called the hippocampus, where morphine was found to alter RNA synthesis.

132.
ISOTOPE LABELED CANNABIS APPEARS IN FRONTAL LOBES AND CORTICE OF MONKEYS

In 1971, William McIssac and his associates demonstrated that with isotope labeled cannabis, the concentration of the drug was located in the frontal lobes and cortice of monkeys.

Chapter V

THE CONNECTION WITH CANCER

133.
FOUND PRECANCEROUS LESIONS IN LUNGS OF CANNABIS-USING AMERICAN SOLDIERS

An investigation of cannabis-using American soldiers in Germany by Dr. Forest S. Tennant, Jr., has shown an alteration of cell structure in the lung air passages. Bronchial biopsies were performed on 30 soldiers whose average age was 21 and who had smoked 25-30 grams of hashish per month for a few months. This is approximately four times as much THC as is received by a person smoking one (two percent) marijuana cigarette, or an estimated 80-90 milligrams of THC, per day. Of the 30 young men studied, 24 had precancerous lesions detected in the biopsied specimen. Such lesions are not seen in tobacco cigarette smokers until much later in life and after three decades of cigarette smoking.

134.
LONG TERM INHALATION MAY CONTRIBUTE TO LUNG CANCER

Dr. Cecile Leuchtenberger as head of the Department of Cytochemistry at the Swiss Institute for Experimental Cancer Research, reported before the United States Senate Subcommittee on Internal Security that: "Marijuana cigarette smoke has a harmful effect on tissues and cells of humans and of animals. The observation that marijuana cigarette smoke stimulates

41

irregular growth in the respiratory system which resembles closely precancerous lesions would indicate that long-term inhalation of marijuana cigarette smoke may either evoke directly lung cancer or may at least contribute to the development of lung cancer."

135.
DOCTORS ALARMED AT SIMILARITY BETWEEN CELLULAR LESIONS AND LUNG CARCINOMA

Dr. Forrest S. Tennant, Jr., head of the United States Army's European drug program from 1968-1972, studied the relationship between the high incidence of respiratory disease and the use of marijuana. Dr. Tennant observed, "Even though (a person) can get bronchitis and emphysema from cigarette smoking, one must usually smoke cigarettes for 10-20 years to get these complications. We became alarmed about this because we began seeing (these conditions) in 18, 19 and 20-year-old men. The cellular lesions found in bronchial biopsies of these men were identified as squamous metaplasia, a condition well known to be 'statistically and anatomically linked with carcinoma of the lung.'"

136.
MARIJUANA SMOKE CONTRIBUTES TO DEVELOPMENT OF MALIGNANT LESIONS IN LUNGS

Cecile Leuchtenberger and Rudolf Leuchtenberger, "Cytological and Cytochemical Studies of the Effects of Fresh Marijuana Cigarette Smoke on Growth and DNA Metabolism of Animal and Human Lung Cultures," in *Pharmacology of Marihuana*, vol. 2., eds. M.C. Braude and S. Szara (New York: Raven Press, 1976), p. 609.

Cecile Leuchtenberger and Rudolf Leuchtenberger report that fresh smoke from marijuana cigarettes harms lung cells in cultures. Furthermore, marijuana smoke contributes to the development of malignant and premalignant lesions.

137.
MARIJUANA SMOKE ENHANCES MALIGNANT CELL TRANSFORMATION IN HAMSTER TESTS

Cecile Leuchtenberger and Rudolf Leuchtenberger, "Cytological and Cytochemical Studies of the Effects of Fresh Marijuana Cigarette Smoke on Growth and DNA Metabolism of Animal and Human Lung Cultures," in *Pharmacology of Marihuana*, vol. 2., eds. M.C. Braude and S. Szara (New York: Raven Press, 1976), p. 609.

The exposure of hamster lung cultures to whole marijuana smoke or the gas vapor phase of marijuana cigarettes, enhances malignant cell transformation. This transformation is also evident after exposure to whole tobacco smoke or the gas vapor phase of tobacco cigarettes, according to Cecile Leuchtenberger and Rudolf Leuchtenberger.

138.
IMPAIRMENT OF LYMPHOCYTES

Several studies show impairment of lymphocytes in marijuana smokers. "There is growing evidence that lymphocytes play a significant role in the body's resistance to cancer," noted Dr. George K. Russell. He adds that "any impairment of the system of defense mechanism and immune responses, therefore, carries with it the distinct risk of malignancy and other serious pathological conditions."

139.
LUNGS OF CHRONIC TEENAGE HASHISH SMOKERS SHOW ABNORMALITIES ASSOCIATED WITH LUNG CANCER

Dr. Forest S. Tennant, Jr., reported that he found in hashish smokers in their teens and early 20s a type of acute bronchitis, and tissue changes in lung biopsies, that are associated with patients who had smoked cigarettes for years. "The abnormalities," said Dr. Tennant, "were the same that are associated with lung cancer."

140.
"ITS TAR IS CARCINOGENIC"

In testimony before the United States Senate Internal Security Subcommittee, Dr. W.D.M. Paton, Professor of Pharmacology at the University of Oxford, stated that marijuana is cumulative, persistent and its tar is carcinogenic. Experimentally, it has been found to be teratogenic and "psychotic phenomena may occur with a single dose . . . it seems to me that cannabis shares the disadvantages of alcohol and tobacco, together with its own psychotogenic and biochemical actions, its chronic effect being accentuated by its cumulative tendency, giving it much earlier adverse action."

141.
HEAVY MARIJUANA SMOKERS MAY HAVE PRECANCEROUS LESIONS IN THEIR LUNGS

"There is evidence that the products of marijuana smoke cause cancer cells in test tubes in a similar way as the tar of tobacco cigarettes produce cancer cells. There is evidence that heavy marijuana smokers have precancerous lesions present in lungs," according to Dr. G. Nahas.

142.
CELLULAR CHANGES FROM MARIJUANA SMOKE SIMILAR TO CHANGES FOUND IN CANCER VICTIMS

"Of interest is the fact that lungs of animals exposed to marijuana smoke have showed cellular changes which are similar to what is seen in patients who develop lung cancer. Tar from marijuana painted on the backs of animals has produced cancers," reported Dr. Nicholas A. Pace.

Chapter VI
WEAKENS RESISTANCE TO DISEASE

143.
MEDICAL SCIENTISTS PRESENT EVIDENCE MARIJUANA LOWERS BODY'S RESISTANCE TO DISEASE

At the Helsinki conference, considerable evidence supporting the idea that marijuana lowers the body's resistance to disease was presented. The strongly immuno-suppressive effects of THC in rodents was disclosed by Rosencrantz; evidence of changes in the white blood cells of chronic hashish smokers in Greece was introduced by Stefanis and Issidorides; the paralysis of cells in the lungs that are thought to be highly important in protecting the lungs from disease was shown by Chari-Bitron.

144.
INTERFERES WITH BODY'S IMMUNE SYSTEM

Dr. Nicholas A. Pace stated that marijuana brings about "interference with the immune system of the body. Studies have shown that marijuana use causes a reduction in the number of chromosomes in the white blood cells plus abnormal white blood cells."

145.
WEAKENS BODY'S IMMUNITY SYSTEM

"Marijuana is a harmful substance. It is not a mild, mind-expanding herb. I deplore efforts to make it socially acceptable or readily available," stated

45

Dr. Gabriel G. Nahas of Columbia Presbyterian Medical Center. Dr. Nahas found evidence that the main substance in marijuana, tetrahydrocannabinol (THC), slows down the production of DNA in the body and thus weakens the body's immunity system by interfering with the production of white blood cells. Additional evidence pointing to the harmful effects of marijuana on the body's immunity system has been reported by other reseachers at many universities and medical centers throughout the country.

146.
INHALED CANNABIS SMOKE SUPPRESSED IMMUNE RESPONSE IN RATS

"A recently published animal study using high, but still humanly relevant doses of inhaled cannabis smoke, found that it had an immune response suppressing effect in rats that justifies further research," stated the report of the National Institute on Drug Abuse.

147.
AFTER ONE YEAR OF HASHISH SMOKING IMMUNITY DEFENSES WERE CUT BY 60%

"Habitual hashish smokers age prematurely and become more vulnerable to cancer and other diseases," reported Dr. Gabriel G. Nahas to an international congress on therapeutics in Geneva in 1973. He said that "his team found that the active agent in hashish causes serious damage to body cells. After two years of smoking hashish three times a week, the damage may be irreparable.

"Prof. Nahas said his team tested a group of 32 hashish users with an average age of 22 years. . . . The scientists found that after one year the users' immunity defenses were reduced by 60 percent, their body cells were no longer capable of reproducing at normal rate and they were as exhausted as much older people."

148.
DIMINISHES IMMUNE RESPONSE SYSTEM OF WHITE BLOOD CELLS

Dr. Hardin B. Jones has found that the average marijuana user is likely to have a large number of broken chromosomes in the cultures of his white blood cells. Furthermore, "his white blood cell immune response is lowered. The immune response of skin cells has been shown to be unaffected; the difference is probably a consequence of the high exposure of blood cells to THC, whereas skin cells are less exposed. It is estimated that skin cells receive fifteen percent of the exposure of blood cells."

149.
NATIONAL INSTITUTE ON DRUG ABUSE REPORTS MARKED
REDUCTION IN IMMUNE RESPONSE SYSTEM

Studies by doctors Nahas, Suciu-Foca, Armand, and Morishima indicate that a marked reduction in the immune response as measured in white blood cell cultures was found in marijuana smokers compared to non-smokers.

150.
IMPAIRMENT OF T-LYMPHOCYTES

Impairment of T-lymphocytes in chronic marijuana smokers has been reported by Cushman and associates.

151.
DELTA-9-THC DEPLETES SPLEEN CELLS

In a study of the effect of delta-9-THC on the immune response in animals, Lefkowitz and Yang found a "reduced response to SRBC in delta-9-TRC-teated mice" and a depletion of spleen cells.

152.
IMMUNOSUPPRESSIVE EFFECTS IN RODENTS

Strong immunosuppressive marijuana effects in rodents have been described by Rosencrantz.

153.
LOWERS RATE OF DIVISION OF LYMPHOCYTES

The immune response of 51 marijuana smokers, 16 to 35 years of age, who had smoked an average of four marijuana cigarettes a week for at least one year, were tested by Dr. Gabriel G. Nahas and his associates. The researchers removed lymphocytes from the subjects and stimulated these lymphocytes to undergo cell division. Lymphocytes usually divide very rapidly when the body is attacked by a virus or foreign tissue. The rate of division of the cells of the subjects was found to be 41 percent lower than in a control group of non-smokers.

154.
MARIJUANA TRACED TO SPLEEN IN ANIMAL TESTS

Marijuana metabolites have been traced to the spleen, an organ closely involved in the body's immunity system. By injecting tagged THC into rabbits and rats, a Swedish scientist found lasting remains of radioactivity.

The urine and feces of the animals remained radioactive for at least three days. In dissected portions of their liver, spleen, kidneys and adrenal glands, similarly lasting concentrations of radioactivity were found.

155.
DIMINISHED IMMUNE RESPONSE CONFIRMED

"A diminished immune response by certain white blood cells . . . has been found in marijuana users," reported Dr. G. Nahas. His findings have been confirmed by studies in which monkeys, when exposed to marijuana smoke also showed this suppression of immue response and by additional studies on human cells.

156.
CELLS FROM MARIJUANA SMOKERS FOUND TO HAVE LOWERED IMMUNITY

The immunity response to marijuana smokers was tested by Dr. Paul Cushman using a test called the "rosette formation." This test is described by Dr. Gabriel G. Nahas: "When lymphocytes are placed in a test tube with red blood cells, taken from an animal, such as a sheep, they have the ability to attract these foreign sheep cells in a form that appears to be a rosette. This property of attracting foreign cells is considered to be an index of cellular immunity. Healthy lymphocytes with good immunity potential will form many rosettes." In the experiments performed by Cushman, the lymphocytes that had been taken from marijuana smokers had lost some of their ability to form rosettes. This indicated that the cells had a lowered immunity.

Chapter VII

AFFECTS HUMAN CELLS AND CHROMOSOMES

157.
HUMAN AND ANIMAL STUDIES PROVE USE AFFECTS CHROMOSOMES

One of the most significant results of current studies on marijuana is that "it has been demonstrated in humans and in animals that marijuana, in socially used doses, affects chromosomes. Chromosomes are what determine our inheritance. They are also the determiners of the function of every cell."

158.
POT SMOKER OFTEN HAS LESS THAN NORMAL NUMBER OF CHROMOSOMES

"The Perils Of 'Pot' Start Showing Up," *U.S. News & World Report,* June 10, 1974, p. 58. Reprinted from 'U.S. News & World Report.'

". . . Findings by another researcher raise suspicions that cancer, genetic mutation and birth defects may result.

"According to Dr. Akira Morishima of the Department of Pediatrics, Columbia University, such problems may occur in marijuana smokers because of a substantial decrease in the number of chromosomes—specs of matter that carry hereditary characteristics—in each cell. This shortage

often leaves the 'pot' smoker with less than the normal complement of 46 chromosomes. . . ."
Copyright 1974 U.S. News & World Report, Inc.

159.
LUNG CELLS OF USERS SHOWN TO HAVE ABNORMAL NUMBER OF CHROMOSOMES

In an experiment studying the effects of marijuana on human lung cells in laboratory cultures, Leuchtenberger and Leuchtenberger found an increase in the number of cells having an abnormal amount of chromosomes.

160.
GENETIC ALTERATIONS MAY BE INDUCED

Dr. Louis Souza of Paterson, New Jersey, has conducted experiments designed to determine the effects of marijuana. His research suggests that marijuana induces alterations of genetic material caused by the destruction of DNA, the macromolecule responsible for human heridity.

161.
CHROMOSOME DAMAGE FROM MODERATE CANNABIS USE SAME AS DAMAGE FROM RADIATION EXPOSURE

Dr. Hardin B. Jones, consultant to the Atomic Energy Commission on the effects of radiation and protection against radiation states: "As an expert in human radiation effects I point out that the chromosome damage found by Professor Stenchever, even in those who use cannabis moderately, is roughly the same type and degree of damage as in persons surviving atom bombing with a heavy level of radiation exposure—approximately 150 roentgens. The implications are the same."

162.
"MAGNITUDE OF THE PROBLEM COULD BE OVERWHELMING"

After his studies showed that more than 60 per cent of marijuana users developed "a significant increase in chromosome breaks," Dr. Morton A. Stenchever wrote:
"The magnitude of the problem could be overwhelming when one considers the number ofaf25young people using this drug (marijuana). The priorities assigned to such studies should be the highest possible."

163.
RESEARCHERS CONFIRM CHROMOSOME AND CELLULAR DAMAGE

". . . Other researchers have confirmed genetic cellular damage: broken chromosomes, alteration of chromosome numbers per cell, depressive effects of marijuana on the synthesis of two nucleic acids—(DNA and RNA), depression of cell division, and interference with some of the important protein synthesis by cells. Here one of the clear examples is deficiency of human sperm in content of certain proteins."

164.
"THC DESTROYS THE BUILDING BLOCK OF ALL LIFE"

"Prof. Nahas reported that tests revealed that the active hashish agent—tetrahydrocannabinol—enters the body cells and with repeated smoking begins destroying the inherent nucleic acid DNA, often called the building block of all life.

"Recent research has shown that DNA determines the cells and the cell organism's characteristics, including such things as shape, size and color. DNA destruction is held responsible for aging and lowers defenses against all metabolic diseases, including cancer," the scientist explained. "He said the team thus concluded it is wrong to consider hashish a soft drug."

165.
INTERFERES WITH SYNTHESIS OF DNA, RNA AND PROTEIN

At an international conference on marijuana held in Helsinki in the summer of 1975, it was stated that 12 medical research groups documented the finding "that cannabis substances strongly interfere with synthesis of DNA, RNA and protein in a wide variety of cell types . . . that cells treated with cannabinoids undergo abnormal division, producing aberrant nuclei with subnormal amounts of DNA."

166.
DISTURBS CELL DIVISION AND CELL GROWTH

Studies have been undertaken to exhibit the consequences of exposure of cells to amounts of different cannabinoids. Investigators at the 6th International Congress of Pharmacology held in Helsinki reported that in every instance in which different cells were exposed to minute amounts of cannabinoids, cell division was disturbed and normal cell growth was prevented.

167.
CAN AFFECT THE PROCESS OF CELL MULTIPLICATION

"Considering the various studies of Drs. Stenchever, Leuchtenberger and Nahas together with the data presented, I believe that we can conclude that there is an increasing body of evidence to suggest that cannabis can affect the process of cell multiplication and induce profound cytogenetic changes," stated Dr. Akira Morishima, Associate Professor in the Department of Pediatrics of the College of Physicians and Surgeons at Columbia University, in a 1974 appearance before the United States Internal Security Subcommittee.

168.
BENEFICIAL ACTION OF WHITE BLOOD CELLS REDUCED

Macrophages taken from the blood of marijuana smokers have an impaired function. Macrophages are the large white blood cells that move around in our tissues, like amoebas to swallow up foreign substances such as dead bacteria. Dr. B.N. Petersen headed a group from Lilly Laboratories in Indiana and showed that the migrating ability of the macrophages was reduced in marijuana smokers.

169.
DOCTORS WATCH WHITE CELL BECOME PARALYZED IN UNUSUAL MOVIE

In commenting on some of the highlights of the 6th International Congress of Pharmacology held in Helsinki, Dr. Gabriel G. Nahas reported that the "high point of the session was a striking movie. It showed a white blood cell (our body's first line of defense against infection) that had been removed from the lining of the lung. In a natural medium, the cell and all of its parts were moving continuously. After a small amount of THC was added, the cell became completely paralyzed, as if it had lost all life."

170.
PROMINENT DOCTOR FINDS CELLULAR DAMAGE

". . . This destructive psychological effect is not the worse effect of marijuana when it's taken on a regular basis. It is the destructive effect of marijuana on cells of the body that has been one of the most compelling aspects of my work in the past ten years," reported Dr. Gabriel G. Nahas.

171.
DOCTOR URGES RESEARCH TO INVESTIGATE LONG TERM MUTAGENIC ASPECTS

"The observation that marijuana cigarette smoke interferes with the DNA stability in cells and in chromosomes, that is, it disturbs the genetic equilibrium of the cell population, strongly suggests that long-term inhalation may alter the hereditary material DNA and may also have mutagenic potentialities," stated Dr. Cecile Leuchtenberger, as head of the Department of Cytochemistry at the Swiss Institute for Experimental Cancer Research. At the United States Senate Subcommittee on Internal Security, Dr. Leuchtenberger recommended that research should be conducted to investigate the possible mutagenic aspects of the drug.

172.
MODERATE AMOUNT DAMAGES BODY CELLS

Marijuana, even when used in moderate amounts, can cause various kinds of damage to body cells, "actions on microsomes, on mitochondria, on neurones, fibroblasts, white blood cells, and on dividing cells, affecting metabolism, energy utilization, synthesis of cellular constituents, and immunological responses," said Professor W.D.M. Paton of Oxford University to sum up some recent research.

173.
HOW MARIJUANA DAMAGES THE NUCLEUS OF A HUMAN CELL

A study relating marijuana use to chromosome breakage was conducted by Dr. Morton Stenchever and several of his colleagues at the University of Utah College of Medicine. "When you find a chromosome breaking agent," Dr. Stenchever reported, "what you have is an agent which is capable of getting into the nucleus of a cell and causing damage." Another thing that "an agent that can break chromosomes can potentially do is damage the genes in the chromosomes and, therefore, bring about a mutation.. . . ."

174.
INTERNATIONAL CONFERENCE OF SCIENTISTS REPORT MARIJUANA SUBSTANCES AFFECT CELLULAR PROCESSES

THC and other marijuana products have inhibiting effects on cellular processes. This is among the findings of some of the 50 medical scientists who attended the International Conference on Marijuana held in Helsinki in July, 1975.

It was recently noted by Dr. George K. Russell that this finding was documented by a dozen groups of independent research teams. He adds that the "scientists reported that cannabis products interfere with the synthesis of DNA (the chemical substance of which genes are composed), RNA and protein in a wide variety of cell types, including a selection of human cell lines, and that cells treated with cannabis products undergo abnormal division, producing malformed nuclei with subnormal amounts of DNA."

175.
WHITE BLOOD CELL CHANGES IN CHRONIC HASHISH SMOKERS

White blood cell changes in chronic hashish smokers in Greece have been reported by Stefanis and Issidorides.

176.
PREVENTS PROPER DIVISION OF CELLS

"Marijuana has been shown to prevent proper formation of DNA, the chemical which carries the genetic code, in dividing cells. When a cell divides into two parts, the resulting cells have characteristics identical to the mother cell, thanks to DNA. Of course, when DNA is altered in a germ cell, there is the danger that incomplete genetic information will be transmitted to the offspring. This does not mean that the offspring of marijuana smokers will have serious birth defects similar to those which were observed after thalidomide, but there is a great danger that there will be subtle changes in physical or psychological characteristics which might not be detected until much later in life. These subtle alterations might include, for instance, minimal brain dysfunctions," explained Dr. G. Nahas.

177.
MARIJUANA BLOCKS CELL GROWTH

"There is biochemical interruption of cellular metabolism with the prevention of the proper formation of the building blocks essential for cell growth when marijuana is exposed to cell cultures," stated Dr. Nicholas A. Pace. "Scientists agree that marijuana interferes with the synthesis of proteins and causes a decrease in the rate of cell division."

178.
"INACTIVE" MOLECULES IN MARIJUANA JUST AS DANGEROUS AS THC

Dr. Gabriel G. Nahas describes a set of experiments that disclosed that cannabinoids other than THC can impair the division of cells: "This time we took lymphocytes from non-smokers and incubated them in a test tube with three different chemicals of marijuana: Delta-9-tetrahydrocannabinol

(THC), cannabinol (CBN), and cannabidiol (CBD). The THC, as we knew, was a proven psychoactive substance. The CBN and CBD, however, were considered to be non-active components of marijuana that seemed to have no effect whatever on the body. To our surprise, the CBN and CBD molecules were even more potent than THC when it came to inhibiting DNA production."

179.
LOWERS NUMBER OF CHROMOSOMES IN WHITE BLOOD CELLS

Experiments developed to investigate the effects of delta-9-THC (tetrahydrocannabinol) on white blood cells, found that this main constituent of marijuana caused an increased number of cells with an unusually low number of chromosomes.

180.
WHITE BLOOD CELLS REDUCED IN CANNABIS USERS

An impairment of lymphocyte activity in cannabis users has been described by Peterson and Lemberger. In addition, white blood cells that engulf foreign substances (polymorphonuclear phagocytes) were also reduced in number.

181.
CHEMICALS IN MARIJUANA DISRUPT CELLULAR METABOLISM

"In minute amounts chemicals contained in marijuana (cannabinoids) disrupt cellular metabolism and prevent the proper formation of DNA, RNA and proteins, the building blocks essential for cell division and growth," testified Dr. Gabriel G. Nahas.

182.
THC AND RADIATION EXPOSURE PRODUCED SIMILAR EFFECTS

"In animal studies, interference with DNA metabolism, delayed cell division, mutations, broken chromosomes, abnormal chromosome numbers, and malformed embryos have been found to be the effects of exposure to radiation. With the exception of mutations, these effects have been observed in laboratory animals exposed to THC. . . . With the exception of mutations and malformed embryos, these effects have also been observed in humans exposed to THC."

183.

MARIJUANA SHOWN TO AFFECT NORMAL BIOLOGICAL PROCESSES OF CELLS

A number of studies have shown that marijuana, or certain ingredients in marijuana, have an effect on normal biological processes of cells. It is suspected that a chromosome damaging agent is present in marijuana or that some agent in marijuana is convertible to a breaking agent by some metabolic process *in vivo*. Morton A. Stenchever described the effects of such an agent: A "chromosome damaging agent could have a teratogenic effect on the developing fetus, or a damaging effect on germ cells which could lead to a mutagenic response, or it could effect a normal somatic cell to produce a neoplastic change."

184.

EFFECT ON CELL DIVISION

By diminishing the body's capacity to synthesize DNA, RNA, and protein, THC appears to lower the rate of cell division. Scientists have confirmed related effects in other experiments involving human cells.

185.

THC INHIBITS DNA, RNA AND PROTEIN SYNTHESIS

In a recent study by Blevins and Regan, it was found that "adding Delta-9-THC to various types of human and animal cell cultures inhibits DNA, RNA, and protein synthesis."

186.

LYMPHOCYTES REACT ABNORMALLY

"When normal lymphocytes sampled from healthy volunteers who did not smoke marijuana were exposed to very small amounts of THC (a few millionths of a gram), they did not divide normally and their growth was markedly decreased." This result, as stated by Dr. Gabriel G. Nahas, has also been found by Dr. Arthur Zimmerman in his experiments to decrease the growth of tetrahymena.

187.

CAUSES CELLULAR DAMAGE

Marijuana has been shown to cause cellular damage in experimental animals. Experiments leading to such results were performed by two biochemists, Drs. Patrick McGreer and Alexander Jacubovic of the University of British Columbia.

188.
ALTERATION IN CHROMATIN TEMPLATE IN RATS

According to John R. Hodgson, Edward J. Woodhouse, and Thomas R. Castles, THC can significantly depress "brain chromatin template activity in rats." They reported that there appears to have been an alteration in the chromatin template, which could have been caused by the THC joining with the DNA or the chromatin protein, or by an indirect effect on the coding system.

189.
MAY INTERFERE WITH CHROMOSOMAL SEGREGATION

According to Drs. Morishima, Milstein and Nahas of the Departments of Pediatrics and Anesthesiology at Columbia University College of Physicians and Surgeons, THC may interfere with chromosomal segregation. In an experiment the researchers added THC to lymphocyte cultures of healthy adults. They observed an increase in metaphase cells containing less than 30 chromosomes.

190.
MARIJUANA SMOKE MORE HARMFUL THAN GASOLINE FUMES

"The absorption of THC in the body fat means that the THC affects the lipoproteins and the lipid layers of the cell membranes. Absorption of THC into the cell substances is not the only consequence of this process, but many other results which follow this process are still not comprehensively understood. Gasoline and kerosene vapors also have a high affinity for the fatty tissue of the body, but marijuana inhalation seems to be more harmful."

191.
RESULT OF THE THC ACCUMULATION IN CELL MEMBRANES

Alteration of membrane structure and, by inference, alteration of cell function is one of the consequences of the accumulation of THC in cell membranes. This type of change is called fluidification of the membrane.

192.
IMPAIRS CELLULAR DIVISION

In an investigation by Dr. Gabriel G. Nahas, it was demonstrated that when normal lymphocytes from the blood of non-marijuana smokers were cultured in the presence of THC, cannabadiol (CBD), or cannabinol (CBN), they were seriously impaired in their capacity to undergo cellular division.

193.
BREAKS IN CHROMOSOMES FOUND IN HEAVY CANNABIS USERS

A significant increase in breaks in chromosomes has been found by
Kumar and Kunwar in heavy cannabis users. Two out of seven of the
subjects examined exhibited such an increase.

194.
CELL REGRESSION AND DISRUPTION OF SPERMATOGENESIS
FOUND IN MICE

Dixit, et al., found Leydig cell regression and disruption of spermatogenesis in mice to be a result of daily administration of high doses of
cannabis extract.

Chapter VIII

HARMS MALE SEXUAL FUNCTION

195.
ADVERSELY AFFECTS THE REPRODUCTIVE PROCESS

"There is also a growing body of evidence that marijuana adversely affects the reproductive process in a number of ways, and that it poses a serious danger of genetic damage and even of genetic mutation," reported Senator James O. Eastland, chairman of the United States Senate Subcommittee on International Security. Specific, scientific testimony pointed to the following conclusions:

a. Marijuana lowered the testosterone level by 44 percent in young males who had used marijuana at least 4 days a week for a minimum of six months.

b. In the same group of users, sperm count was dramatically reduced, falling almost to zero with heavy smokers, so that they had to be considered sterile. A similar result was found with mice.

c. Very heavy smoking in a number of cases resulted in impotence. Potency was recovered in *some* of these cases when marijuana was given up.

d. In animal experiments, spermatids (which develop into sperm) were found to be abnormal in the sense that they carried reduced amounts of DNA.

e. Regular marijuana use, even down to the once a week level, results in roughly three times as many broken chromosomes as are found in nonusers. While further research is necessary, this suggests the possibility of genetic abnormalities.

f. In a number of animal experiments, marijuana was found to cause a very high rate of fetal deaths and fetal abnormalities, including runting and a lack of limbs. . . .

196.
FOUND TO ALTER SPERM CELLS

"Marijuana has been found to alter sperm cells. Two mouse studies showed a reduction in DNA content of cells destined to become sperm (spermatids) from exposure to marijuana smoke and one showed degenerating forms of spermatids and fragmented sperm from exposure to THC," reported C. Leuchtenberger.

197.
MALE HORMONE LEVEL FOUND TO DECREASE

Dr. Gabriel G. Nahas writes that five scientists have found "evidence that the male hormone level was reduced by forty-four percent in young males who had used marijuana at least four times a week for a minimum of six months; evidence that the sperm count in this same group dropped in proportion to the amount of marijuana smoked, falling to almost zero—or sterility—in some very heavy smokers; evidence that sperm cells in some animals exposed to marijuana carried reduced amounts of DNA; evidence that regular marijuana use resulted in roughly three times as many broken chromosomes as are found in nonusers; evidence that in some animal experiments marijuana caused an increased incidence of fetal deaths and fetal abnormalities."

198.
ABNORMAL FEMALE HORMONE FOUND IN CELLS OF MALE HASHISH USERS

Stefanis and Issidorides have found "a possible confirmation of abnormal female sex hormone influences in the cells of male hashish users. The white blood cells of women have a small characteristic drumstick protrusion from the cell nucleus; this structure is rarely found in white blood cells of men. This female characteristic was found . . . in 10 percent of the white cells from 21 out of 34 men who regularly smoked hashish. None of the nuclei in the white blood cells from the men in the control group showed drumsticks."

199.
CHRONIC HEAVY USE OF MARIJUANA LEADS TO BODILY DETERIORATION

"The chronic heavy use of marijuana . . ." stated Dr. D. Harvey Powelson, "leads to a deterioration of bodily functions that is difficult, sometimes impossible, to reverse. Heavy pot smokers lose their normal appetite. They have trouble sleeping regular hours. They can become sexually impotent."

200.
REDUCTION IN SPERM

Dr. Hembree and his associates "found a 66 percent reduction in sperm after one month of marijuana use."

201.
MARIJUANA USE MAY DELAY ONSET OF PUBERTY IN MALES

Dr. Robert C. Kolodny et al., studied 20 heterosexual males, 18 to 28 years of age who used marijuana at least four days a week for a minimum of six months. He found that "there is . . . a possibility that marijuana use by the prepuberal male may delay the onset or completion of puberty if hypothalmic or pituitary suppression occurs. Investigation of this aspect of marijuana use seems called for."

202.
CHRONIC HASHISH USE MAY LEAD TO IMPOTENCE

"Chronic hashish smoking . . . reduces sexual power and may lead to impotence. These are the same phenomena as in alcohol abuse, particularly in morphinism," contends Dr. Nils Bejerot.

203.
SUPPRESSION OF MALE HORMONE PRODUCTION PROPORTIONAL TO AMOUNT SMOKED

In a 1974 study by Dr. Kolodny, it was shown "that testosterone, the most potent of the male sex hormones, was depressed in the blood of a group of marijuana users." The study, whose participants smoked at least 5 marijuana cigarettes per week, who took the drug at least 4 times a week, and for at least 6 months, found that "the significant effects, which were proportional to the degree of marijuana use, suggest that the suppression of male hormone production is about four percent for each marijuana cigarette smoked per week. It was also observed that sperm production in six of the twenty subjects was significantly depressed. In those six men, there was a significant correlation between sperm count and the blood level of the pituitary hormone known to activate sperm production. The group smoking 10 or more marijuana cigarettes per week had significantly less sperm and less of the pituitary hormone that controls sperm production than those smoking about half as much marijuana."

204.
ONE MARIJUANA CIGARETTE DECREASED TESTOSTERONE LEVEL

Robert C. Kolodny et al., "Depression of Plasma Testosterone with Acute Marihuana Administration," in *Pharmacology of Marihuana*, vol. 1., eds. M.C. Braude and S. Szara (New York: Raven Press, 1976), pp. 219-221.

The smoking of a single marijuana cigarette caused a substantial and progressive decrease in testosterone levels in a study conducted by Kolodny, et al. Additional smoking of marijuana cigarettes further decreased testosterone levels. The study also documented decreases of both plasma testosterone and plasma luteinizing hormone after smoking a single marijuana cigarette.

205.
INTERFERES WITH PRODUCTION OF REPRODUCTIVE HORMONES

"A new study of men who smoked marijuana daily under controlled conditions has shown that the drug can interfere with production of reproductive hormones, in some cases suppressing the male sex hormone, testosterone, to levels that could result in impotence or infertility," Jane E. Brody reported.

The "new study clearly indicates that the drug is the actual cause of this hormonal effect and that the effect can be reversed within two weeks of stopping marijuana use." Described at the first meeting of the International Academy of Sex Research, the study undertaken by researchers at the Reproductive Biology Research Foundation and the University of California, "showed that the testosterone effects of marijuana do not show up until five weeks after continued heavy use of the drug. Thereafter, testosterone levels continued to fall. . . ."

206.
AFTER ONE MONTH OF HEAVY SMOKING MILD DECREASE IN
SPERM OCCURS

"We have also studied sperm cells because they can readily be sampled and collected. In our experiments on young men we have shown that after one month of heavy marijuana smoking there is a mild decrease in sperm.

However, this is not the most serious effect. The most serious and alarming effect is that there is a large incidence of abnormal sperm cells."

207.
HIGH DOSES OF MARIJUANA MAY PRODUCE SEXUAL DYSFUNCTION

"When the sedative effects of high doses of marijuana are predominating, it is quite possible that acute and transient episodes of sexual dysfunction might occur."

208.
DOCTOR FINDS 5% DECLINE IN MALE HORMONE PRODUCTION PER MARIJUANA CIGARETTE SMOKED PER WEEK

Dr. Hardin B. Jones made reference to the findings of Dr. Robert C. Kolodny which indicate a five percent decline in male hormone production for each marijuana cigarette smoked per week. This is the relationship in mature males; it is likely that the effect is relatively larger in the adolescent. Since Kolodny finds that the effect is mediated through the pituitary, and both gonadotropic hormones are diminished, it is likely that a similar effect occurs in women.

209.
INCREASED LEVELS OF MARIJUANA USE CAUSE REDUCTION IN SEXUAL ABILITY

"In interviews with 500 men who were regular users, Dr. Robert C. Kolodny found that with increasing levels of marijuana use, the men reported lower frequency of coitus and orgasm and increasing difficulties with potency and ability to control the time of ejaculation. Yet, the more marijuana the men used, the more they were likely to say that the drug enhanced their enjoyment of the sexual experience," reported *The New York Times*.

210.
HEAVY USERS EXPERIENCE DECREASED SEXUAL FUNCTION

The "observations of Kolodny, et al., confirm clinical reports from India and Morocco which state that heavy users of cannabis preparations display a decreased sexual function in which a lack of desire is coupled with an inability to perform."

Drs. Gabriel G. Nahas and his associates commented that this indicates that smoking marijuana causes a hypothalmic or pituitary dysfunction resulting in a decrease in the plasma testosterone levels and also impotence in chronic users of the drug.

211.
STUDY SHOWS MARIJUANA DECREASES TESTOSTERONE LEVEL

Tharp, Paul, "Cannabis Conference: The Latest Word from Science," *The Village Voice*, February 9, 1976.

Dr. Sidney Cohen of the University of California told the New York Academy of Science's Cannabis Conference about the results of a study of the effects of smoking marijuana on male sex organs. The amount of male sex hormone—testosterone—in the plasma decreases by thirty percent with an intake of six joints of marijuana a day, according to the study.

212.
DELTA-9-THC AFFECTS SEXUAL PERFORMANCE IN RATS

Merari, et al., noted a deterioration of sexual performance when high doses of delta-9-THC were administered to male rats.

213.
SPERM STRUCTURE FOUND DEFECTIVE IN CHRONIC HASHISH USERS

In 1976, Stefanis and Isidorides found consistent defective structure of the sperm in chronic hashish users due to an impairment of protein synthesis.

214.
CHANGE IN SEXUAL ACTIVITY

The relationship between marijuana use and sexual activity has been studied by Dr. Hardin B. Jones. He reports the absence of sexual activity in male smokers, including the absence of sexual dreams. Masturbation is common. The pot smoker does not perceive these changes, due in part to induced depression of pituitary and gonadal function. The clinical result is well-established although the mechanisms are unknown at this time.

215.
HEAVY USE OF MARIJUANA FOUND TO HAVE "STRIKING ESTROGENIC EFFECTS" IN HUMANS AND ANIMALS

Drs. Jolane Solomon and Douglas X. Shattuck of Boston College conducted experiments on 25-day-old male rats in order to verify the findings of various colleagues who found that in human males "heavy use of marijuana has been found to have striking estrogenic effects" and depressed testosterone levels. After treating the rats with 20mg per kilogram of delta-9-THC for 10 weeks, "the depression in skeletal and somatic growth, the increase in adrenal weight, and the decrease in seminal-vesicle weight lend further support to the possibility that large doses of THC have an estrogen-like effect in male rats."

216.
CHRONIC USE LOWERS MALE HORMONE

Professor Reese Jones of the Department of Psychiatry of the University of California has confirmed that chronic marijuana smoking causes a lowering of testosterone, the male hormone.

217.
THC INHALATION CAUSED REDUCTION IN MALE SPLEEN AND TESTES WEIGHTS

Harris Rosenkrantz, "Cellular, Immunological, and Hormonal Effects," in *Pharmacology of Marihuana*, vol. 1, eds. M.C. Braude and S. Szara (New York: Raven Press, 1976), p. 141.

In tests on animals, using the inhalation route, male spleen and testes weights were reduced by delta-9-THC by the 28th day. After the prolonged treatment of 87 days, the weight losses for adrenal weights and testes were increased.

218.
MARIJUANA SMOKE DECREASED TESTOSTERONE

Rosenkrantz and Braude have found decreased testosterone in rats exposed to marijuana smoke.

219.
"THAT'S TRUE IMPOTENCE"

"There can be true impotence among marijuana users—no sexual dreaming, no surges of sexual desire in either the male or the female. That's true impotence."

220.
SEXUAL URGE DIMINISHES

"Researchers claim that the anatomical structures that control sexual functions are first irritated and then impaired by cannabis use. The user in his early experiences reports a good feeling and his sex becomes more sensual. As he progressively smokes more cannabis, however, his sexual urges diminish steadily. Frequent marijuana users report an absence of sexual activity, a lack of sexual connotative dreams and a disappearance of nocturnal emissions. Perhaps these results are related to induced depression of the pituitary and gonadal functions. The exact physical reasons remain unknown at this time, but the clinical consequences are becoming clearer."

221.
MAY CAUSE LOW TESTOSTERONE LEVEL FOR SOME MEN

M.C. Braude and S. Szara eds., *Pharmacology of Marihuana*, vol. 1, (New York: Raven Press, 1976), p. 226.

Dr. Robert C. Kolodny speculates that there is at least a possibility of low testosterone level as a result of marijuana use. He suggests that in men with marginal (sexual or procreative) functions, a lowering of their testosterone level may result in partial or complete impotence or difficulty in conception.

222.
SIGNIFICANT DECREASE IN SPERM FOUND AFTER 2 WEEKS

"Over a 2 year period, 16 marijuana smokers aged 18 to 23, were hospitalized in the Research Ward of the Psychiatric Institute of Columbia University. Each subject was studied for 8 to 12 weeks. The study was divided in 3 periods: a 3 to 4 week drug-free period; a 4 week smoking period, and a 3 to 4 week wash out phase. All subjects were carefully selected from a large pool of marijuana smokers, and only those in good physical and mental health were retained," reported Dr. Gabriel G. Nahas, who conducted this investigation along with Drs. Hembree, Morishima and Zeidenberg.

"During the smoking period, the subjects smoked an average of 5 to 15 cigarettes of marijuana a day (0.9 gm of marijuana, 2% THC). The highest daily consumption was 36 in one subject. The subjects claimed to have smoked such large amounts on certain occasions, when marijuana was available. Twelve of the sixteen subjects had significant and sustained decrease in sperm concentration occurring only after 2 weeks of marijuana smoking and sustained for at least 2 weeks," they reported.

223.
EFFECT OF MARIJUANA ON GONADS

"Studies of the effects of marijuana on the function of the gonads have so far been conducted only on men. However, because the gonad-stimulating hormones are controlled through the pituitary, similar changes may also be detected in women who smoke marijuana," wrote Dr. Hardin B. Jones and Helen C. Jones.

224.
ABNORMAL SPERM CELLS

Dr. Nicholas A. Pace has found that "there was . . . a decrease in the mobility of the sperm (movement of the sperm). The most potentially damaging effect of marijuana on the sperm was the marked increase in abnormal forms of the sperm cell. This brings forth the genetic possibility of transmitting abnormally viable sperm with decreased genetic information to a fertilized egg."

225.
MAY ALTER MALE REPRODUCTIVE SYSTEM

In a study of 20 heterosexual males, 18 to 28 years of age, using marijuana four days a week for a minimum of six months (without the use of other drugs), the findings suggest that chronic use of marijuana over a period of time may produce alterations in the male reproductive system, causing a decrease in testosterone level. Six of seventeen men showed oligospermia, and two men were impotent. "Now the possibility of an adverse effect of frequent marijuana use on male sexual functioning must be considered," stated the research team members.

226.
MEN WHO SMOKE VERY HEAVILY MAY DEVELOP GYNECOMASTIA

"There is a strong similarity," stated Dr. Aliapoulios as a member of the Harvard Medical School faculty, "between an ingredient of marijuana, delta-9-tetrahydrocannabinol, and the female hormone, estradiol. Young men who smoke pot heavily, and by that I mean one or two hours per day or two to three hours, three or four times a week, such men stand a very good chance of developing gynecomastia," (enlarged breasts in the male).

In a 1972 article that Dr. Aliapoulios wrote with John Harmon, "the surgeons pointed out . . . that they had treated three young men in the 22-26 age group for gynecomastia and that all three turned out to be heavy pot smokers.

"Since then . . . (they) have treated 10 more young men with the same affliction and have come to the conclusion that there is a positive correlation between heavy marijuana use and breast enlargement.

"Not only do their breasts enlarge and swell painfully but their nipples begin to discharge a white, milky liquid. Obviously marijuana contains a feminizing ingredient.

"All young men who smoke pot heavily, will not, of course, develop breast enlargement. Some, however, will, and swollen breasts in young men are particularly painful and psychologically harmful."

227.
RELEASES SEXUAL INHIBITIONS . . . THEN DECREASES SEXUAL URGE

Excerpt from THE SEEKERS by Jess Stearn. Copyright © 1968, 1969 by Jess Stern. Used by permission of Doubleday & Company, Inc.

Marijuana is a tricky drug which at different times has different effects upon the user. It releases sexual inhibitions at the onset but with continued use, reported Dr. Constandinos J. Miras, Chairman of the Biological Chemistry Department at the Athens University School of Medicine. "This increased sexual activity was altered to complete sexual apathy even at the age of forty."

228.
MARIJUANA AND SEX

In the habitual user, there is a combination of indifference to the opposite sex and extreme promiscuity. There are feelings of unrivaled sexual potency but they are without affection. If the choice were necessary, marijuana is chosen rather than women.

229.
DIRECT RELATIONSHIP BETWEEN MARIJUANA USE AND SEXUAL RELATIONS

"What I found was that all measures of sexual activity correlated significantly and powerfully with all measures of drug abuse. Marijuana users were far more likely to have engaged in premarital sex than nonusers." These are the comments of Dr. Erich Goode, Associate Professor of Sociology, State University of New York at Stony Brook. In an article about marijuana and sex, he stated that "the more frequently marijuana was used, and the greater number of drugs experimented with, the greater the number of sexual partners the respondent had intercourse with." Dr. Goode added that "there was an almost perfect linear relationship between frequency of smoking marijuana and premarital sexual intercourse."

230.
PROBLEMS OF USERS MAY BE TRACED TO MARIJUANA

It "is conceivable that some marijuana smokers use the drug to avoid meaningful contact with members of the opposite sex. It is certainly possible that some users experience difficulty in their lives which can, at least in part, be traced in some way or another to their use of marijuana. And no doubt some users engage in a compulsive, self-flagellating form of 'promiscuity' that they themselves despise and condemn," reported Dr. Erich Goode.

231.
MARIJUANA AND PROMISCUITY

In a large northeastern university, Ibtihaj Arafat and Betty Yorburg surveyed women on campus. They found that the women who used drugs, principally marijuana, tended to be having sex relations. The non-users were less likely to be engaging in sex relations. The marijuana users were also likely to be having sex relations with more than one person.

232.
LOWERS MORAL STANDARDS

J.S. Hochman and N.Q. Brill of U.C.L.A. found that the students who used marijuana often, had greater sexual experience as compared to a group of non-users. They also experienced sex at an earlier age and with more than one partner.

Chapter IX

DANGER TO PREGNANT WOMEN AND THEIR BABIES

233.
MARIJUANA MAY AFFECT SEXUAL DIFFERENTIATION IN MALE EMBRYO

Dr. Hardin B. Jones reported that "at least some of the active constituents of marijuana cross the placenta and enter fetal circulation (and can also pass into breast milk). Thus, there may be a significant risk of depressed testosterone levels in the developing fetus when marijuana is used by a pregnant woman. Since normal sexual differentiation in the male embryo depends on adequate testosterone stimulation during critical stages of fetal development, maternal use of the drug may disturb that development."

234.
MARIJUANA USERS EXPERIENCE RISK FROM SOMATIC GENETIC CHANGE

"Of primary concern to the individual is the risk from somatic genetic change, the greatest danger being carcinogenesis. Though not all mutagens are necessarily carcinogens, there does seem to be a relationship. A large number of known carcinogens, when tested in non-mammalian systems, have been found to be mutagenic," stated Steven S. Matsuyama.

There is "the possibility of an increase in neoplastic diseases which may

71

affect today's young people many years from now, as well as the possibility of an increase in deformed infants in the next or successive generations as a result of present day marijuana use.

"In addition, adverse genetic effects from the consumption of marijuana and related compounds during the organogenesis stage of pregnancy may cause teratogenic consequences."

235.
FETAL ABNORMALITY AND DEFORMITY WHEN ADMINISTERED TO ANIMALS

The "administration of cannabis during the vulnerable period of pregnancy has been found to cause fetal death and fetal abnormality in three species of animals. The deformity includes lack of limbs—reduction deformity," observed Dr. W.D.M. Paton of Oxford University. Additionally, he explained that marijuana "is taken for its psychic action; it is cumulative and persistent; . . . experimentally it is teratogenic (producing fetal deformities); psychotic phenomena may occur with a single dose; . . . the price for overuse is paid in adolescence or in early life."

236.
PREGNANT WOMEN WARNED TO STOP SMOKING

"Researchers from the St. John's University College of Pharmacy in Jamaica, N.Y., warned that pregnant women should stop smoking marijuana. The warning was based on findings linking marijuana with 'high incidence' of a kidney malformation, as well as death and stunted growth, in the offspring of mice exposed to low doses of Cannabis sativa while pregnant."

237.
TESTS ON RHESUS MONKEYS SHOW IMPAIRMENT IN REPRODUCTIVE FUNCTION

A study by Sassenrath and Chapman on rhesus monkeys indicated impairment in reproductive function, produced by chronically administered delta-9-THC. Their data suggest that:

"1. Failure to conceive or resorptions are associated with THC-treatment of the female parent;

"2. Abortions, stillbirths, and neonatal deaths are associated with THC-treatment of the male parent."

238.
ANIMAL STUDIES BRING WARNING ON USE DURING PREGNANCY

"Robert J. Staab and Vincent de P. Lynch of St. John's University College of Pharmacy warn pregnant women against smoking marijuana in the light of the 'high incidence' of kidney malformation as well as death and stunted growth in the offspring of mice exposed to low doses of cannabis during pregnancy."

239.
HARMFUL EFFECTS SHOWN IN MICE AND RAT TESTS

Dr. Paton's experiments were similar to those in which pregnant rats were injected with cannabis in amounts "not far from the equivalent of the dose that could be received by someone smoking cannabis." The rats produced only 13 percent normal offspring. The balance of the rats gave birth to fifty-seven percent deformed offspring and nearly 30 percent of the rats suffered miscarriages.

"If one were to view cannabis simply as a new drug which might be introduced into medicine," said Dr. Paton, "the evidence we already have of health hazards would rule it out."

240.
A DOCTOR TESTIFIES ON POSSIBLE SERIOUS CONSEQUENCES OF SMOKING MARIJUANA

Dr. Robert Kolodny of the Reproductive Biology Research Foundation in Missouri explains why he is opposed to the legalization of marijuana. ". . . There is evidence currently, based on both animal and human experimentation, that indicates the possibility of consequences that potentially are serious ones . . . such as disruption of sperm production, the possibility of birth defects, the possibility of impairment of hormone balance, and the possibility of either inhibition of puberty or disruption of normal sexual differentiation during fetal development. . . ."

241.
MARIJUANA CAUSES BIRTH DEFECTS IN MICE

The effects of marijuana on mice has been studied by Dr. Vincent de Paul Lynch. He found that marijuana smoke caused birth defects in the offspring of the animals for two generations. This suggests that marijuana should not be used by pregnant women.

242.
GENETIC DAMAGE FOUND IN TWO GENERATIONS

"Professor Sassenrath has established marijuana induced genetic damage in monkey breeding experiments. The work is also confirmed independently in experiments involving mice and rats. When the male parent alone is exposed to marijuana, there are significant increases in congenitally malformed offspring. This means genetic damage." In addition, "one study has gone through two generations in two separate experimental runs."

243.
RATS AND MICE EXPOSED TO MARIJUANA GIVE BIRTH TO DEFORMED YOUNG

The National Institute of Mental Health has performed experiments on the long range physical and psychological effects of the drug. "Preliminary findings of these experiments have shown that rats and mice with no previous history of genetic defects—after exposure to marijuana smoke—gave birth to dwarfs and young with bizarre developments of the lower jaw."

244.
GENETIC ABNORMALITIES FOUND IN 2ND GENERATION OF ANIMALS EXPOSED TO MARIJUANA

"Two major studies have shown genetic and developmental damage in laboratory rodents after exposure to marijuana. One unpublished study, conducted by Vincent Lynch of Saint John's University, New York, examined the transmission of defects to succeeding generations. Excessive abnormalities appeared in two generations after exposure to the original animals. In this instance only two generations were studied. The other study conducted by Peter Fried of Carlton University, Canada, establishes a variety of genetic changes in offspring of rats exposed to marijuana. Developmental abnormalities were found to be equally frequent after the exposure of either male or female parents."

245.
MALFORMATIONS FOUND IN OFFSPRING OF MONKEYS EXPOSED TO MARIJUANA

"E. Sassenrath . . . has reported recent findings on the increase in malformations in the offspring of monkeys exposed to marijuana. These results, the first definitive findings on primate malformation associated with marijuana, confirm the results of earlier studies involving laboratory rodents. As many developmental abnormalities were found in the offspring when the father monkey alone was exposed to marijuana as when the mother was."

246.
MARIJUANA AFFECTS PREGNANCY & OFFSPRING IN ANIMAL EXPERIMENTS

Dr. Hardin B. Jones reported that animal experiments have shown that marijuana affects pregnancy and offspring. Enough has been demonstrated about the effects of marijuana on the endocrine and cell systems to suggest a similar effect on humans. When administered to pregnant mice, THC was found to accumulate in the placenta and embryonic tissue. In a group of experimental animals, the number of liveborn babies, the size of litters, and the size of the offspring all declined.

"It has been established in three species of animals that crude cannabis administered during pregnancy causes fetal death or fetal abnormality and that these effects are dose related. The doses used in these animal studies were high, but the results should not therefore be discounted."

247.
THC MAY BE TRANSMITTED THROUGH MOTHER'S MILK IN TESTS ON RATS

Dr. Peter A. Fried of Carlton University in Ottawa studied young suckling rats whose mothers had been exposed to marijuana smoke. His findings suggest that THC may be transmitted to the offspring through the mother's milk.

248.
THC SHOWN DANGEROUS TO MICE OFFSPRING

Bernardo Mantilla-Plata and Raymond D. Harbison, "Influence of Alteration of Tetrahydrocannabinol Metabolism on Tetrahydrocannibinol-Induced Teratogenesis," in *Pharmacology Of Marihuana*, vol. 2., eds. M.C. Braude and S. Szara (New York: Raven Press, 1976), p. 733.

THC, when administered to pregnant mice at critical times of fetal organogenesis has been shown to induce cleft palate in the fetus, according to Mantilla-Plata et al.

249.
EFFECT ON PREGNANT RODENTS

Bernardo Mantilla-Plata and Raymond D. Harbison, "Influence of Alteration of Tetrahydrocannibinol Metabolism on Tetrahydrocannabinol-Induced Teratogenesis," in *Pharmacology Of Marihuana*, vol. 2., eds. M.C. Braude and S. Szara (New York: Raven Press, 1976), p. 733.

It is reported by several scientists that THC (delta-9-tetrahydrocannabinol) produces fetocidal and embryocidal effects when it is administered to pregnant mice and rats.

250.
MAY DISRUPT SEXUAL DIFFERENTIATION IN MALE EMBRYO

There is "the possibility that frequent intensive marijuana use during critical stages of pregnancy might result in disruption of normal sexual differentiation patterns in the male embryo . . . Until this area is better understood, it would appear to be judicious for pregnant women to avoid the use of marijuana or hashish oil."

251.
AFFECT ON FETUSES REVEALED IN 1969

That "marijuana, like LSD, may affect the development of fetuses and the genetic characteristics of organisms," has been revealed by Dr. William F. Geber.

252.
POSSIBILITY OF GENETIC DAMAGE

In discussing the effect of marijuana on children born to young men with a large incidence of abnormal sperm cells, Dr. Gabriel G. Nahas noted that "there is a danger of genetic damage to the offspring." He believes that the effect of marijuana on the offspring, if the woman smokes as much as the man is "more serious, I believe, because men manufacture large amounts of sperm daily. However, a woman has only 400,000 germ cells at birth. Every germ cell that is impaired will remain imperfect. This again raises the possibility of genetic damage to her future offspring."

253.
MARIJUANA CROSSES PLACENTAL BARRIERS

"It is possible that a drug that has an affinity for brain tissue in adults may have a greater affinity for brain tissue in the developing fetus, and that it may induce malformations in the development of small areas of the brain," reported Morton A. Stenchever. "Marijuana certainly has this potential since it is lipophilic and does cross both the placental and bloodbrain barriers."

254.
A WARNING FOR FUTURE PARENTS

"No other environmental hazard is as likely to influence the health of those yet to be born. Persons smoking marijuana should pause and reflect on their responsibility for the health of their future children."

255.
NOT ADVISABLE DURING PREGNANCY

The National Commission on Marijuana and Drug Abuse reports that "since fetal damage cannot be ruled out, the use of marijuana like that of many other drugs, is not advisable during pregnancy."

256.
MEMPHIS PAPER WARNS MARIJUANA COULD CHANGE GENETIC MAKE-UP FOR GENERATIONS

The Memphis Commercial Appeal editorialized that the "possibility that the offspring of marijuana smokers could be adversely affected is of extreme concern, for it could change the genetic make-up of generations to come."

Chapter X

HARMFUL EFFECTS ON SENSES, RESPIRATORY TRACT, LIVER, HEART, GLANDS, CENTRAL NERVOUS SYSTEM AND SLEEP PATTERNS

257.
DIRECT EFFECT ON CONJUNCTIVAL BLOOD VESSELS OF THE EYE

Conjunctival congestion, or the reddening of the eyes, is a proven characteristic of cannabis smoking. This congestion is still apparent over 90 minutes after smoking cannabis. This effect is not due to irritation from the cannabis smoke but due to a direct effect of THC on the conjunctival blood vessels of the eye. Yellow deposits around the conjunctiva of chronic users in India as a result of cannabis use remain for years, reported G.S. Chopra.

258.
ALTERATION OF PERIPHERAL VISION

One of the dangers of marijuana that is not commonly known is the fact that a marijuana user suffers an alteration of peripheral vision, stated Dr. Robert W. Baird of the Haven Clinic in New York.

259.
REDDENING OF EYES OCCURS

Reprinted from DRUGS AND THE MIND, New Revised Edition, by Robert S. De Ropp. Copyright © 1957, 1976 by Robert S. De Ropp. Used by permission of the publisher, Delacorte Press/Seymour Lawrence.

All "investigators agree that reddening of the conjunctiva of the eyes takes place as a result of the action of this drug (marijuana). It has nothing to do with irritation of the eyes by the smoke. It is a specific effect of the drug and occurs whether it is smoked or taken by mouth. The size of the eye pupil is not affected by marijuana."

260.
INCREASES COMPLEX VISUAL REACTION TIME

"Marijuana has been reported to increase complex visual reaction time, and especially to increase variability in performance because of occasional lapses of attention," stated Dr. I.R. Rosengard.

261.
HASHISH AFFECTS SIGHT AND HEARING

During hashish intoxication the sensations of sight and hearing are altered. It is difficult for the abuser to judge time and distance and even the length of his own limbs. Muscle coordination deteriorates which may result in serious misjudgments, according to Dr. Nils Bejerot. He also found that drivers and pedestrians who are hashish smokers are dangerous on the roads.

262.
EFFECTS OF MARIJUANA ON THE MOUTH AND TONGUE

Drs. Paton and Pertwee report that: "The smoking of cannabis characteristically produces a dry mouth. This may become intense and affect the tongue, throat, and nose, with a feeling of thirst and difficulty in swallowing. There may be some burning and irritation of the tongue, a resinous taste, and an anesthesia of the tip of the tongue (compared with the effect of menthol). Numbness and paresthesiae around the mouth have been noted."

263.
"TELL-TALE" SIGN OF MARIJUANA USE

According to Dr. L.E. Hollister, "A regular sign of the drug (marijuana) is conjunctival injection, which is not dependent upon irritation, as it appears equally when the drug is ingested as well as when it is smoked. Its duration tends to parallel that of the drug's actions, so it may be a reliable clinical sign of intake. Dryness of oral and pharyngeal mucous membranes also is commonly observed."

264.
SMOKING SIZEABLE QUANTITY CAUSES BLOODSHOT EYES

Some "drug effects will be fairly distinct and will not vary a great deal, and there will be widespread agreement on their occurrence. In almost every case the whites of a person's eyes will become bloodshot after he has smoked a sizeable quantity of marijuana."

265.
COMMON RESULT IS REDDENING OF THE EYES

One of the more common reactions to the use of marijuana is conjunctival injection, more commonly known as reddening of the eyes.

266.
PHYSIOLOGICAL AND SUBJECTIVE REACTIONS NOTED IN 1944

"Physiologic responses to marijuana include tachycardiamydriasis and suffusion of the conjutiva. Subjective sensations often include feelings of heaviness or pressure in the head, dryness of the mouth, and a 'floating sensation'," stated Dr. S. Allentuck.

267.
RESPIRATORY DIFFICULTIES LINKED TO MARIJUANA SMOKING

Chronic cannabis smoking can produce "sinusitis, pharyngitis, bronchitis, emphysema and other respiratory difficulties in a year or less, as opposed to ten to twenty years of cigarette smoking to produce comparable complications." This was brought out at United States Senate hearings by several medical researchers.

268.
AFFECTS FIRST LINE OF DEFENSE IN LUNGS

It has been shown by researcher Chari-Bitron that THC leads to paralysis of alveolar macrophages. These cells are considered to be the first line of defense in the human lung.

269.
"LUNGS OF THE MARIJUANA SMOKER CHANGE PERMANENTLY FROM PINK TO BLACK"

"The lungs of the marijuana smoker become more irritated than those of the tobacco smoker. The irritation is greater because THC is more tightly bound to the carbon particles in the smoke than nicotine is, and, in order to get an effect, the marijuana smoker must inhale deeply and hold the smoke in his lungs. After even a short period of exposure, as the carbon particles accumulate, the lungs of the marijuana smoker change permanently from pink to black," stated Dr. Hardin B. Jones of the Donner Laboratory.

270.
CHRONIC CANNABIS SMOKING MAY LEAD TO EMPHYSEMA IN YOUNG PEOPLE

Professor Paton of Oxford University has pointed out that emphysema which normally occurs late in life is appearing more and more frequently in young people, "opening up the prospect of a 'new crop of respiratory cripples' early in life," due to their chronic cannabis smoking.

271.
HEAVY CHRONIC USE COULD LEAD TO CHANGE IN LUNG FUNCTION

The National Institute on Drug Abuse reported on the effect of marijuana on lung functioning: "Because marijuana is characteristically smoked in the United States and because of the known adverse effects of cigarette smoking, this has been a continued source of concern . . . although there is now good evidence that marijuana and delta-9-THC administered acutely produce an increase in the diameter of the air passages of the lung . . . chronic use may have quite different implications. Previously reported research has indicated impairments in pulmonary function in chronic marijuana smokers. More recent work using still more sophisticated measures has demonstrated detectable impairment in lung functioning after six to eight weeks of heavy cannabis smoking. The changes found, while still within normal limits, persisted at least one week after smoking. This suggests that heavy chronic use could well lead to clinically important changes similar to those found in heavy cigarette smokers.

272.
FIND STATISTICALLY SIGNIFICANT IMPAIRMENTS IN PULMONARY FUNCTION

"We found statistically significant impairments in pulmonary function tests, vital capacity, $FEV_{1.0}$, or both, in 14 of our subjects at the outset of these studies, suggesting the possibility that their prior marijuana smoking may have adversely affected their lungs. When tested within an hour of marijuana smoking, these subjects exhibited a further reduction in pulmonary function. This suggests an apparent adverse effect of marijuana on the respiratory tract."

273.
BRONCHITIS AND RESPIRATORY AILMENTS

"Eastern scientists and others report a high frequency for bronchitis and other respiratory problems in their studies of chronic user populations. . . . Doctors recently have reported on a group of soldiers in West Germany who used hashish very heavily. A majority had respiratory complaints which included bronchitis, sinusitis, asthma, and inflammation of the nose and throat. In five patients who showed evidence of bronchitis, pulmonary function studies showed a mild obstructive condition," reported Dr. I.R. Rosengard in a recent issue of Science Digest.

274.
LUNG DAMAGE DISCOVERED AFTER 6 TO 8 WEEKS OF HEAVY SMOKING

Doctor Robert L. DuPont, Director of the National Institute on Drug Abuse, reported that "research on heavy marijuana smokers found that lung impairment can be detected after six to eight weeks of heavy smoking (5 to 20 cigarettes or joints a day). This suggests that heavy chronic use could lead to damage similar to that found in heavy cigarette smokers."

275.
EFFECT ON RESPIRATORY TRACT

"Eight of the subjects showed some further reduction in pulmonary function test results when tested within an hour of marijuana smoking, again lending credence to the apparent effect of marijuana on the respiratory tract," reported Jerrold G. Bernstein and his associates.

276.
PATIENTS WITH LUNG DISEASES ARE WARNED

Patients with existing lung disease are warned by physicians against the use of cannabis. According to Dr. Hardin B. Jones, "there is a well-founded claim that marijuana smoking makes breathing easier during the immediate period of exposure to the smoke. The effect seems to be due to drug-induced relaxation of the bronchioles. This observation has led to a claim by some people in the movement to legalize marijuana that the drug offers a benefit to asthmatics. It has been noted just as frequently in the literature, however, that marijuana is likely to bring on an asthmatic attack. These are not contradictory sets of observations; the induction of attacks of asthma seems to be caused by the chronic irritation by the marijuana smoke, an inflammation due to the cytotoxic impact of the THC itself. It certainly appears necessary to warn young asthmatics that aggravation is the more likely result of marijuana smoking."

277.
IRRITANT EFFECTS

Evidence of irritant effects with chronic cannabis use has been noted by Drs. Paton and Pertwee. Investigators have found "chronic pharyngitis and laryngitis, edema of the uvula, with hoarseness and catarrh, an increase in flow of bronchial mucous after an initial reduction, sinusitis and changes in alveolar macrophages. Inspiratory or expiratory dyspnea may occur. Bronchitis or asthma was diagnosed in 10 of 31 subjects believed to be heavy users. . . ."

278.
CHRONIC SMOKING CAUSES . . . ABNORMAL MICROSCOPIC CHANGES IN LUNG TISSUE

Dr. Phillip Zeidenberg as research associate in psychiatry at Columbia University and senior research psychiatrist at New York State Psychiatric Institute stated that "chronic marijuana smoking causes bronchitis, diminished lung capacity, and abnormal microscopic changes in lung tissue. In the long run, marijuana smoking may have many of the pulmonary effects of tobacco."

279.
HEAVY USERS IN MOROCCO MORE SUSCEPTIBLE TO TUBERCULOSIS

The relation between heavy use of marijuana and tuberculosis in Morocco was mentioned by Dr. Gabriel Nahas in his testimony before the United States Internal Security Subcommittee. While on a trip to the Rif Mountains of Morocco, Dr. Nahas was told "by the Under Secretary of Health of Morocco that heavy marijuana users were more susceptible to tuberculosis which in that area constitutes a major public health problem."

280.
HEALTHY SUBJECTS SHOWED BREAKDOWN IN BRONCHIAL MECHANICS

L. Vachon et al., "Bronchial Effect of Marihuana Smoke in Asthma," in *Pharmacology of Marihuana*, vol. 2., eds. M.C. Braude and S. Szara (New York: Raven Press, 1976), p. 783.

A significant bronchodilatation in normal human subjects is shown in the data of Vachon, of the Boston University School of Medicine from a study of the effect of marijuana smoke on bronchial mechanics. This report has been confirmed in an independent study by Taskin, Shapiro, and Frank.

281.

Carlton R. McCarthy et al., "The Effect Of Marihuana on the In Vitro Function of Pulmonary Alveolar Macrophages," in *Pharmacology of Marihuana*, vol. 1, eds. M.C. Braude and S. Szara (New York: Raven Press, 1976), p. 215.

The alveolar macrophage (the key cell of the lung's defense against pulmonary disease and environmental pollutants) is impaired by the presence of fresh marijuana smoke. This impairment of alveolar macrophages may be caused by any of the different components of the smoke. Impairment of alveolar macrophages' function may in turn render the organism more susceptible to pathologic processes and bacterial infection in the lungs.

282.
"MARKED BRONCHITIS" REPORTED BY PHYSICIAN

From MARIJUANA AND YOUR CHILD by Jules Saltman. Copyright © 1970 by Jules Saltman. Used by permission of Grosset & Dunlap, Inc.

Respiratory ailments in pot smokers have been noticed by American physicians. Dr. Milton M. Waldman reports that one of his patients who had smoked five or six cigarettes a day for several years had a "marked bronchitis."

283.
RESEARCHERS REPORT EFFECT ON WORKING ABILITY OF THE LIVER

The effects of marijuana on the body are very complex. Drs. Paton and Crown noted that "another cannabinoid of marijuana smoke, cannabidiol, in addition to modifying the lipid structure of the cell membrane differently from the THC, impairs liver cell microsomal activity. The suppression of microsomal activity in liver cells causes a general reduction in the ability of the liver to decompose toxic substances."

284.
HEPATIC DEGENERATION & DYSFUNCTION FOUND IN CANNABIS USERS

In the follow-up of a case of hematemesis due to cirrhosis of the liver in a young cannabis smoker, signs of hepatic degeneration were found in three out of 12 cannabis users and dysfunction found in eight out of 12.

285.
NATIONAL INSTITUTE ON DRUG ABUSE REPORTS MARIJUANA CAN BLOCK LIVER FUNCTION

"Some of the metabolites of marijuana are very active in themselves . . ." reported the National Institute on Drug Abuse. "Additionally some constituents can block important drug metabolizing enzymes in the liver (i.e., block natural chemicals which play an essential role in metabolizing drugs or preventing the accumulation of potentially injurious substances). Such blocking might cause toxic reactions were marijuana to be ingested simultaneously with other drugs normally detoxified in the liver."

286.
NATIONAL INSTITUTE OF DRUG ABUSE REPORTS POT IS DANGEROUS FOR THOSE WITH HEART DISEASE

"Effects on cardiovascular functioning have been extensively studied. Indeed, tachycardia (an accelerated heart rate) is the most common and prominent physiological response to marijuana use . . . the effects of marijuana may be dangerous for those with cardiac abnormalities. Evidence that marijuana not only increases heart rate, but may also temporarily weaken heart muscle contractions has led the researchers who originally studied patients with heart disease to express concern about marijuana use among individuals with such problems. The research on the effects of marijuana on patients with angina (cardiac related chest pain) illustrates that effects on those with any type of health problem cannot always be predicted from studies of normal volunteers. Studies of normal young men have not revealed any serious effects on heart functioning."

287.
INCREASES HEART RATE

The increase in heart rate caused by marijuana is moderate but significant. The pulse will rise from 72 beats per minute to over 90 beats per minute. After you start smoking the heart beats faster, peaks and then decreases.

288.
ABNORMAL HEART ACTION

Bernstein et al., reported that "sinus tachycardia (abnormal heart action) was generally seen after marijuana smoking, being particularly pronounced when subjects were standing."

289.
EFFECTS OF MARIJUANA ON PATIENTS WITH CORONARY CONDITION

Drs. Wilbert S. Aronow and John Cassidy conducted an experiment in which they evaluated 10 patients with a history of chest pain and coronary conditions in regard to the effect of smoking marijuana compared to smoking placebo marijuana: "Smoking marijuana significantly decreased the exercise time until angina (occurred) more than smoking marijuana placebo." Also, it was found that smoking marijuana "probably increases the myocardial oxygen demand and decreases myocardial oxygen delivery, causing patients with angina to experience angina after exercise sooner, and with less work."

290.
30 MG. OF THC DOUBLED HEART BEAT OF USER

Reprinted from DRUGS AND THE MIND, New Revised Edition, by Robert S. De Ropp. Copyright © 1957, 1976 by Robert S. De Ropp. Used by permission of the publisher, Delacorte Press/Seymour Lawrence.

Although a subject in an investigation by E.E. Domino "seemed extremely tolerant of the psychic effects" of marijuana, he exhibited an increase in heart rate from 55 to 120 beats per minute after smoking marijuana containing 30 mg. of THC.

291.
MAY ALTER AUTONOMIC TONE OF HEART

"The two most consistent physiological effects of marijuana are an increase in pulse rate and reddening of the eyes. Perhaps the most consistent physiological occurrence . . . is an increase in heart rate. The increase is dependent on the dose of THC administered. . . . There is a gradual return to normal or near normal by 85 minutes after smoking. . . . Experiments suggest that marijuana may have its effect on heart rate by altering normal autonomic tone," reported Dr. I.R. Rosengard.

292.
INCREASE IN HEART RATE IS DOSE-RELATED

Edward F. Domino et al., "Short-Term Neuropsychopharmacological Effects of
Marihuana Smoking in Experienced Male Users," in *Pharmacology of Marihuana*, vol. 1., eds. M.C. Braude and S. Szara (New York: Raven Press, 1976),
p. 401.

Several groups of investigators including Kiplinger, Manno, Rodda,
Forney, and Johnson and Domino, report that smoking marijuana produces
an increase in heart rate that is dose-related.

293.
PATIENTS WITH DISEASED CORONARY ARTERIES EXPERIENCE CHEST PAINS WITH USE

Another concern over marijuana use raised by Dr. Robert L. DuPont,
"relates to the types of persons who become users. From a public health
standpoint, we may be fortunate that marijuana users are now concentrated
among young adults, persons who are generally healthy. . . .

"Many patients with diseased coronary arteries experience chest pains
when they use marijuana. Similarly, the implications for the use of
marijuana by persons having greater problems with coping, or fewer skills
for doing so, may be quite different from those of the more competent,
advantaged youth who predominate in current-using populations."

294.
ALTERS SLEEPING PATTERNS

According to Dr. Hardin B. Jones, the "diurnal cycle of sleep and waking
is largely inverted. The marijuana user stays up at night."

295.
"SLOW-WAVE SLEEP" CHANGED

Normal sleep is divided into several stages as shown by the study of brain
waves using an electroencephelograph. "Slow wave" sleep seems to be
altered by marijuana use, according to studies by Dr. Ernest Barrat and his
co-workers. The sleep patterns of marijuana users were studied for two
weeks. The subjects smoked one joint of marijuana before going to sleep,
with their sleep being monitored by continuous EEG recordings. At first,
there was an increase in the length of time spent in slow-wave sleep, but
then there was a reversal. This decrease in slow-wave sleep was present
even after the subjects stopped smoking marijuana.

296.
BRINGS ON SLEEPINESS

The accumulated data from animal research by many investigators can interpret the pharmacologic action of tetrahydrocannabinol as both a depressant and a stimulant. There are many reports of marijuana bringing on sleepiness in humans and many users report that they use marijuana occasionally "to go to sleep."

297.
HIGH USAGE MAKES SLEEP POORER

The effects of marijuana intoxication on the sleep patterns of 150 experienced smokers have been studied and reported by Tart and Crawford. They found that moderate levels of marijuana intoxication have a sedative effect on the user. High levels of intoxication, however, may overstimulate the user and make sleep poorer.

298.
PROPERTIES POTENTIALLY DANGEROUS TO EVERYONE

"Marijuana should be placed in the category of a central nervous depressant with hallucinatory and narcotic properties. It should be realized that these properties are potentially dangerous to everyone," said Dr. Robert W. Baird, Director of the Haven Clinic in Harlem.

299.
MAY ACT ON CENTRAL NERVOUS SYSTEM

"The results of the present study suggest that the effect (of marijuana on time perception) is mediated directly through the action of delta-9-THC on the central nervous system," reported A. Michael Rossi and John O'Brien.

300.
INVOLUNTARY HYPERACTIVITY MAY OCCUR

Cannabis causes involuntary hyperactivity in some users. Drs. Paton and Pertwee reported that: "Restlessness and impulsive activity have been mentioned. . . In a few subjects, probably with higher or repeated doses of cannabis, involuntary twitching, jerking movements during sleep and painful muscle spasms have been recorded."

In one case, "there was some sort of convulsion, with crying and uncontrollable arm movements, and researcher Ames noted jumping with arching of back in patient A, muscle twitches of limbs and abdomen in patient F, and painful and prolonged arm and leg movements in patient G which could only be momentarily controlled when the patient was urged to do so.

"These phenomena strongly suggest, as with laughter, a disinhibiting process allowing myoclonic jerks or liability to choreiform activity."

301.
HEMP PLANT'S RESIN HARMFUL TO NERVOUS SYSTEM OF INSECTS AND ANIMALS

Hashish is a crudely separated resin. "The hemp plant's resin is a pesticide; it is harmful to the nervous system in insects and animals."

302.
INFLUENCE OF MARIJUANA ON THE ENDOCRINE SYSTEM

Harris Rosenkrantz, "Cellular, Immunological, and Hormonal Effects," in *Pharmacology of Marihuana*, vol. I, eds. M.C. Braude and S. Szara (New York: Raven Press, 1976), p. 146.

The influence of cannabis on endocrine systems is very well documented. There is an alteration of levels of pituitary hormones, stimulation of adrenal hormones, and an influence on reproductive biochemistry and physiology. Sufficient evidence exists to warrant further evaluation of the effects of the constituents of marijuana on the endocrine systems.

303.
PITUITARY-THYROID FUNCTION DISTURBED BY THC IN ANIMAL TESTS

". . . The hypothalamus is the master endocrine gland and nerve control center; its many functions include regulating the secretion of the pituitary, which, in turn, regulates the secretions of other endocrine glands. . . . In rats, the function of the hypothalamus has been found to be disturbed by marijuana. A dose of THC administered locally in the hypothalamus of rats inhibited the pituitary-thyroid function (production of the thyroid-stimulating hormone and the thyroid hormone)."

304.
MAY ACT AS "FALSE HORMONE" INTERFERING WITH NATURAL HORMONES

Stephen Szara, "Clinical Pharmacology of Cannabis: Scientific and Nonscientific Constraints," in *Pharmacology of Marihuana*, vol. 1, eds. M.C. Braude and S. Szara (New York: Raven Press, 1976), p. 28.

At the Copenhagen meeting of the CINP, (1972) Szara made the speculative suggestion that delta-9-THC may act as a "false hormone" interfering with the normal functions of natural hormones.

305.
EFFECTS OF THC RESEMBLE EFFECTS OF ESTROGEN

"A recent experiment of spayed female rats exposed to THC (in doses that fell within the range of heavy, chronic doses used by humans) demonstrated that the effects of THC are much like the effects of estrogen. This effect was determined by the uterine weight gain in spayed rats."

Chapter XI

DAMAGES MEMORY

306.
USERS EXPERIENCE POOR MEMORY RETENTION

Drs. Paton and Pertwee reported that among marijuana smokers "information is poorly retained in the short-term memory and therefore not passed on to a long-term memory." Abel suggests that "this arises because cannabis impairs the rehearsal of information required for successful short-term remembering, this itself being a result of a failure of concentration."

307.
AFFECTS STORAGE OF INFORMATION IN BRAIN

"Short-time memory has been singled out by many investigators as the mental faculty most affected by marijuana. . . . It was shown that . . . marijuana interferes with initial learning, considerably affecting acquisition processes involved in storage of information," stated Doctor I.R. Rosengard.

308.
TEMPORAL DISINTEGRATION

A recent article in *Science Digest* noted that: "Scientists also investigated the relationship of temporal disintegration to impairment of immediate or short-term memory by marijuana. They have shown that increased concentration on the present covaries noticeably with a confusion of past, present, and future and the emergence of a sense of timelessness."

309.
TESTS SHOW HARMFUL EFFECT ON MEMORY

A group of nonusers were compared by Drs. Elliot Entin and Paul Goldzung to a group of students who had been using marijuana every day for at least six months. None of the students in the smoking group were under the influence of marijuana at the time of the experiment. Non-users performed significantly better than the marijuana smokers on learning and recall tasks. These investigators did another verbal memory task experiment using subjects who had used marijuana and no other drugs, daily for at least six months and a new control group of nonsmokers. As before, the control group performed better than the marijuana smokers.

310.
MEMORY IMPAIRMENT SHOWN BY CONCEPTUAL CLUSTERING MEMORY TESTS

Edward F. Domino et al., "Short-Term Neuropsychopharmacological Effects of Marihuana Smoking in Experienced Male Users," in *Pharmacology of Marihuana,* vol. 1., eds. M.C. Braude and S. Szara (New York: Raven Press, 1976), p. 406.

Researchers Domino, Rennick and Pearl reported that one of the most common effects of marijuana intoxication is the impairment of the short-term memory. As part of a study, short-term memory was tested by the Conceptual Clustering Memory Test. The results of this test showed that marijuana has a detrimental effect on the number of words that were recalled. They also found that this effect was dose-related.

311.
ACUTE EFFECT ON SHORT-TERM MEMORY

Marijuana clearly has an acute effect on short-term memory. Dr. Stanley F. Yolles offers one explanation for this effect: The "drug reduces the ability to concentrate while intoxicated, preventing the implicit reversal that may be essential to remembering newly acquired information."

312.
ABILITY TO CONCENTRATE REDUCED

According to Dr. Hardin B. Jones, the "marijuana user's attention span and ability to concentrate have been reduced. Memory, especially short-term memory, is shortened."

313.
EFFECT OF CHRONIC USE ON ACQUISITION AND RETENTION CAPACITY

Simone Radouco-Thomas et al., "Effect of Chronic Administration of delta-9-Tetrahydrocannabinol on Learning and Memory in Developing Mice," in *Pharmacology of Marihuana*, vol. 2., eds. M.C. Braude and S. Szara (New York: Raven Press, 1976), p. 487.

A toxicological study was undertaken by Radouco-Thomas, et al. in mice to study the long-term and short-term consequences of chronic marijuana use by young adolescents. The major areas under observation were acquisition and retention capacity. The results from this study of mice of comparable stages of development (from weaning to adulthood) disclosed three major characteristic behavioral trends: (1) inhibition of retention of avoidance behavior that occurred irregularly but was strain-independent; (2) strain-independent difficulty in keeping up sustained efforts that occurred systematically; and (3) improvement of acquisition rate in naive mice that was strain-dependent.

314.
INTERFERENCE WITH MEMORY FUNCTIONS

"Marijuana users consistently report interference with short-term and immediate memory functions," reported author Ronald Bruce.

315.
LEARNING AND SHORT-TERM MEMORY HURT IN TORONTO TEST

Dr. Ernest Abel of the University of Toronto, is one of many investigators to study the effects of marijuana on short-term memory and learning. Lists of words were read off to his subjects, and they were asked to recall as many of the words as they could, given five minutes for this task. Abel found that short-term memory and learning ability of the subjects are poorer under the influence of marijuana. During an interview of the subjects after the experiment, many of the subjects disclosed that they felt they were less able to concentrate, and therefore not able to perform well. This lack of concentration, believes Abel, may well be responsible for marijuana's effects upon memory.

316.
ABILITY ON "MEMORY TEST" DECREASES AFTER THC IS ADMINISTERED

The "ability to rearrange and say back in correct numerical order a series of random digits was . . . sensitive to 20mg THC administered orally, with the impairment lasting up to 24 hours in some of the subjects," reported Drs. Paton and Pertwee.

317
DISRUPTS TRANSFER OF INFORMATION IN BRAIN

Cannabis disrupts the transfer of information in the brain from short-term to long-term memory in a manner similar to alcohol and other drugs. This was discovered by Dr. Leo Hollister of the Veterans Administration Research Hospital after he examined many of the effects of single doses of cannabis.

318.
AFFECTS RECENT MEMORY AND ALERTNESS

"Clark suggests that marijuana affects the mental processes involved in recent memory and types of decision requiring recent memory and sustained alertness."

319.
IMPAIRS ABILITY TO REMEMBER

Dr. Leo Hollister, of the Veterans Administration Research Hospital in Palo Alto, California, found that marijuana use reduces both the ability to remember and to complete a train of thought during a conversation.

320.
AFFECTS TRANSFER PROCESS

"Marijuana has an effect on the short-term memory and also the transfer process between the short-term and the long-term memory. Because of this, heavily affected marijuana users behave much like senile individuals. They can't remember from one five-minute period to the next what they were intending to do. . . . They don't get as much filed away in their permanent memory as people ordinarily do."

321.
CAN INTERFERE WITH MEMORY FUNCTION OF BRAIN

"In both inexperienced and experienced users marijuana can also cause what has been called temporal disintegration. This may be related to an interference with the short-term memory function of the brain. Temporal disintegration is associated with the user's common inability to estimate the passage of time accurately and with his difficulty in carrying on a detailed conversation while under the influence of marijuana."

Chapter XII

IMPAIRS LEARNING AND CONCENTRATION

322.
INTERFERES WITH LEARNING TASKS

Studies have shown that marijuana use interferes with cognitive functions such as "the learning of a digit code, digit-symbol substitution, reading comprehension, speech, and goal-directed arithmetic tasks."

323.
"DISTORTS TIME . . . IMPAIRS MEMORY . . . REDUCES ABILITY TO REASON"

According to Dr. Harvey Powelson, former chief of the Department of Psychiatry in the Student Health Center at the University of California, the dangers of marijuana are so subtle that users of the drug do not realize how it affects them. He stated that marijuana distorts the sense of time, impairs memory, reduces clarity and the ability to reason. He says chronic heavy users of the drug lose sight of reality in that they are apt to accept easy solutions to personal and societal problems.

324.
INTERFERES WITH LEARNING

In his testimony before the United States Subcommittee on Internal

Security, Dr. Phillip Zeidenberg of Columbia University said "a child who needs an education can go into the washroom and smoke a couple of marijuana cigarettes in the morning and not learn a single thing for the rest of the day and nobody is going to know it."

325.
CANNABIS USE LOWERS STUDENTS' GRADES

Ian Campbell of the Sir George Williams University in Canada conducted a study by interviewing 127 students who used cannabis during the year. "A year by year analysis of final examination averages of these students showed that the greater their use of cannabis the greater the tendency for a decline in final averages."

326.
PERMANENT LEARNING IMPAIRMENT OCCURRED IN
LABORATORY TESTS ON RATS

Permanent learning impairment in rats has occurred after chronic heavy exposure to cannabis. Ten mg/kg. of THC, which corresponds to heavy human use, was administered orally for six months. The animals gained weight normally and were in good health throughout the experiments although they were visibly intoxicated for at least four hours after each dose. Permanent impairment of learning on two different tasks in a food motivated maze task occurred after six months of treatment. "EEG changes in the present work tend to support the interpretation that we are dealing with organic damage for which histological confirmation is being sought," stated Kehr and Kalant.

327.
MANY USERS WHO APPEAR NORMAL CANNOT THINK CLEARLY

"We have all seen examples of the tragic effects of marijuana on the mind. Marijuana smokers seem to suffer from distorted emotional responses, disordered thinking, dullness, and slothfulness. Early in the use of the drug, these behavioral changes appear to be reversible, but as exposure continues, recovery is less and less complete. Those most severely affected are usually not employed. There are, however, many marijuana users in factories and offices who appear to be normal but who suffer chronically from an altered judgment that may affect the quality of their work," according to Dr. Hardin B. Jones.

328.
IN-DEPTH EGYPTIAN STUDY OF HASHISH USERS

In 1954, a group of scholars were commissioned by former Egyptian President Nasser, to conduct an in-depth study of the effects of hashish consumption on the Egyptian people. Harold Pascal reports that this was a thoroughly controlled enquiry and probably the most knowledgeable study of chronic cannabis intoxication ever done.

"The comparison of 850 cannabis users to 839 controls showed that the former often need more powerful doses of drugs to have the desired effects on the central nervous system, their learning powers slow down, they are more anxious than controls, they present memory impairment, flight of ideas and difficulty in concentration."

329.
ALTERS JUDGMENT

The chronic user of marijuana eventually experiences an alteration in his judgment and memory. After a while the user may become easily upset, confused, and even disoriented.

330.
IRREVERSIBLE LOSS OF LEARNING ABILITY IN TESTS ON RATS

In a study conducted at the University of Toronto, Dr. Harold Kalant discovered that rats exposed to marijuana smoke over a five-month period suffered an irreversible loss of learning ability as measured by standard psychological tests.

331.
COHERENCE AND CLARITY OF THOUGHT DECREASES AS DOSES INCREASE

"Work performed under the influence of cannabis showed decreased accuracy. With larger doses, there was a marked decline in coherence and clarity. The performance impairment of complex tasks appears to arise from difficulty in maintaining a logical train of thought.

332.
INTELLECTUAL FUNCTIONS ADVERSELY AFFECTED BY MARIJUANA

According to Dr. L.E. Hollister, "intellectual functions, such as performance of simple arithmetic problems or copying a figure by connecting dots, show decrements in speed on the former case, or decrements of accuracy in the latter," under the influence of marijuana. "Previously, the digit-symbol substitution test was found to be impaired as well."

333.
LARGE DOSES HAVE ADVERSE EFFECT ON LOGICAL THINKING

According to the National Institute of Mental Health, small quantities of marijuana may cause little impairment of mental ability; large doses of marijuana definitely have an adverse effect on logical thinking and rational functioning.

334.
MARIJUANA AFFECTS ATTENTION AND CONCENTRATION

Drs. Paton and Pertwee summarized their observations of various research findings as follows:

"Loss of attention is episodic. This affects the ability to act, and subjects report how difficult a simple sequence of actions such as putting on a kettle becomes because of the difficulty in concentrating on a task or the difficulty of completing a sentence.

"Circumstantial talk, lackadaisical behavior, and difficulty in self-expression or in speaking are noted by observers. Action fails, too, because the subject is unable to keep up with the pressure of ideas, and, in attempting to write, it might be impossible for him to write a single intelligible sentence.

"Related to these phenomena, perhaps, is the feeling of loss of control or of will power."

335.
IMPAIRS COMPREHENSION

Impairment of comprehension in a silent reading test given to subjects under the influence of marijuana has been found proportional to the complexity of the test.

336.
BREAKDOWN IN THOUGHT PATTERNS

"Temporal disintegration," the breakdown in thought patterns and organized speech, has been reported by Drs. Hollister, Clark and Nakashima. This disruptive effect of cannabis may cause damage when learning patterns and background information are being developed during the formative years.

337.
PEOPLE UNDER THE INFLUENCE OF MARIJUANA MAKE MORE ERRORS AND IMPROVE LESS

In his experiments, E.L. Abel found that ". . . while the capacity to solve anagrams was not impaired, subjects under the influence of marijuana improved less with practice . . . and errors increased."

338.
"I CAN'T EVEN READ A BOOK . . . ANYMORE"

"There are too many youngsters who should be getting their Ph.D.'s by now who are drifting along smoking marijuana. . . . A few of the brighter ones will even tell you: 'I can't even read a book from cover to cover and grasp its meaning anymore. I tell myself that I don't care what's in it, that their topics are not important. But I really can't do it. Of course, I really don't care,'" reported Louis West, Department of Psychiatry, Neurology and Behavioral Sciences, Oklahoma Medical Center.

339.
IMPAIRMENT OF REASONING

The impairment of reasoning and thinking caused by cannabis is dose-related. Other, more complex types of reasoning are influenced more by cannabis. "Information rehearsal" is prevented from taking place because of an inability of the user to concentrate when intoxicated.

340.
MORE THAN 1,500 SUBJECTS OBSERVED IN EGYPTIAN STUDY

Gabriel G. Nahas, *Marijuana: Deceptive Weed* (New York: Raven Press, 1973), p. 22.

The most thorough study of chronic cannabis intoxication was performed in Egypt where 850 cannabis users were compared with 839 non-using controls. Dr. Gabriel G. Nahas, Columbia University Professor of Anesthesiology, writes that a "positive relationship was established between duration of hashish use and opium taking; *Cannabis* takers crave for agents acting on the central nervous system more than non-takers do. Cannabis users are slow learners compared with non-takers; controls scored significantly better than hashish takers on most of the objective tests."

341.
IS AN AGENT WITH HARMFUL EFFECTS

As one sees "a number of patients where smoking marijuana is in the foreground of the clinical picture, you do begin to feel that this is an agent which has harmful effects, and one which reduces the effective capability of many students in both their personal life relationships and their academic performances. Speaking as a clinician without being able to back it with precise hard data, it seems probable that the continued use of marijuana is reducing the potential ceiling level of functioning of a number of these students, both emotionally and academically," testified Dr. Robert Galbrieth Heath, as chairman of the Department of Psychiatry and Neurology at Tulane University School of Medicine.

Chapter XIII

ALTERS THOUGHT PROCESSES

342.
LOSS OF MENTAL FUNCTIONING

Dr. Harvey Powelson of the University of California at Berkeley summarizes why he feels marijuana use is dangerous:

"(1) Its early use is beguiling. It gives the illusion of feeling good. The user is not aware of the beginning loss of mental functioning. I have never seen an exception to the observation that marijuana impairs the user's ability to judge the loss of his own mental functioning.

"(2) After 1 to 3 years of continuous use the ability to think has become so impaired that pathological forms of thinking begin to take over the entire thought process.

"(3) Chronic heavy use leads to paranoid thinking.

"(3) Chronic heavy use leads to deterioration in body and mental functioning which is difficult and perhaps impossible to reverse.

"(5) . . . its use leads to delusional system of thinking which has inherent in it the strong need to seduce and proselytize others."

343.
CAUSES LOSS OF JUDGMENT IN TIME AND SPACE . . .

"The student who uses marijuana loses all judgment in time or space. If he is driving a car, what looks blocks away may be feet away. If she is a

103

mother who think she's fed her infant one hour ago, it may have been six hours."

Dr. Katherine Hess as Narcotics Coordinator for the New York Board of Health also contended that: "There is real evidence that some brain damage may occur from its frequent use."

344.
EFFECTS ON TIME PERCEPTION

The effects of marijuana on time perception include "timelessness, time standing still, loss of sense of time, something like a fragmentation of the normally smooth succession of events, with long intervals between events, as though individual frames of a movie were being shown; a tendency to concentrate on the present; and a blurring of the distinction between past, present and future, a temporal disintegration found to be significantly correlated with the degree of depersonalization," reported Paton and Pertwee, summarizing the findings of many other investigators.

345.
ALTERS NORMAL CONSCIOUSNESS

According to Dr. Dana L. Farnsworth, as Director of the Harvard University Health Services, marijuana produces a chemical effect which alters normal consciousness. Thought formation may be rapid, disconnected and uncontrollable. There may be periods of elation and well being followed closely by periods of moodiness, panic and fear of death. High doses of marijuana may produce confusion, disorientation, and increased anxiety as well as psychoses similar to those produced by LSD.

346.
DISTRESSING SUBJECTIVE EFFECTS

In the May 1978 issue of Science Digest, Dr. I.R. Rosengard stated that "recent reports of adverse reactions embrace a wide variety of distressing subjective effects, including such things as panic, fear, depersonalization, confusion, disorientation, depression, and paranoid ideation."

347.
EVEN SMALL AMOUNT OF POT HAS AN EFFECT ON THE MIND

The United States Drug Enforcement Administration, describing the effects of marijuana upon users who smoke just one or two cigarettes, states that the results can be "alteration of sensory perceptions, including expansion of space and time . . . and subtle changes in thought formation and expression." Higher use dulls the attention of the user and has other effects which "can produce feelings of panic and anxiety in an individual who has little experience with drugs."

348.
HARMFUL EFFECTS VARY BY DOSAGE

The reactions of squirrel monkeys to marijuana were similar to those of users and experimental subjects. These are the results of a study by Dr. W. McIssac and his associates. The researchers found that low doses of marijuana produce euphoria along with a distortion of time perception. Medium doses cause stimulation and talkativeness. High doses of the drug lead to hallucinations. Very high doses impair mental and physical functioning.

349.
COMMON RESULT IS DISTORTED PERCEPTION

Excerpt from THE SEEKERS by Jess Stearn. Copyright © 1968, 1969 by Jess Stearn. Used by permission of Doubleday & Company, Inc.

"It was hard to see how any marijuana-watcher could dismiss the drug as harmless unless he were on it so much himself that his own senses were dulled," stated Jess Stearn. "Marijuana obviously built up a dependence, withdrawing habitual users from painful challenges, and often sexually stimulating the casual user. But the most common result was a state in which ideas seemed disconnected, uncontrolled, perception disturbed, minutes seemed hours, and seconds minutes. Spatial images were distorted, and the near seemed far, and the far near."

350.
BRINGS ON DISORIENTED THINKING AND HALLUCINATIONS

"There is general agreement between the findings of the present study, the LaGuardia studies, and subjective users, all claiming that as marijuana is used, persons experience disoriented thinking, depersonalization, and hallucinations," stated Jess R. Lord.

351.
MARIJUANA CHANGES TIME PERCEPTION

"One of the most regular effects of cannabis is to change time perception, and almost all investigators use phrases such as 'alteration in sense of time,' 'tremendous increase in sense of time,' 'distortion of time perception,' or 'disoriented in time.'

352.
HASHISH INTOXICATION CAUSES BIZARRE DELUSIONS

Doctor Nils Bejerot has found that the hashish smoker is easily irritated. Bad trips (severe agitation) often occur during heavy intoxication. Alarming hallucinations and bizarre delusions of his surroundings plague the individual and can result in panic by the user.

353.
PSYCHOLOGICAL EFFECTS OF ACUTE INTOXICATION

At higher dose levels acute intoxication by marijuana may be accompanied by illusion, hallucination, depersonalization, restlessness, confusion, excitement and paranoid ideas.

354.
SOME VERY COMMON ADVERSE EFFECTS

A study in 1954 by Penfield and Jasper reported that "abnormal discharges in or near the limbic cortex may produce feelings of depersonalization, distortions of perception, alterations in time sense, and feelings of fear or paranoia. All these subjective states may occur and some are very common, as part of the marijuana experience," said Dr. Gabriel G. Nahas.

355.
HEAVY HASHISH SMOKERS LOSE SENSE OF REALITY

"Our ordinary reality is experienced by the heavy hashish smoker as increasingly uninteresting and meaningless, while the intoxication experiences become more important and essential," reported Dr. Nils Bejerot. The heavy smoker glides in a world of daydreams, and loses interest in work or school.

356.
"DRUG IS AN ILLUSIONOGEN"

Dr. Andrew Malcolm, as a member of the Drug Advisory Committee of the Ontario College of Pharmacy reported that "virtually nothing, however, has been done to determine the relationship between marijuana and the vulnerability of the intoxicated person to persuasion. But this drug is an illusionogen. In sufficiently high doses it is capable of producing what has been called the altered state of consciousness."

357.
HASHISH HALLUCINATIONS

Pseudohallucinations when the eyes of the hashish user are closed are a prominent phenomenon, but direct hallucinatory phenomena also occur. According to Dr. Nils Bejerot: "There are even hallucinations in regard to the body; for instance it is not uncommon that the hashish smoker feels that his arms and legs are extremely long or very short."

358.
CANNABIS PRODUCES VISUAL IMAGERY

Drs. Paton and Pertwee found that visual and other sensory experiences can become more vivid than normal under cannabis. Cannabis produces visual imagery when one looks at a bare surface (wall or ceiling) or when the eyes are closed.

359.
UNPREDICTABLE ILLUSIONARY REACTIONS

"Self-reports from marijuana users indicate that at the higher level of a 'high,' two different effects may be experienced because of the intensity of their inner experiences. The user may become less sociable and may withdraw from the group in order to enjoy his inner experiences, or if he continues to interact, he may feel that his interaction becomes extremely profound, including such phenomena as merging with another person—of feeling so aware of another person that a telepathic-like communication seems to exist between them. Usually these two reactions also show illusionary characteristics."

360.
USERS HALLUCINATE

As the marijuana smoker ingests more and more of the drug, he is not apt to collapse as is the alcoholic. Rather, the drug user develops feelings of great strength and power along with hallucinations. He soon thinks he can accomplish unbelievable feats, often endangering himself and others as a result.

361.
DELUSIONAL THINKING OCCURRED WHEN SUBJECTS WERE GIVEN CANNABIS EXTRACT ORALLY

F. Ames conducted an experiment by giving 10 subjects between .24 and .46 grams of cannabis extract orally. Five of the subjects exhibited delusional thinking in some degree and one experienced intense anxiety.

362.
WEST GERMAN STUDY FINDS HARMFUL EFFECTS

In commenting on the study by Dr. H. Isbell, the West German pharmacologist, who used doses of 4 and 18 mg. smoked THC, Russell notes that this dosage produced a "marked distortion of visual and auditory perception, low sense of reality, depersonalization and, in some instances, hallucinations."

363.
ALTERED STATE OF CONSCIOUSNESS

The use of marijuana can bring about an altered state of consciousness, that is "a condition of the mind that deviates from that which is experienced by a person in a state of alert waking consciousness," reported Dr. Andrew Malcolm. He believes that "the administration of a great variety of chemicals, particularly such illusionogens as marijuana and LSD, will also result in the A.S.C. (altered state of consciousness). It was on the basis of this observation that I developed a few years ago, a hypothesis that the use of certain drugs might be one of several factors in the causation of attitudinal change and that this might be related to the observed diffusion of social alienation in Western society."

364.
HALLUCINATIONS MAY OCCUR AS DOSAGE IS INCREASED

"It appears that it is only with high doses, for instance when consumption rises from 1-2 marijuana cigarettes a week to 4-5 doses a week for a period of months or when, after only one or two previous cigarettes, the subject smokes continuously for 1-2 hours, that the frankly hallucinatory phenomena appear," stated Drs. Paton and Pertwee. "The content of the imagery and hallucinations does not seem to offer any particular clue to the action of cannabis beyond the general emphasis on visual phenomena. . . ."

365.
ADVERSE EFFECTS FOUND OVER A CENTURY AGO

Moreau de Tours first described the acute effects of marijuana intoxication over a century ago and his description is still relevant today. The effects he mentions include excitement, euphoria, illusions and hallucinations, alterations in the perception of time and space, disturbed associations, rapidly changing emotions, increased sensitivity to sound and fixed ideas.

366.
1840 EXPERIMENT FINDS INGESTING HASHISH HARMFUL

The father of clinical psychopharmacology, Jacques Joseph Moreau, experimented with hashish in 1840 in order to be able to describe the mental effects of cannabis intoxication. For Moreau, the process of intoxication was similar to mental illness. He experienced hallucinations, euphoria and incoherence after ingesting hashish.

367.
USERS REPORT LOSING CONTACT WITH REALITY

"A frequent report (by the cannabis user) is that of feelings of unreality. It has been expressed as 'losing contact with reality,' 'loss of feeling real,' 'seeing reality in glimpses,' 'conscious of reality leaving him,' 'perceiving voice thoughts and appearance as unreal,' 'being in an unreal state.' Related to it are feelings of change of personality or loss of personality," wrote Paton and Pertwee summarizing relevant research.

368.
MARIJUANA DISTORTS CLEAR THINKING

Exceprt from THE SEEKERS by Jess Stearn. Copyright © 1968, 1969 by Jess Stearn. Used by permission of Doubleday & Company, Inc.

"To an observer, he (the marijuana user) appears to have abandoned the usual efforts to be clean, neat and presentable; he has failed in college, has no job (and doesn't want one), yet insists that he has achieved happiness," reported Dr. Dana Farnsworth of Harvard University.

Chapter XIV
CAUSES LOSS OF MOTIVATION. . . . APATHY

369.
DISINTEGRATES MOTIVATION

Despite the fact that little is known about many of the mind altering drugs being used today, millions of young people continue to experiment, unaware of the dangers of these chemical substances. In an attempt to escape the problems facing them, many teenagers use marijuana and wind up with new problems in addition to the old ones. Marijuana "disintegrates motivation, will power, resistance to drug pushers, reasoning ability, capacity to experience real joy, and ability to form meaningful relationships."

370.
DIMINISHED DRIVE

"Marijuana smokers suffer personality changes that occur gradually over a period of time. These personality changes include diminished drive, lessened ambition, decreased motivation, apathy, shortened attention span, poor judgment, diminished capacity to carry out complex plans or prepare realistically for the future, and a variety of other deleterious changes," stated Dr. Nicholas A. Pace.

111

371.
NATIONAL INSTITUTE OF MENTAL HEALTH REPORTS: MARIJUANA IS NOT HARMLESS

The concern over the unknown long-term hazards of smoking marijuana continue to grow among physicians, according to Dr. Sidney Cohen, former director of the Division of Narcotics and Drug Abuse at the National Institute of Mental Health. "The notion that marijuana is harmless just is not so," he stated. Dr. Cohen said that more research is needed to scrutinize such cases as those involving "losses of drive, motivation and memory in some chronic marijuana smokers."

372.
CAN MARIJUANA AFFECT MY PERSONALITY?

"Yes," says Dr. Stanley Yolles, and with use it apparently can also contribute to severe emotional problems in some individuals. You may become very passive and apathetic, lose your motivation and interest in activities that once seemed important to you, experience memory difficulties."

373.
APATHY APPROACHING INDOLENCE

In 1974 Dr. Robert Heath, Chairman of the Department of Psychiatry and Neurology at Tulane University School of Medicine, mentioned some common effects of marijuana use. He noted that the "most notable and consistent clinical changes that have been reported in heavy marijuana smokers include apathy approaching indolence, lack of motivation often referred to as an emotional state, reduced interest in socializing, and attraction to intense sensory stimuli. . . . Less frequent are reports of overt psychotic behavior characterized by losing contact with reality, having hallucinations and so forth and the induction of dyskinesias—abnormal muscle movements."

374.
LOSS OF PERSONAL EFFECTIVENESS

From MARIJUANA AND YOUR CHILD by Jules Saltman. Copyright © 1970 by Jules Saltman. Used by permission of Grosset & Dunlap, Inc.

Drs. McGlothlin and West say "it appears that regular use of marijuana may very well contribute to some characteristic personality changes, especially among highly impressionable young persons. "Such changes include apathy, loss of effectiveness, and diminished capacity or willingness to carry out complex long-term plans, endure frustration, concentrate for long periods, follow routines, or successfully master new material."

375.
FORMER USERS REPORT SURPRISING IMPROVEMENT AFTER QUITTING

Dr. George K. Russell recently wrote about an interesting challenge which was made by a professor to his students. Dr. Hardin B. Jones of the University of California, asked his students to make careful notes on any changes they felt after abandoning marijuana for a period of three months. The students "almost invariably came back" and reported that they "wouldn't have believed it possible, but you were right. I feel as though a layer of fog has been lifted from my mind. I know that I am better focused; I can remember better; I am performing better."

376.
NEGATIVE IMPACT ON ACHIEVEMENT

"Physicians with academic responsibilities particularly see a negative impact of marijuana use on achievement and motivation."

377.
LOSS OF MOTIVATION

"I have personally observed in persons, usually frequent marijuana users, a goallessness and grave loss of motivation—they resembled an anchored row-boat rising and falling with the ebb and flow of the tide. These persons became moored in the ebb and flow of life's events seemingly unable to care about where or how the tide of life carried them as long as they had the 'weed.' Most of them appeared older than their age and seemed tired of the struggle to live meaningful lives. Most of them were unaware of their disjointed speech, their loss of a sense of time and their unintelligible thinking patterns (they were victims of the 'wily weed's illusion). Cleanliness, grooming, neat dressing, usually went by the wayside as shabbiness became their normal living pattern."

378.
USERS HAVE LOWER GRADE POINT AVERAGES THAN NON-USERS

In a study of high school students conducted by R. Jessor, it was found that high school users as compared with non-users placed lower value on achievement and higher value on independence, tended to be more alienated and critical, more tolerant of deviance, less religious, less influenced by parents as compared to friends, and had a lower grade point average.

379.
LEADS TO LISTLESSNESS

A disease directly resulting from using marijuana "is listlessness, the lack of self-activation."

380.
"ACADEMICALLY IT IS LETHAL"

"In our service, we observe four well-defined areas of risk associated with marijuana use. The first of these is an acute anxiety reaction most commonly manifested by a racing pulse, a highly intensified awareness of the heart beat, pain in the chest, and occasionally pain in the arm. Not surprisingly, the students came to us seeking treatment for a 'heart attack'" wrote Dr. Roswell Johnson, as director of University Health Services at Brown University.

"A second common difficulty is a chronic anxiety, frequently accompanied by relatively severe and visible tremor. . . .

"The third problem area displays a group of reactions that threaten the reality system. . . . Illustratively, a 25-year-old student came in for help and reassurance because he had just finished writing an exam during which he felt he was standing behind his own chair watching himself write. . . .

"Annoying and disconcerting as all these reactions may be, they do not carry the hazard of the fourth category. This is the student who embraces the whole mystique of a cult and whose life becomes centered around marijuana, its origins, varieties, modes of use. He uses it at least once a day and usually more. . . . Nothing else in life matters much any more because he now has 'close friends with whom he can truly communicate.'

"Academic application is virtually ignored. As a chemical means of avoiding psychological pains and problems marijuana may be an efficient anodyne, but academically it is lethal."

381.
LOSS OF GOALS

"A common concern among members of the medical profession is that marijuana—particularly at the heavier levels of use—will produce lethargy, leading to a loss of goals and a draining off of potential adolescent talent into frivolous and shiftless activities."

382.
MAJOR MANIFESTATIONS ARE IMPAIRMENT OF JUDGMENT— MEMORY—CONCENTRATION

According to several psychiatrists who appeared before the United States

Internal Security Subcommittee in early 1974, use of marijuana leads to the so-called "amotivational syndrome." For example, Dr. Forest S. Tennant, Jr., a medical director for several drug abuse programs in the Los Angeles area, testified that the "major manifestations (of marijuana use) were apathy, dullness and lethargy with mild to severe impairment of judgment, concentration, and memory . . . physical appearance was stereotyped in that all patients appeared dull, exhibited poor hygiene, and had slightly slowed speech. . . ."

383.
MARYLAND STUDY FINDS THOUGHT DISORDERS

"In a study in Maryland . . . hundreds of drug addicts from high schools, universities, prisons, and drug programs were studied for six to nine years. The researchers observed thought disorders in the chronic marijuana users that they identified as the *cannabis syndrome*. A major thought disorder of this syndrome was found to be diminished drive, lessened ambition, decreased motivation, and apathy."

384.
INCREASED APATHY IN STUDENT USERS

Ian Campbell reported that his "interviews with and observations of . . . 127 students who used cannabis . . ." suggested that apathy increased and vitality diminished as frequency of cannabis intoxication increased. This could be attributed to many sources, including their heavy cannabis use, their participation in a subculture that did not tend to stress academic success, or to a general decline in motivation."

385.
LACK OF AMBITION FOUND IN CONSTANT SMOKERS

Excerpt from THE SEEKERS by Jess Stearn. Copyright © 1968, 1969 by Jess Stearn. Used by permission of Doubleday & Company, Inc.

"In my own research, more pragmatic than scientific," reported Jess Stearn, "I had discovered a telltale lack of ambition among constant pot smokers, accompanied by a bristling resentment of any suggestion that their lethargy was induced by their habit. . . . In some cases, young high school and college athletes, taking up pot, soon gave up their athletic pursuits."

386.
HARMFUL EFFECTS ON STUDENTS

"The most common behavioral changes we detect resulting from drug usage, including marijuana, are lack of academic productivity and under-achievement in general. Normal curricular and extracurricular activities lose their meaning and their importance; the individual becomes at best apathetic and at worst the victim of a considerable sense of unreality. He loses the ability to cope with the very demanding nature of this school," commented John Richards, II, Dean of Students at Phillips Academy, Massachusetts, and panelist at an Andover-Exeter alumni meeting on drugs in New York, May 6, 1970.

387.
LOSS OF WILL POWER

Dr. Franz Winkler wrote: "An early effect of marihuana and hashish use is a progressive loss of will power, already noticeable to the trained observer after about six weeks of moderate use. This loss of will power weakens the ability to resist coercion, so that marihuana users too often fall victim to hard drug pushers, extortionists and deviates. Soon all ability for real joy disappears, to be replaced by the noisy pretense of fun."

388.
STUDENTS' INCREASING LACK OF MOTIVATION RELATED TO CANNABIS USE

Testimony before a United States Senate Subcommittee in 1974 indicated that a common complaint of high school teachers is that a growing number of students are "already afflicted by the amotivational syndrome which shows a general lack of motivation." The teachers say that "the growth of this phenomenon in recent years has roughly paralleled the spread of the cannabis epidemic."

389.
DOCTOR DESCRIBES DISTRESSING CONSEQUENCES OF SMOKING MARIJUANA

Dr. Andrew Malcolm testified before the United States Senate Subcommittee on Internal Security about the effects of marijuana on the chronic or habitual user: "As a clinician, I have seen numerous people who presented a most distressing picture that resembled in varying degrees simple schizophrenia, the sociopathetic personality, and chronic brain syndrome. That is to say, these people seemed to be lackadaisical, passive, uninterested in the world around them and demonstrably unreliable. They would often be verbally quite facile but the range of their thought and feeling would be very limited, I might even say impoverished. Their attention spans would be short and they would seem interested only in experiencing each moment as it occurred without reference either to the past or the future. Their thinking would be frequently nonlogical and they would be very fascinated by magical explanations for natural phenomena. They presented . . . a version of what actually happens when a person consumes a sufficient quantity of marijuana to achieve a state of disinhibition, mild euphoria, self-centeredness and some degree of detachment from reality. "Now this clinical picture has been called the amotivational state."

390.
MOST CLINICIANS HAVE TREATED USERS FOR THE "AMOTIVATIONAL SYNDROME"

Thomas H. Maugh, II, noted that "many scientists argue that the continued presence of tetrahydrocannabinol in the brain induces a set of mental characteristics termed the 'amotivational syndrome.' This syndrome is familiar to most clinicians who have treated cannabis users."

391.
MARIJUANA USE AND DROPOUTS

According to Dr. Robert W. Baird, Director of the Haven Clinic in New York, marijuana smoking decreases both high school and college students' motivation, causing them to drop out of school.

392.
THE AMOTIVATIONAL SYNDROME

Suffering from a sense of aimlessness, depression, an "inability to get it together," a lack of motivation, trouble thinking through personal problems and premature ejaculation, R.F., a 24-year-old unmarried male visited Dr. Roy H. Hart.

In therapy it came out that "he had failed his first year of college, living through two semesters in a perpetual stoned state via LSD, barbiturates, amphetamines, and marijuana. Now, six years later, he was drug-free— according to his criteria. He discounted his use of marijuana and his newly acquired taste for whisky as drug experiences. His daily intake of marijuana was 1-2 joints or a pipeful of high-grade Colombian or Jamaican grass. Marijuana smoking had become as commonplace for him as cigarette smoking was for others, and he indulged in his habit nightly while reading the newspaper or watching TV in solitude.

"Although gifted with an I.Q. of 145, he worked in his father's laundry. His attendance was unpredictable, as he slept right through much of the day on many occasions. When at work, his performance was poor, his interpersonal relationships were hampered by irritability, and his judgement so unsound as to cost the business business."

393.
"SOME DEGREE OF CHANGE—IN EVERY MARIJUANA USER"

An average marijuana user shifts from being a self-activating, interesting and interested person to one who is withdrawn and given to disordered thinking.

Dr. Hardin B. Jones has "observed some degree of change of this kind in every marijuana user. When it becomes clearly noticeable as a change in life style, it is often called the 'amotivational syndrome.' This is more than a shift to sedation because thinking is affected in many ways."

394.
USERS UNDERGO SUBTLE CHANGES IN PERSONALITY

"Several psychiatrists believe they have detected clinically that some heavy marijuana-using individuals appear to undergo subtle changes in personality and modes of thinking, with a resulting change in life style. In adopting this new life style, a troubled youth may turn toward a subculture where drug use and untraditional behavior are acceptable," reported The Official Report of the National Commission on Marihuana and Drug Abuse.

395.
AMERICAN MEDICAL ASSOCIATION CALLED MARIJUANA A "MENTAL CRUTCH"

A report of a Council of the American Medical Association made it clear that marijuana produces adverse physical consequences, psychological dependence and called it a mental crutch.

Dr. Edward R. Pinckney, former editor of the AMA *Journal*, pointed out that: "This psychological dependence . . . was frequently reflected in listlessness, apathy, neglect of personal appearance, indifference to accomplishment." Additionally, the council of the American Medical Association "warned that repeated use (of marijuana) could result in illusions and delusions that predispose to antisocial behavior. Other direct results after long usage were clearly physical—chronic bronchitis and asthma, low blood sugar, sleep disturbance, impaired coordination."

396.
"THE DRUG OF ALIENATION"

"The conditioned social responses, such as affection for parents and tolerance for their suggestions, are impaired. Throughout the literature, cannabis is known as 'the drug of alienation.' Perhaps the cause is that pleasure centers for social conditioning have been affected. There is a loss of other conditioned responses; for example, an unkempt appearance is common. . . . Concern for consequences is reduced, and concern for the rights and well-being of others may be largely absent," reported Dr. Hardin B. Jones.

397.
CAUSES LOSS OF EMOTIONAL MATURATION

Dr. Robert Baird, as Director of the Haven Clinic, New York City, testified before the 1970 Select Committee on Crime:

"There is a complete loss of the emotional maturation so the individual cannot cope with the everyday situations with the result he starts to develop antisocial behavioral patterns. The longer one smokes grass or marijuana the more conditioned this way of living becomes, seeking those things that make him happy, regardless of those about him who must have to suffer."

398.
DANGERS OF CONSISTENT HEAVY USE

"Consistently heavy marijuana use can impair some mental functions. A wide variety of sensory distortions can occur, ranging from illusions to hallucinations. If the user is anxious about his actions, he may have feelings of persecution.

"One other danger in the repeated use of marijuana is the chance that the user may become drug-oriented. He loses sight of goals and values while concentrating his attention on drugs and their effects. Once this has occurred, he may drop out of the mainstream of life altogether."

This is an excerpt from a pamphlet distributed by the New York State Narcotic Addiction Control Commission.

399.
EXCESSIVE PERSONALITY INADEQUACIES FOUND IN HEAVY CANNABIS USERS

"Excessive (cannabis) use is associated with personality inadequacies. Persons who exhibit emotional immaturity, low frustration tolerance, and failure to assume responsibility tended to be overrepresented in (a group of) heavy cannabis users. In behavioral terms, these traits are manifested in an unrealistic emphasis on the present as opposed to the future, a tendency to drift along in a passive manner, failure to develop long-term abilities or skills, and a tendency to favor regressive and magical rather than rational thinking processes."

400.
CHRONIC USERS DRIFT OUT OF SOCIETY

Excerpt from THE SEEKERS by Jess Stearn. Copyright © 1968, 1969 by Jess Stearn. Used by permission of Doubleday & Company, Inc.

In studies started at the University of California, Dr. Constandinos J. Miras observed chronic marijuana smokers for twenty years. He reveals that because of their habit, many of his subjects drifted out of society. "A degree of responsibility remained in some of them to the extent of finding the minimum money required to cover their living and hashish purchasing expenses," he explained.

401.
CAUSES SELFISHNESS AND INTROVERSION

Marijuana smokers grow increasingly introverted and develop more and. more antisocial behavior. Dr. Robert W. Baird said this is due to "a complete loss of emotional maturation and the individual cannot cope with the everyday situations. . . ." He contends marijuana smoking causes selfishness and introversion to the point where the drug user cares about nothing other than his own personal pleasure and satisfaction, regardless of others around him.

402.
CHANGES IN GOAL DIRECTION

"Some clinicians have described the existence of a complex of subtle social, psychological and behavioral changes related to a loss of volitional goal direction in certain individuals, including some long-term heavy users of marijuana," reported The National Commission on Marihuana and Drug Abuse. "Such persons appear to orient only to the present. They appear alienated from generally accepted social and occupational activities, and they tend to show a reduced concern for personal hygiene and nutrition."

403.
"HEAVY MARIJUANA SMOKING ASSOCIATED WITH STAGNATION. . . ."

Dr. Gabriel Nahas recently reported: "There's no question that heavy marijuana smoking is associated with stagnation, with lack of ambition, with what some older psychiatrists describe as mental and physical deterioration or 'amotivational syndrome.' There's no question that heavy marijuana users drop out of society into their own little world. People who smoke marijuana tend to be careless in their physical appearance, in their social duties, in their religious performance."

404.
CONSPICUOUS CHANGES IN HABITUAL USERS

Excerpt from THE SEEKERS by Jess Stearn. Copyright © 1968, 1969 by Jess Stearn. Used by permission of Doubleday & Company, Inc.

Conspicuous changes are noticeable in habitual users, over relatively short periods, months and even weeks. "What the hell difference does it make? . . . I'm happy," stated a habitual user who originally was an ambitious young man in his early 20's. He became passive and indolent, refused to clean his room or wash his person. It became too much of an effort to keep a job or pursue his original ambitions.

405.
RESEARCHERS FIND PERMANENT BEHAVIORAL ALTERATIONS

Researchers Chopra and Jandu from India report that "subjects who take smaller doses tend to be quiet, apathetic, and disinterested in their surroundings; these changes are followed by permanent behavioral alterations, which are more marked under stress, starvation, poor health, and so on, resulting in an 'amotivational syndrome.'"

406.
ALTERS INTERPERSONAL RELATIONS

Dr. I.R. Rosengard reported that interpersonal relations are altered by marijuana use. At the lower to moderate levels of use, the drug may enhance social relationships. Many users therefore feel that marijuana is a "social drug par excellence." At higher levels, however, marijuana may have the opposite effect, with the user becoming less social and more withdrawn.

407.
DOCTOR CAN SPOT USERS FROM AFAR

Dr. Constandinos J. Miras of the University of Athens, Greece, spoke of the "amotivational syndrome" which marijuana stimulates in the user. He says he can spot a chronic marijuana user by the way he walks, talks, and acts. Among his personality traits one can find "slowed speech . . . lethargy . . . lowered inhibitions . . . loss of morality."

408.
USERS UNAWARE OF ACTIONS

Many investigators report that the use of cannabis reduces physical activity and lessens the desire to work. In a review of such findings, Drs. Paton and Pertwee noted that such feelings as "lethargy, laziness and disinterest . . . have the expected result. . . . Activity can sometimes be 'automatic,' with, for example, an individual stopping at a traffic light or pushing a button in a test without being aware of it. . . ."

409.
SYMPTOMS OF "WITHDRAWAL"

"The symptoms of marijuana withdrawal are typical and predictable—malaise, headache, restlessness, sleeplessness, and some kind of gastrointestinal disturbances."

410.
EGYPTIAN HASHISH SMOKING IS PROBLEM OF "NATIONAL DIMENSION"

Gabriel G. Nahas, *af17Marihuana: Deceptive Weed* (New York: Raven Press, 1973), p. 22.

In 1971 Sami-Ali indicated that hashish intoxication is related to general stagnation and lowered productivity of the Egyptian population. He stated that "the habit of taking hashish which prevails in all the strata of the population raises a problem of national dimension."

411.
UNIVERSITY STUDY REPORTS SYMPTOMS OF WITHDRAWAL

Tharp, Paul, "Cannabis Conference: The Latest Word From Science," *The Village Voice*, February 9, 1976.

Some effects detected during the marijuana withdrawal period include irritability, tremors, slight depression, and loss of weight and appetite according to a University of California, San Francisco study.

Chapter XV

UPSETS TIME SENSE

412.
USERS TEND TO OVERESTIMATE TIME LENGTH

"In experiments on 'reported' time, a low dose of smoked marijuana led to the reporting by three out of nine subjects that a period of speech lasting five minutes appeared to last about 10 minutes, to an overestimation by about one-third of tasks lasting on the average 15, 90, or 180 seconds, and to a significant rise in the estimation of an interval of 15 seconds from a control level of 14.9 to 15.6 seconds," reported Drs. Paton and Pertwee.

413.
ALTERED TIME SENSE AND EFFECTS ON PERCEPTION AND MEMORY

". . . The occurrence of a marijuana induced altered time sense has been well documented. . . . It is likely that distortion of time sense is incidental to . . . effects on perception, memory, and organization of thought," suggested Clark et al.

414.
REAL TIME APPEARS TO PASS SLOWLY

An acute effect of marijuana is "to speed up the hypothetical internal clock so that real time appears to pass slowly. The presence of this acute effect was further suggested by the correlation of the 180-second time estimate scores with time elapsed since marijuana was smoked (up to two hours)," reported A. Michael Rossi and John O'Brien.

415.
AFTER 3 JOINTS MEMORY AND TIME SENSE ARE INTERFERED WITH

In 1974, Dr. Harvey Powelson of the University of California, and former chief of the University's Psychiatric Division of the Student Health Service from 1964 to 1972, said: "The essence of the pattern is that with small amounts of marijuana, approximately three joints of street grade, memory and time sense are interfered with. With regular usage the active principles cause more and more distorted thinking. The user's field of interest gets narrower and narrower as he focuses his attention on immediate sensation. At the same time his dependence and tolerance is growing. As he uses more of the drug, his ability to think sequentially diminishes. Without his awareness, he becomes less adequate in areas where judgment, memory and logic are necessary. As this happens, he depends more and more on pathological patterns of thinking. Ultimately all heavy users, that is daily users, develop a paranoid way of thinking."

416.
SENSE OF TIME AND MEMORY ALTERED

"The marijuana-induced illusion of well-being causes students not to report real symptoms of illness because they aren't aware of them. The real happenings which are affecting them deeply are out of their reach. Even small amounts of the drug interferes with their sense of time and with their memory storage. They are not aware that they are becoming less adequate in areas where judgment, clarity, memory, and reasoning are necessary. Their own pathology becomes more entrenched without their becoming aware of it—they are deluded by their own illusion."

417.
IMPAIRED PERFORMANCE

"Both experienced and inexperienced users demonstrate impaired performance on certain psychological tests that were specifically designed for this drug (marijuana)."

Chapter XVI

DANGEROUS WHEN USED PRIOR TO DRIVING

418.
ACCIDENT RATES COULD TRIPLE IF MARIJUANA IS LEGALIZED

"Marijuana is highly dangerous if used before or during the use of an automobile. If it were legal, and use became widespread, accident rates would triple. It never should be legalized," stated Dr. I.R. Rosengard, a member of the Illinois Research Hospital in Chicago.

419.
MORE AND MORE STUDIES SHOW TYPICAL SOCIAL DOSE OF MARIJUANA IMPAIRS DRIVING SKILLS

"Evidence that marijuana use at typical social levels definitely impairs driving ability and related skills continues to accumulate. There is now data indicating impairment from laboratory assessment of driving related skills, driver simulator studies, test course performance, actual street driver performance, and most recently, a study conducted for the National Highway Traffic Safety Administration of drivers involved in fatal accidents."

420.
MAKES DRIVING HAZARDOUS ESPECIALLY AT NIGHT

Marijuana users "are classified as dangerous drivers while under the influence of the drug. They have been shown to be more dangerous at night than in the daytime, perhaps because marijuana intensifies and prolongs the effect of glare on the eyes.

"Some scientists state that regardless of the time of day or night, their extensive tests reveal drivers under the influence of marijuana react as erratically as do drunken drivers. Their reaction time is slow, their judgment is poor, and they have trouble performing complicated tasks such as simultaneously putting on a directional signal, changing lanes, and stopping for a red light."

421.
ACUTE EFFECTS IMPAIR DRIVING SKILLS AND PSYCHOMOTOR FUNCTIONING

Supported by research, Dr. Robert L. DuPont stated that the "acute effects of marijuana intoxication do impair both driving skills and the kinds of psychomotor functioning which are required in many occupations. . . .

"We now urgently need a practical roadside test of marijuana intoxication and sound national studies of this problem."

422.
FREQUENT CAUSE OF AUTOMOBILE ACCIDENTS

Drs. Dana Farnsworth and Curtis Pound of the Harvard University Health Service reported that marijuana slows down the user's reflexes. When this is added to other effects, such as distortion of time and distance perception, "the drug is frequently a cause of automobile accidents."

423.
SLOWS DRIVERS' REACTION TIMES

Many investigators, in actual as well as simulated driving tests, have found that when subjects were under the influence of marijuana, they exhibited poorer automobile handling, slower reaction times and incorrect or inadequate responses.

424.
NORMAL USE IMPAIRS DRIVER PERFORMANCE

The National Commission on Marijuana and Drug Abuse states that marijuana intoxication significantly impairs a driver's performance. Even at dosage levels normally consumed in social settings visual perceptual performance is impaired to a significant degree.

425.
EFFECTS ON COORDINATION AND MOTOR ACTS

From THE DRUG SCENE by Donald B. Louria. Copyright 1968 by Donald B.
Louria. Used with permission of McGraw-Hill Book Company.

"A more mundane but possibly even more serious danger results from
the effect of marijuana on coordination and the performance of motor acts.
Tests show that simple motor acts are performed normally under the
influence of marijuana, but that complex ones are clearly impaired. Skilled
motor acts are performed more rapidly, but less accurately; furthermore,
marijuana distorts time and space perception. Obviously, then, those
driving an automobile under the influence of marijuana are potentially
dangerous to themselves and to others," reported Donald B. Louria.

426.
EMERGENCY TREATMENT CENTERS REPORT INCREASE IN AUTO
ACCIDENT RATE

Studies confirm the fact that "marijuana definitely impairs driving
ability," wrote George K. Russell. He has also noted that emergency
treatment centers indicate an increase in the accident rate of users of the
drug.

427.
ONE OF MOST SERIOUS PROBLEMS WITH MARIJUANA IS ITS USE
WHILE DRIVING

According to Dr. Forest S. Tennant, Jr., former chief of the Special
Action Office for Drug Abuse of the United States Army in Europe, one of
the most serious problems with marijuana is its use while operating motor
vehicles. He states ". . . that we have no reliable, inexpensive routine test
to detect THC or cannabis products in the urine, breath, blood, et cetera.
And, therefore, there is no way to accurately detect . . . whether someone
is intoxicated with cannabis. . . ."

428.
COMPARISON WITH DRUNKEN DRIVING

There is a danger in driving an automobile while under the influence of
marijuana. The National Commission on Marijuana has concluded that such
action, like driving under the influence of liquor, should be penalized.

429.
HIDDEN DANGER OF MARIJUANA

Dr. Robert W. Baird of the Haven Clinic in New York City told a Congressional Committee that one of the most treacherous aspects of marijuana use is that there is an absence of outward signs of intoxication in the smoker. The fact that someone has been using the drug will go unnoticed until that person tries to drive a car or perform some other activity that requires skill.

430.
DRIVERS EXPERIENCE DIFFICULTY RECOVERING FROM GLARE

Orally administered marijuana caused a significant dose-related increase in brake time on simulated driving tests. Additionally, "scientists report a marked increase in the time required to recover from glare." This lasted for several hours after smoking marijuana, reported Dr. I.R. Rosengard.

431.
MARIJUANA AND MOTORCYCLES: NOT A GOOD MIXTURE

Dr. Henry Brill has described an interview he had with a marijuana-using group in Chicago. "We point-blank asked them what they thought about having people ride motorcycles under the influence of marijuana; and these were marijuana users, middle-class cultured people. They agreed completely that that was not a good mixture, and would not approve of it. . . ."

432.
MAY DRAMATICALLY INCREASE DEATHS ON HIGHWAYS

"Physicians consider marijuana dangerous and not to be legalized or made freely available. . . . It deteriorates one's motor coordination, rendering the handling of a machine, particularly an automobile, hazardous. The fear is that the current slaughter on the highways of America—partly due to drunk driving—will increase dramatically with the increase in marijuana use."

433.
WARNING TO DRIVERS FROM NATIONAL INSTITUTE ON DRUG ABUSE

One of the most serious and dangerous effects of marijuana smoking is the persistence of perceptual impairment possibly as long as several hours after intoxication. This is hazardous with regard to both driving and flying, where the operator is not aware that he or she is still impaired even though marijuana has not been used for some time.

434.
LOGICAL THINKING IMPAIRED

"Like alcohol, marijuana affects judgment, and an individual may find it much harder to make decisions which require logical thinking. At the same time, he may erroneously believe that his judgment is unimpaired, or even that his mental functioning has been enhanced by the drug. The performance of any complex task which requires good reflexes and clear thinking is impaired, making such tasks as driving or flying particularly dangerous," stated Lt. Col. David H. Karney, M.D.

435.
TESTIMONY OF INTOXICATED DRIVERS

Automobile drivers under the influence of marijuana have reported rushes of distracting thought. In a 1971 study, one driver testified: "Your mind wanders off to something else." Another driver remarked, "I think it is too easy to forget that you are driving a car. It is easy to become distracted by music or lights."

436.
MARIJUANA IS BECOMING SIGNIFICANT FACTOR IN AUTOMOBILE ACCIDENTS

"Although drunk driving is still the primary cause of traffic accidents, marijuana use is beginning to be identified as a significant factor. In one study, fourteen persons admitted to the emergency room of Denver General Hospital who had been in single-car accidents and charged with operating a motor vehicle under the influence of drugs were given laboratory tests to verify drug use. In six persons, test results were positive for alcohol alone; in five, for marijuana alone; in one, for marijuana and opiates; and in two, for opiates alone."

437.
FREQUENT HALLUCINATIONS OF SPACE AND TIME

Dr. Sidney Cohen, Director of the Division of Narcotic Addiction and Drug Abuse of the National Institute of Mental Health, warned that marijuana produces frequent hallucinations of space and time and users of the drug should not operate heavy machinery or automobiles.

438.
IMPAIRS DRIVERS' ABILITY TO JUDGE SPEED, TIME, DISTANCE

Subjects in one study conducted by Dr. O.J. Rafaelsen, were tested on a driving simulator after receiving oral doses of marijuana. The simulator gave the subject the illusion he was driving on a test course. These subjects exhibited an impaired ability to brake and an impaired ability to estimate speed, time and distance. The subjects might estimate they were driving forty miles an hour when they were actually going twenty.

439.
MARIJUANA AND DRIVING PERFORMANCE

The Official Report of the National Commission on Marihuana and Drug Abuse believes "that driving while under the influence of any psychoactive drug is a serious risk to public safety; the acute effects of marijuana intoxication, spatial and time distortion and slowed reflexes may impair driving performance."

440.
AUTOMOBILE ACCIDENTS RESULTING FROM DISTORTION OF TIME

According to Dr. Robert W. Baird, Director of the Haven Clinic in New York, one of the changes that occurs from marijuana is the distortion of time. He said this would be dangerous while driving an automobile, for example, and an accident might result.

441.
POTENTIAL EFFECT ON AUTOMOBILE ACCIDENTS IS A MAJOR CONCERN

"The greatest concern I have about this drug—and marijuana is an intoxicating drug—is its potential effect on automobile accidents in this country. As marijuana becomes more acceptable to society more users are likely to drive cars while under its influence," reported Robert L. DuPont, M.D., Director of HEW's National Institute on Drug Abuse.

442.
HASHISH SMOKERS ARE A DANGER ON ROADS

Dr. Nils Bejerot reported that hashish smokers have "poor estimation of time and distance and reduced ability to coordinate movement, so that (they) are a considerable danger on the roads."

443.
OBJECTS CLOSE BY WILL SEEM FAR AWAY

The Farmers' Almanac noted that marijuana "distorts time and space so that minutes may seem hours and objects close by will seem far away. Obviously, anyone under its influence should not drive a car or operate machinery as the ability to perform is impaired."

444.
MARIJUANA SMOKERS KNOW THEY CANNOT DRIVE SAFELY

"We simply asked our subjects when they were high (marijuana), 'Do you think you could drive a car?'" reported Dr. L.E. Hollister. "Without exception the answer from those who had really gotten high has been 'no' or 'you must be kidding.'"

445.
WHY USERS GET INTO AUTOMOBILE ACCIDENTS

The marijuana user's sense of depth perception is altered. This can cause confusion in the operation of the gas and brake pedals, and, not knowing exactly where his foot might be, the user might become involved in an automobile accident, stated Dr. Robert W. Baird.

446.
LEADS TO MORE MOVING TRAFFIC VIOLATIONS

J.S. Hochman and N.Q. Brill asked their students at U.C.L.A. if any of them had been arrested for traffic violations. They found that the students who had used marijuana more often were the ones who had received more citations for moving traffic violations.

447.
INTERFERES WITH PERIPHERAL VISION WHILE DRIVING

Dr. H. Moskowitz reported that in experiments studying the effects of marijuana on visual functions while driving, he found that marijuana interferes with central vision and peripheral vision. This, he claims, is perhaps a result of lapses in attention during marijuana intoxication.

448.
WILL INCREASE DANGERS ON HIGHWAYS

". . . Of course, the mayhem on the highways will only increase, as pot adds to the toll already caused by alcohol. As stated elsewhere by me—and by others—cannabis has no place in a technological society."

449.
CAUSES AUTO AND BUS ACCIDENTS IN MEXICO AND CUBA

According to Dr. Pablo Wolff, in Mexico and in Cuba numerous auto accidents result from drivers using marijuana including bus drivers. He feels this is dangerous because marijuana distorts perception of bth time and space.

450.
"IT NUMBED MY BRAIN. . . . I COULD NOT DRIVE WELL"

A marijuana user told of his experiences while driving under the influence of the drug. He said that he was unable to operate the car normally. "In driving, you might think you are going 60 if you are only going 30 mph . . . it numbed my brain and I could not think right. I could not drive well," he added.

451.
ALTERS DISTANCE PERCEPTION

According to Dr. Robert W. Baird: "Distance perception is altered. . . . Ask any of these people who have been on it. They might think the car, when they are on marijuana, is over here . . . but in actuality he will be tailgating. . . . He applies brakes—accident."

452.
MAKES DRIVING DANGEROUS

"Most recent evidence indicates that driving while under the influence of marijuana is dangerous."

453.
MARIJUANA AND AUTOMOBILE ACCIDENTS

Marijuana smoking impairs judgment and perception and, therefore, could be a factor in automobile accidents, stated Dr. Stanley F. Yolles.

454.
MAKES DRIVING HAZARDOUS

"The marijuana user is difficult to recognize unless he is actually under the influence of the drug and even then he may be able to work reasonably well. The drug may distort his depth and time perception, making driving or the operation of machinery hazardous.

"a. In the early stages of marijuana usage, the person may appear animated with rapid, loud talking and bursts of laughter. In later stages, he may be sleepy.

"b. Pupils may be dilated and the eyes get pink.

"c. May have distortions of perception and rarely, hallucinations."

455.
DRIVING PERFORMANCE OF CHRONIC USERS MAY BE IMPAIRED EVEN BETWEEN USES

"The severely altered behavior typical of the chronic marijuana user suggests that driving performance would be impaired even between uses; the user is never free from the burden of active material."

456.
STUDY FINDS MARIJUANA A FACTOR IN FATAL AUTOMOBILE ACCIDENTS

The U.S. Department of Health, Education and Welfare reported that "a recent study of 300 drivers responsible for fatal accidents in Boston found that 39% were intoxicated on alcohol and 16% had used marijuana."

457.
AUTOMOBILE ACCIDENTS AND IRRESPONSIBLE ACTS

"No one, of course, recommends the use of marijuana nor does anyone deny that there are evil effects and consequences associated with using it. The fact that the use of marijuana is outlawed, for example, means that it is often obtained through association with unsavory types, often used in an underworld environment, and the user takes the risk of criminal prosecution. It is also undeniable that marijuana intoxication may sometimes lead to automobile accidents and to irresponsible or criminal acts," stated Alfred R. Lindesmith, Professor of Sociology at Indiana University.

458.
NEAR FATAL DRIVING ACCIDENTS

Many marijuana users have had the experience of a near-fatal accident because they have become so immersed in concentrating on a light or sound that they took their hands off the wheel while they still had their foot on the accelerator.

459.
AFFECTS ABILITY TO DRIVE

The influence of using marijuana before driving "affects judgment, the ability to keep more than one thing in your mind at the same time, to take into account all the factors at once which have to do with driving instead of just where you are going."

460.
CANADIAN STUDY FINDS MARIJUANA TO BE A CAUSE OF DRIVING ERRORS

"That marijuana is a cause of driving errors has been determined by a study done in Canada, stated Frank Fioramonti, as regional director of the National Organization for the Reform of Marijuana Laws (NORML).

"Fioramonti said the study tested people who had three drinks, people who had a one gram marijuana cigarette with 5 per cent THC, people who had a 'joint' with 1.4 per cent THC, and people who had no drugs."

The results of the driving tests showed that those who made the most errors were those who had consumed the alcohol. Close behind in the number of errors made were those who had the more potent marijuana. Those with the lower quality pot made only a few driving errors.

"We don't believe anyone should drive after using any drug," stated Fioramonti. "That includes both alcohol and marijuana."

Chapter XVII

THREAT TO AVIATION SAFETY

461.
100% OF PILOTS MADE "DANGEROUS MISTAKES" AFTER SMOKING MARIJUANA

Jack D. Blaine et al., "Marihuana Smoking and Simulated Flying Performance," in *Pharmacology of Marihuana*, vol. 1., eds. M.C. Braude and S. Szara (New York: Raven Press, 1976), p. 446.

The entire pilot group of a study by Blaine, et al., made errors in simulated flight situations that, if made during actual flight situations, would have such dire consequences as getting lost, fuel exhaustion, misjudging gross altitude or navigational deviations, or stalling. The magnitude of the errors made by these pilots under the influence of marijuana varied but each pilot experienced a deterioration in flying performance.

A half hour after consumption of marijuana, all of the pilots showed a decreased ability to maintain assigned altitudes and headings, or to follow radio-navigation procedures, and committed major and minor errors.

462.
INTOXICATED PILOTS EXPERIENCED "A COMPLETE LOSS OF ORIENTATION"

Lt. Col. David H. Karney, M.D., discussed the performance of pilots who were intoxicated with marijuana during a flight simulated test: "At times they exhibited a complete loss of orientation with respect to the navigational fix. This loss of orientation occurred when the pilots were either daydreaming, lapsing, or focusing on one certain part of their specified routine. Although the results noted were quite dramatic in the flight simulator, it is believed that pilot performance in actual flight situations would be even more adversely affected by marijuana. The pilots tested performed a memorized flight sequence and had the instructions for the pattern in front of them at all times. In actual flight situations, instructions come sequentially from an air traffic control specialist and must be accurately noted and repeated (i.e., read back) by the pilot."

463.
PILOTS WHO SMOKE MARIJUANA MAKE MANY MISTAKES IN FLIGHT-SIMULATED TESTS

A test conducted by the University of California "revealed that social marijuana smoking is not an uncommon practice among civilian-type aviators, some of whom reported that they had even flown while 'high' on marijuana. For this reason, the University conducted an experiment to determine the effects of the drug on the aviators' ability to operate an aircraft. The test was conducted in instrument flight simulators using seven professional and three private pilots who had smoked marijuana socially for several years." The flying patterns they would have to perform "required coordination as well as short term memory, concentration, and orientation in time and space. . . . These flight profiles were carefully chosen to demand a high level of flying skill to correctly complete the sequence." The marijuana "caused a gross decrement in flying performance with increased prevalence of major and minor errors, altitude and heading deviations, and radio navigational errors. The effects of the drug persisted for at least 2 hours, generally disappearing within 4 to 6 hours after it was administered."

464.
PILOTS' EFFECTIVENESS DECREASED

"Pot's detrimental influence on pilots can be substantiated by scientific data. Last year Dr. David Janowsky and his group in San Diego studied the effects of marijuana intoxication on the ability of 10 certified pilots to operate a flight simulator. All 10 pilots showed a significant decrease in measurements of flying performance 30 minutes after smoking active marijuana.

"The authors went on to state: 'Our data do not support safe instrument flight for at least 4 hours after smoking marijuana.'

"These pilots, ranging in age from 21 to 40, are not that much different in their general tastes than white-collar workers, college students, et cetera.

So merely thinking about flying and flyers who smoke pot introduces yet another devastating condemnation against the trend for the relaxation of laws governing the regulation and supply of cannabis."

465.
AFFECTS PERFORMANCE OF ALL AIRLINE PERSONNEL

"Unfortunately, there has been little research into the effects of marijuana intoxication on personnel performing specific jobs such as aircraft maintenance, air traffic control, or other support duties. However, the effects of marijuana upon human performance, particularly those tasks requiring a high level of skill, memory, interpretation, awareness, and judgment, have been well documented. Based on this research and on the detrimental effects of marijuana intoxication on the performance of aviators, it is logical to assume that job performance of all aviation-related personnel would be affected."

466.
HARMFUL EFFECTS LISTED BY U.S. ARMY AGENCY FOR AVIATION SAFETY

"The psychological effects on the emotions and senses vary widely, depending on what the user expects from the drug, the circumstances under which it is used, and the strength and quality of the drug. Time is distorted and five minutes may seem like an hour. Space may seem enlarged or otherwise distorted and sound and colors sometimes seem intensified. Thought frequently becomes dreamlike and some individuals believe they are thinking better than usual. Recent evidence shows that there is a loss of immediate recall and that it is difficult to think or speak due to disorganization of recent memory," reported Lt. Col. David H. Karney of the Medical Division, U.S. Army Agency for Aviation Safety.

467.
MARIJUANA AFFECTS PILOTS' ABILITY TO FLY

Lt. Col. David H. Karney, M.D., reported the results of a University of California study done on the effect of marijuana on pilots while "flying" simulator courses. "Several major problems were noted in flying the simulator while under the influence of marijuana—the most significant being its effect on short-term memory and time sense. Aviators often forgot where they were in a given flight sequence or had difficulty recounting how long they had been performing a given maneuver in spite of the presence of written instructions and a stopwat·h. Marijuana also appeared to cause alterations in concentration and attention, so that pilots would become preoccupied with one task. . . ."

468.
POT CALLED POTENTIAL THREAT TO AVIATION SAFETY

In an article written for The U.S. Army Aviation Digest, Lt. Col. David H. Karney, M.D., reported that "marijuana (affectionately known by users as pot, tea, grass, weed, or Mary Jane) (is) a growing concern in our society and a potential threat to aviation safety. When smoked, marijuana quickly enters the bloodstream and within a few seconds (minutes at the most) begins to affect the user's mood and thinking for two to four hours."

469.
USE BY AIRPLANE MAINTENANCE PERSONNEL MAY BE CAUSING ACCIDENTS

Lt. Col. David H. Karney of the U.S. Army Agency for Aviation Safety stated that "marijuana, like all intoxicating drugs including alcohol, has no place in our aviation environment. While few aviation accidents have been reported in which marijuana usage by maintenance personnel or aircrew members was a factor, it is a well known fact that the use of the drug is widespread among servicemen and it would be naive to think the aviation population has not been affected. The absence of documented marijuana-caused accidents is grossly misleading since proof of intoxication is, for all practical purposes, impossible at the present time."

Chapter XVIII

FOUND HARMFUL IN THE ARMED FORCES

470.
KNOCKS FIGHTING EDGE OFF AMERICAN TROOPS

During the Vietnamese conflict, an army division issued a bulletin to its men stating that the Viet Cong was supplying marijuana to United States troops with the intention of rendering them less effective in combat. The bulletin informed the GI's that the drug was in fact a substance that could decrease the military abilities of fighting men in battle.

471.
HASHISH CAUSED HOSPITALIZATIONS IN U.S. ARMY HOSPITALS

While testifying before the United States Senate Subcommittee on Internal Security, Dr. Forest S. Tennant, Jr., described the hospitalization of persons at the U.S. Army Hospitals in Europe requiring treatment for non-violent type activities after smoking hashish: ". . . Many people believe that if you smoke hashish or marijuana, it will never result in hospitalization because the drug is harmless. But our data . . . does not support this belief. We had many admissions each month to our ten hospitals, which showed that there were a number of hashish-caused hospitalizations."

139

472.
USE BY AMERICAN SAILORS IS A SERIOUS PROBLEM

In addition to being a problem in the Army, marijuana smoking goes on in the Navy as well. Captain George H. Sult, special assistant for drug abuse in the Bureau of Naval Personnel in Washington, says that marijuana use by American sailors is a serious problem.

473.
HASHISH USE BY U.S. SOLDIERS

Gabriel G. Nahas, *Marihuana: Deceptive Weed* (New York: Raven Press, 1973), p. 44.

A three-year study on the chronic use of hashish by 110 United States soldiers in Germany showed that daily heavy use of cannabis for three to 12 months "was accompanied by significant physical and mental deterioration as well as decreased work performance."

474.
MILITARY POLICE REMOVED FROM DUTY BECAUSE OF HASHISH ABUSE

A report released by the Subcommittee to Investigate The Administration of the Internal Security Act and Other Internal Security Laws stated that 33 U.S. Army MP's (military police), who were stationed at a nuclear weapons depot in Germany had to be removed from their duty because of hashish abuse.

475.
DANGEROUS WHEN USED BY SOLDIERS

There is evidence that American GI's have been killed because they were intoxicated with marijuana. In some cases men actually thought that smoking marijuana would speed up their reactions and make them better soldiers, whereas they actually "were missing what they should have seen and seeing what was not there."

476.
"DANGEROUS THING IN BATTLE"

From MARIJUANA AND YOUR CHILD by Jules Saltman. Copyright © 1970 by Jules Saltman. Used by permission of Grosset & Dunlap, Inc.

Many psychiatrists and military men regard a marijuana high as a dangerous thing in battle. It leads to mistakes that could be fatal to the soldier as well as to others.

477.
ARMY MORE CONCERNED WITH MARIJUANA THAN VENEREAL DISEASE

From MARIJUANA AND YOUR CHILD by Jules Saltman. Copyright © 1970 by Jules Saltman. Used by permission of Grosset & Dunlap, Inc.

According to a psychiatrist who served in Vietnam in late 1968, "30 to 50 percent of the troops had smoked pot at least once and it was a growing problem for the medical department." Dr. John A. Talbott remarked that "the Vietnamese war is the first in which the Army has been more concerned with marijuana than with venereal disease."

478.
HARMFUL EFFECTS IN U.S. ARMED FORCES

"The use of cannabis (by the United States Armed Forces) was a good deal more prevalent than the use of heroin. And, also, it has a persistent effect in making soldiers sloppy in their thinking, susceptible to all sorts of suggestions of an absurd nature, and careless in all matters," reported Dr. Hardin B. Jones.

479.
ACUTE TOXIC PSYCHOSIS FOUND IN SOLDIERS IN VIETNAM

An acute toxic psychosis following the inhalation of cannabis cigarettes was observed in twelve soldiers seen in Vietnam. Drs. J. Talbot and J. Teague concluded that it is a definite clinical syndrome.

Chapter XIX
REDUCES COORDINATION

480.
MARIJUANA INTOXICATION AFFECTS PSYCHOMOTOR FUNCTIONS

"Intoxication with psychoactive substances affect psychomotor and cognitive functions. That marijuana is no exception is apparent from the assertions of users. Experimental confirmation is evident from a wide range of studies."

481.
THC FOUND IN MOTORMAN INVOLVED IN FATAL TRAIN CRASH

At a National Transportation Safety Board Hearing investigating the Chicago train crash that killed 11 persons and injured nearly 200, a doctor testified that THC was present in the motorman's urine sample taken after the accident on February 4, 1977. Dr. Monroe Wall, vice-president of Triange Institute in North Carolina, testified that Mr. Martin, the motorman, "could have been normal, or he could have been as high as a kite." In his testimony, Mr. Martin, who was hospitalized for 6 weeks, denied he had smoked marijuana before colliding with the other train.

482.
IMPAIRS PSYCHOMOTOR ABILITIES AND MENTAL PERFORMANCE

William S. Dalton et al., "Effects of Marijuana Combined with Secobarbitol," *Clinical Pharmacology and Therapeutics* 18(3): 298-304, © by the C.V. Mosby Company, St. Louis, Mo., U.S.A.

In various studies it has been discovered that many marijuana users also use other drugs. For example, approximately 30 percent of regular marijuana users are said to ingest barbiturates. It is known that independent use of either drug impairs psychomotor abilities. Researchers conducted an experiment using 12 male volunteers in which they found indications that smoking marijuana causes impairment of stability, hand-eye coordination, and mental performance.

483.
CASUAL USERS MADE 5 TIMES AS MANY ERRORS WHILE HIGH AS THEY DID WITH PLACEBO

Although both casual and heavy smokers showed a small decrease in perception and psychomotor task performance, the "casual smokers showed a greater degree of impairment than did heavy smokers. On a 'Continuous Performance Test' the casual smokers made five times as many errors of omission as they did under placebo, but no increase in errors was found in heavy smokers."

484.
SENSE OF TIME AND REACTION TIME MARKEDLY IMPAIRED IN SCIENTIFIC STUDY

"Motor functions, such as static equilibrium and hand steadiness, are impaired. Tapping speed and simple reaction time were only affected slightly. Complex reaction time was markedly impaired. Although time estimation was said not to be impaired in an earlier study, our current studies," stated Dr. L.E. Hollister, "with doses that are not extraordinarily high, show marked changes in most aspects of time sense. Certainly, clinical descriptions indicate this to be one of the most affected senses."

485.
LOSS OF MENTAL ACCURACY

"The most striking neurological effect of cannabis is ataxia, and it has been frequently reported. . . . as a loss of accuracy when coordination or manual skill is required, as difficulty in fine movements such as picking up a pin, as an unsteady gait, or as difficulty in articulation."

486.
TEST SHOWS THAT HIGH DOSAGE PRODUCES ADVERSE EFFECTS

C.A. Tassinari et al., "The Neuropsychiatric Syndrome of delta-9-Tetrahydrocannabinol and Cannabis Intoxication in Naive Subjects: A Clinical and Polygraphic Study During Wakefulness and Sleep," in *Pharmacology of Marihuana*, vol. 1., eds. M.C. Braude and S. Szara (New York: Raven Press, 1976), pp. 370-371.

The subjects said that the experience was extremely unpleasant and were all unwilling to repeat it. This is the general feeling of the subjects of a study by Tassinari, et al. All of the subjects were naive marijuana smokers except one. They had never tried cannabis in any form, nor had they ever used any other psychoactive drugs.

The effects the subjects experienced were impaired psychomotor performance, lack of subject cooperation, increased drowsiness, incoherent sleepiness, anxiety and difficulty in contacts with other subjects.

487.
IN EGYPTIAN TESTS USERS PERFORM WORSE THAN NON-USERS

Dr. M.I. Soueif of Cairo University in Egypt told the United States Senate Subcommittee on Internal Security that objective psychological tests were used to measure several psychological functions considered to be of crucial importance for adequate functioning in work situations. The results were:

"a. Takers were definitely slow on tests used for the assessment of speed of very simple motor tasks.

"b. They also did poorly on a test measuring speed and accuracy of visual discrimination. This test requires a good deal of concentration of attention.

"c. Takers were definitely below the average for their comparable non-takers on tests for hand-eye coordination with and without speed being explicitly emphasized in the instructions. . . .

"d. We also found that on some tests of immediate memory . . . especially those requiring some kind of mental reorganization of the test material . . . cannabis takers were very low performers.

"e. Cannabis takers tended to overestimate distances of moderate lengths. However, non-takers tended to underestimate such distances."

488.
IMPAIRS PERCEPTION IN CASUAL USERS

Casual users show a greater degree of impairment than do heavy users on perceptual and psychomotor tasks. Heavy marijuana users experience more profound subjective effects after a half hour of smoking marijuana but are less intoxicated than casual users one hour after smoking, according to Meyer and his associates.

489.
MEDICAL TEAM FINDS HEAVY SMOKING DECREASES WORK ABILITY

Tharp, Paul, "Cannabis Conference: The Latest Word from Science," *The Village Voice*, February 9, 1976.

"An individual's work output . . . tends to decrease slightly in days following heavy marijuana use (six joints or more daily). A medical team at Harvard Medical School and McLean Hospital isolated male volunteers in a ward for 31 days—half were casual smokers (one to two joints daily) and the rest heavy smokers.

"Using a simple work-task, the volunteers accumulated work points exchangeable for extra marijuana or money. Heavy users took grass instead of money, and casual users preferred money. And always, casual users accumulated more work points on days following heavy smoking by their counterparts."

490.
LA GUARDIA STUDY LONG AGO FOUND HARMFUL EFFECTS

"Almost all the users experienced some sort of symptom of mental illness, ranging from euphoria to hallucinations to floating sensations to full-blown psychotic episodes," wrote Dr. Gabriel G. Nahas in commenting on the 1938 LaGuardia Report involving 120 prisoner-volunteers. They were given amounts of cannabis from material that had been seized by the Federal Bureau of Narcotics, in both a smoking and a liquid form. Mental, motor and physical examinations were given to both groups.

The "aptitude and manual dexterity tests showed that despite the widespread belief of increased agility and ability while under the influence of marijuana, users consistently performed their motor tasks with less efficiency than nonusers."

This study represented the first medically sponsored systematic examination of the effects of marijuana. The prestigious New York Academy of Medicine conducted this investigation in 1938 at the request of New York's Mayor Fiorello La Guardia.

491.
SLOWS RESPONSE TIME

Subjects were asked to respond as fast as they could to a sound then a visual stimulus by Dr. Rhea Dornbush and her associates. The reaction time of the subjects was slowed by higher dose levels of marijuana.

492.
ALTERS MUSCLE COORDINATION

"Muscle coordination is altered so that in simple tests, just like inserting a pencil into a pencil sharpener or reaching out for a glass, the object in pursuit is missed. They overextend or underextend," commented Dr. Robert W. Baird of the Haven Clinic in New York on one of the effects of marijuana.

493.
LOSS OF COORDINATION AND MANUAL SKILLS

Tests of cognitive function of marijuana-users have shown a loss in accuracy of coordination and manual skills.

494.
TYPISTS USING MARIJUANA MAKE MORE MISTAKES AND TYPE SLOWER

Four typists under the influence of marijuana were given a passage to type, as were four other typists of the same age and group who had never used cannabis. "There were significant differences in the time required to type the passage and in the number of mistakes made. Five to 10% more time was required, and 6-12% more mistakes were made by those under the influence of the drug."

495.
RESULTS OF ACUTE MARIJUANA INTOXICATION

Dr. Stanley F. Yolles stated that recent findings "continue to confirm earlier reported observations that acute marijuana intoxication causes a deterioration in intellectual and psychomotor performance." These observed effects are related to the size of the dose and the difficulty of the task. The deterioration of performance is greater when the task is more complex and demanding.

496.
MARIJUANA MAY HARM JOB PERFORMANCE

It appears that "marijuana use on the job may be of great importance to business and industry based on deterioration of intellectual and psychomotor performances in employees. As the public and the politicians begin to lessen their concern over marijuana use, the knowledge emerging from scientific research may forecast a major area of concern to which business and industrialists must address themselves in evaluating employee performance on the job," reported Dr. Stanley F. Yolles.

497.
MARIJUANA REDUCES PHYSICAL ACTIVITY

Over a period of time the chronic marijuana user may become less and less coordinated although he may be unaware of his condition. Any physical activity requiring effort seems endless and awkward. As a result, marijuana smokers usually engage in activities such as watching television, listening to music, or just sitting.

498.
MARIJUANA AND MUSCLE WEAKNESS

"Muscle weakness is a subjective complaint, which in one of our studies was demonstrated objectively by the use of a finger ergometer. The same subjects also reported a decrease in feelings of aggressiveness."

499.
EX-USER REPORTS PERMANENT LOSS OF MENTAL FACILITIES

Dr. D. Harvey Powelson, former director of the Department of Psychiatry in the Student Health Center at the University of California at Berkeley, reported the following case: An athletic junior faculty member with a degree in mathematics had gone on to take graduate work in philosophy until he started using hashish. He discontinued use of the drug when he realized that it was affecting his athletic timing. But the effects of his use of hashish remain; three and a half years later, he cannot handle mathematics at his prior level. The change is permanent and the patient is convinced that this loss of mental facilities was drug-induced.

500.
CANADIAN RESEARCH TEAM STUDIED AFFECT ON PRODUCTIVITY

The Addiction Research Foundation Team in Canada found that "when large mandatory doses of marijuana were introduced after long periods of abstinence in the laboratory, work productivity tended to be depressed. Discontinuation of marijuana use after a prolonged period of forced daily smoking of high doses resulted in an increase in productivity."

501.
ORAL DOSAGES CAUSE LOWER MUSCLE STRENGTH AND COORDINATION

In various studies of the effects of marijuana on humans, it has been found that the drug affects muscle strength and the performance of simple motor tasks. Researchers have observed decreased strength in leg, hand and finger at oral dosages of 50 to 75 mg.

502.
AFFECTS ABILITY TO PAY ATTENTION

Drs. Sharma and Moskowitz performed the following experiment: Subjects were seated in front of a panel with neon lights that turn off every couple of seconds; when they saw the light, they were supposed to press a key. Subjects who smoked a marijuana cigarette before taking part in this hour long experiment missed the light signals more often than the subjects who smoked a placebo beforehand.

503.
ADVERSE EFFECT ON PERFORMANCE OF HIGH-LEVEL JOBS

"Marijuana has an adverse effect on the performance of high level jobs. The user is frequently lethargic, lacks motivation, is prone to error, has trouble remembering important details, and cannot think practically about the future. These transformations are gradual and are not marked by the obvious signs of impaired ability; it is easy to spot the alcoholic, but not so easy to spot the marijuana user."

504.
BELIEF THAT MARIJUANA ENHANCES CREATIVITY IS FALSE

From THE DRUG SCENE by Donald B. Louria. Copyright 1968 by Donald B. Louria. Used with permission of McGraw-Hill Book Company.

"It has been suggested that in addition to providing a pleasant experience, marijuana has beneficial effects on the user. It allegedly augments creativity, but there is no valid data in support of this contention. On a substantial number of occasions creative people have deliberately been given marijuana and asked to carry out and interpret their artistic activity under the drug's influence. In the majority of cases, during the actual period of marijuana intoxication they felt that their creative activities were enhanced. However, almost uniformly, when the effects of the marijuana had dissipated and they again viewed their creative activities, they found that in actuality they had done very badly . . ." reported Donald B. Louria.

Chapter XX

HARMFUL EFFECTS ON YOUNG PEOPLE

505.
MANY ADVERSE EFFECTS AMONG TEENAGERS

Dr. A. Kornhaber treated 50 marijuana-smoking patients, ranging in age from 13 to 18 years, over an 18 month period. His findings, as summarized by Dr. Roy H. Hart, are that marijuana use "impairs learning ability and judgment by its harmful effect on attention span and ability to concentrate; that it produces an increase in daydreaming, fantasy, and withdrawal; that it brings about an increase in school absence, cutting classes, and problem behavior; and that it also leads to a decrease in personal hygiene, physical activity, and logical thinking."

506.
MARIJUANA PRODUCES CEREBRAL ATROPHY IN YOUNG MEN

"Evidence of cerebral atrophy," reported Dr. A.M.G. Campbell, et al., "was demonstrated by air encephalography in ten patients with histories of consistent cannabis smoking over a period of 3-11 years. The average age of the patients was 22 years; all were males.

"Our findings indicate that there is a particular pattern of cerebral atrophy in a series of young men who smoked cannabis. . . . We feel that our results suggest that regular use of cannabis produces cerebral atrophy in

young adults. . . . Significant cerebral atrophy is rare in young people. . . ."

The researchers contend that "this work on man indicates an urgent need
for further studies of the neurological consequences of drug abuse,
particularly the long-term effects of cannabis smoking."

507.
BRINGS ABOUT APATHY IN YOUNGSTERS AT IMPORTANT TIME

"I think that the worst thing about marijuana is that it infuses a terrible
apathy into youngsters at precisely that time when they should be making
or preparing to make important decisions that will affect the rest of their
lives," stated Dr. W.X. Lehmann, director of a Connecticut drug rehabilitation foundation.

508.
YOUTH BECOME ALIENATED FROM NORMALLY ACCEPTED CONDUCT

"In the past few years," reported The Official Report of the National
Commission of Marihuana and Drug Abuse, "observers have noted various
social, psychological and behavioral changes among young high school and
college-age Americans including many who have used marijuana heavily for
a number of years. These changes are reflected by a loss of volitional goal
direction. These individuals drop out and relinquish traditional adult roles
and values. They become present rather than future oriented, appear
alienated from broadly accepted social and occupational activity, and
experience reduced concern for personal hygiene and nutrition."

509.
ADVERSE EFFECTS RECEIVE LITTLE RECOGNITION IN MEDIA

Doris H. Milman, Letters, *The New York Times*, 2 June 1977. © 1977 by The
New York Times Company. Reprinted by permission.

"I would like to . . . narrow the focus to adolescents, the age group that is
particularly open to experimentation with drugs, has the highest rate of
marijuana usage and is most vulnerable to the untoward effects of
marijuana," wrote Dr. Doris H. Milman in a letter to the Editor of *The New
York Times*.

"I refer specifically to the adverse psychological effects: hallucinations,
paranoid reactions, depressive reactions, acute psychotic reactions, spontaneous flashbacks and chronic withdrawn reactions (i.e., the so-called
amotivational syndrome).

All of these adverse responses have been noted and recorded in scientific
journals, but receive little or no recognition in the lay media.

510.
HEAVY USE MAY JEOPARDIZE SOCIAL DEVELOPMENT OF ADOLESCENTS

"Whichever interpretation one accepts," stated the Official Report of the National Commission on Marihuana and Drug Abuse, "the fact is apparent that the chronic, heavy use of marijuana may jeopardize social and economic adjustments of the adolescent. We believe this is one concern which merits further research and evaluation. On the basis of past studies, the chronic, heavy use of marijuana seems to constitute a high-risk behavior, particularly among predisposed adolescents."

511.
A TRAGIC ASPECT IS HOW YOUNG PEOPLE ARE CONDEMNED TO DISINTEGRATION OF PERSONALITY

"While healthy teenagers will eagerly participate in all kinds of activities, such as sports, hiking, artistic endeavors, etc., a marijuana user will show an increasing tendency to talk endlessly of great goals, while doing nothing about them," said the late Dr. Franz E. Winkler, who made a number of public appearances at colleges and on television to voice his opinion about marijuana.

Dr. Winkler stated that a tragic aspect of marijuana use is that young people, who are merely seeking a diversion or mind-expanding experience, "are thus condemned by sheer ignorance to a gradual disintegration of their personality."

512.
"CAN DESTROY OUR YOUNG PEOPLE IN A COUPLE OF YEARS"

According to Phyllis Schlafly, "marijuana is far more dangerous than tobacco or alcohol. Marijuana damages the lungs and respiratory system ten times as fast as cigarette smoking. It usually takes years for a social drinker to become an alcoholic and drink himself to death or out of a job. Marijuana however, can destroy our young people in a couple of years, before they ever have the chance to know life and the excitement of confronting its challenges."

513.
REDUCES TEENAGERS' MOTIVATION TO SUCCEED

"Chronic marijuana use, particularly in teenagers, contributes to a shift in reality perception in which thinking and action become increasingly divorced from each other," reported Dr. Edleff H. Schwaab, Ph.D., Consultant in Clinical Psychology at The Phillips Exeter Academy in

Exeter, New Hampshire. He observes that marijuana users lose the ability to judge between what is important and what is not, resulting in making unimportant matters significant. "Such a loss of ability to discriminate is often accompanied by a marked reduction in a person's motivation to achieve in life. This renunciation of objectives and of purposes, which are usually accepted as meaningful in our society, turns chronic marijuana smokers into an essentially underproductive people," added Dr. Schwaab.

514.
USERS WILL REMAIN PARTIAL MENTAL CRIPPLES AFTER THEY GIVE UP CANNABIS

According to United States Senator, James O. Eastland, "We may . . . find ourselves saddled with a partial generation of young people—people in their teens and early twenties—suffering from irreversible brain damage. Their ability to function may improve if they abandon cannabis, but they will remain partial cripples, unable to fully recover the abilities of their pre-cannabis years."

515.
A PSYCHIATRIST'S WARNING

"One of the problems of adolescence is to learn to turn wishes into actions. Wishing is a prelude to action and often a substitute for it. But marijuana doesn't help you to carry out wishes. It does just the opposite: it postpones action, slows up the maturing process and results in narcissism, emptiness and decreased self-esteem," said Dr. Paul A. Walters, Harvard University psychiatrist.

516.
YOUNG USERS LOSE INTEREST, AMBITION, DRIVE

According to Dr. Constandinos J. Miras of the University of Athens, experiments indicate that marijuana use causes permanent alterations of the brain structure. He is concerned about young marijuana users who lose interest, ambition, and drive.

517.
DANGER TO PSYCHOLOGICAL DEVELOPMENT OF ADOLESCENTS

"The *chronic* user of marijuana or 'pot-head' may encounter a number of psychological problems. If he is using it to escape life stress, his mental growth is impaired by not learning how to deal with frustration and problems," stated Dr. Stanley F. Yolles, as director of the National Institute of Mental Health. "One needs to be particularly concerned about the potential effect of a reality-distorting agent on the future psychological development of the *adolescent* user. We know that normal adolescence is a time of great psychological turmoil. Patterns of coping with reality developed during the teenage period are significant in determining adult behavior. Persistent use of an agent which serves to ward off reality during this critical development period is likely to compromise seriously the future ability of the individual to make an adequate adjustment to a complex society."

518.
"BLOCKS OFF" ADOLESCENTS' MATURATION

Dr. Robert Baird, as Director of the Haven Clinic in New York City, testified before the Select Committee on Crime:

"The preadolescent-adolescent child, if you put him on grass you are going to block off his maturation. He is going to develop a stereotyped way of reacting to reality. Growth for all of us is a daily painful process of . . . being hurt and learning why you got hurt and what you can do, so you do not get hurt the next time so badly. If you deter this, then you are going to have an individual who is slowly going to become psychotic or neurotic."

519.
RISKS TO NOVICE SMOKERS

From MARIJUANA AND YOUR CHILD by Jules Saltman. Copyright ©℗⋆© 1970 by Jules Saltman. Used by permission of Grosset & Dunlap, Inc.

"A one-time or novice smoker . . . can have fairly serious psychic trouble if he has predisposing mental or emotional traits that might be brought out by pot. Since no one can say just what those traits are or how to spot them ahead of time, the risk is not a small one."

520.
HARMFUL FOR MANY ADOLESCENTS

From MARIJUANA AND YOUR CHILD by Jules Saltman. Copyright © 1970 by Jules Saltman. Used by permission of Grosset & Dunlap, Inc.

"For many adolescents with a pre-existing personality disorder and poorly developed psychological defenses, the drugs (marijuana) are sufficient to dissolve these fragile defenses and facilitate the emergence of a psychotic process," reported Dr. Doris Milman.

521.
MARIJUANA IS NOT A HARMLESS DRUG

"Marijuana is a harmless drug . . ."

This statement is false according to Thomas Weisman: "There is actual and potential hazard in the use of any psychoactive drug. . . . It is known that some people have adverse effects from the acute use of marijuana, and others appear to develop a pattern of psychological dependence on the drug. Also, the use of marijuana by young people as a means of postponing or avoiding the internal conflicts characteristic of adolescence may significantly impair or even arrest the development of a mature personality."

522.
CAUSES A SHIFT IN VALUE ORIENTATION OF YOUNG PEOPLE

Dr. Edleff H. Schwaab, Consultant in Clinical Psychology at The Phillips Exeter Academy in New Hampshire, says that the prolonged use of marijuana causes a "shift in the value orientation of young people." He states that marijuana users suffer a "loss of social conscience" evidenced by "the preoccupation with inner psychic processes and the concomitant disinterest in our environment." He adds that marijuana users see this shift as an asset rather than as a psychological liability.

523.
ROBS YOUNG OF VITALLY IMPORTANT EXPERIENCE

From MARIJUANA AND YOUR CHILD by Jules Saltman. Copyright © 1970 by Jules Saltman. Used by permission of Grosset & Dunlap, Inc.

On the subject of marijuana, Dr. Sidney Cohen of the National Institute of Mental Health, feels that there is a "seductive aspect of the drug for young people, particularly those who are dependent, unsure of themselves or unhappy. The shy, inadequate or chronically perturbed find the marijuana way of life far easier than their ordinary existence. It provides them with a solution to their conflicts about aggression, sexuality and maturation. The painful process of problem solving is bypassed."

524.
PHYSICIANS CONCERNED WITH EFFECT ON ADOLESCENT PERSONALITY

"Physicians are acutely aware of the potential damaging effects of the drug (marijuana) on the adolescent personality. (In fact, even many non-medical observers who take a relatively tolerant view of marijuana use in general are concerned about its possible impact on the young.)"

525.
GROWING NUMBER OF YOUNG USERS LIVING IN A "WORLD OF ... FANTASY AND NON-PRODUCTIVITY"

Dr. John A.S. Hall, as chairman of the Department of Medicine at the Kingston Hospital in Jamaica, testified before the United States Senate Subcommittee on Internal Security that in Jamaica many people smoke ganja (marijuana) without apparent ill effects. However, there is a growing number of young adult marijuana users who have reached the point at which they are living in a "world of chemically-induced, drug-induced fantasy and non-productivity. One can visualize at the national level ganja smoking changing the life style of a society, undermining economic productivity, and impairing a country's military effectiveness."

526.
RISKS GREATER FOR YOUNG USERS AND THOSE MENTALLY ILL

The American Medical Association Council on Scientific Affairs reported that "research and clinical experience have shown that younger users probably are more at risk psychiatrically, and that persons already diagnosed as mentally ill can undergo relapse or exacerbation of their conditions as a consequence of marijuana use."

527.
RESULTS OF MARIJUANA TEST IN A COLLEGE POPULATION

The National Institute on Drug Abuse states that M.P. Naditch in his preliminary work "has found that in a college population, those who are more hypochondriacal, and who feel less in control of their own lives and more at the mercy of external events are more likely to have adverse reactions to marijuana and other psychoactive drugs."

528.
YOUNG USER REPORTS LETHARGY

A young marijuana user reported, "When I smoke it I think about doing great things, but somehow as long as I smoke it I never get around to doing them."

529.
JUNIOR HIGH & HIGH SCHOOL USERS ARE MORE SEXUALLY ACTIVE

A survey by R. Jessors, S.L. Jessors, and J. Finney of junior high school and high school students found that the students currently using marijuana are more sexually active than the other students. The junior high marijuana users engage in petting more frequently than the non-users; in high school, users had sexual intercourse more frequently than non-users.

530.
COLUMNIST MAX LERNER REPORTS ON SERIOUS EFFECTS

"The folklore of the young, which says that smoking pot a few times a week is no different from taking a sociable drink, or smoking cigarettes moderately, just isn't true," stated columnist Max Lerner.

"Some doctors sum it up as a pattern of ego-distortion, others as a serious slowdown in the maturing process. Whatever happens seems to happen through a toxic effect on the nervous system, and when the marijuana use ends the symptoms also level off and diminish. . . . Right now I wouldn't want any son or daughter or student of mine to settle down to a steady diet of marijuana."

531.
CHOICE OF PERSONAL VALUES MAY BE BEYOND USERS' CONSCIOUS CONTROL

Dr. Andrew Malcolm stated that "in my opinion, among the many unusual characteristics of marijuana use one of the most important is that its users may be rendered suggestible and that what they consider to be their voluntary espousal of a new system of values may be due, in fact, to influences beyond their conscious control."

532.
INFLUENCES JUDGMENT

Keith Cowan as an adviser to the government of the Canadian province of Prince Edward Island testified that "a young adult who has developed a desire for the pleasure of the marijuana or hashish high, whether it be physical or psychological, will filter out information which threatens his pleasure and probably let it influence his judgment. . . ."

533.
LEADS TO ALCOHOL ETC. AT AN EARLIER AGE

Marijuana users are more likely to be sexually permissive, to drink alcohol, and to smoke tobacco cigarettes at an earlier age and also more frequently than non-users," reported Dr. Erich Goode.

Chapter XXI
CHANGES BEHAVIOR

534.
14 PERSONALITY CHANGES NOTED AMONG USERS

"There are many young people, including some of the brightest, who have been using marijuana now more or less regularly for three to four years. Addiction or even habituation is denied. The smoking is said to be simply for pleasure. Untoward effects are usually (not always) denied. But the experienced clinician observes in many of these individuals personality changes that may grow subtly over long periods of time: diminished drive, lessened ambition, decreased motivation, apathy, shortened attention span, distractibility, poor judgment, impaired communication skills, less effectiveness, magical thinking, derealization, depersonalization, diminished capacity to carry out complex plans or prepare realistically for the future, a peculiar fragmentation in the flow of thought, habit deterioration and progressive loss of insight. There is a clinical impression of organicity to this syndrome that I simply cannot explain away," reported Louis J. West of The Department of Psychiatry, Neurology and Behavioral Sciences, Oklahoma Medical Center.

535.
ADVERSE EFFECT ON HEAVY SMOKERS

Heavy marijuana smokers are more likely than light smokers to experience difficulties in expressing their thoughts; their energy level is low, and their memory is not as sharp, according to Dr. David Kupfer and his associates.

536.
CHRONIC SMOKING IMPAIRS PERSONALITY

"Personality changes and mental illness have been reported in chronic cannabis smokers of previously normal personality. Addicts often have impairment of recent memory, vegetative symptoms, and a tendency to reversed sleep rhythm suggesting organic brain damage," reported Dr. A.M.G. Campbell, et al.

537.
LONG USE AFFECTS MEMORY AND PLEASURE CENTERS OF BRAIN

Marijuana "can affect both the memory . . . and the pleasure centers of the brain. These pleasure centers are the conditioning centers of the brain, and every experience of life is noted as causing either pain or pleasure. They are also part of the emotional matrix. But when these centers become quiescent, it is unlikely that the person can be self-activating."

538.
EFFECTS UNPREDICTABLE

From MARIJUANA AND YOUR CHILD by Jules Saltman. Copyright © 1970 by Jules Saltman. Used by permission of Grosset & Dunlap, Inc.

"Behavioral toxicity" has been seen by many investigators. According to Drs. Clark and Nakashima, the effects are unpredictable and "the very unpredictability of marijuana on different individuals and on the same individuals at different times and under different conditions increase the risk to the user."

539.
CONNECTION BETWEEN MARIJUANA AND CRIME

"Inspector Burnell Blanchard of the California Attorney General's Bureau of Narcotic Enforcement argues insistently that the connection between cannabis and crime is not coincidental. It has been found that marijuana reduces inhibitions. The danger lies in the fact that immature and psychopathic persons use it to deaden their perception of reality, and when under its effects their inhibitions and judgment are impaired with consequent increase in abnormal behavior."

540.
MARIJUANA AFFECTS PERSONALITY

"The evidence indicates that people become less interested in other people, more apathetic, awkward, defensive, aggressive, bitter, and distrustful when using marijuana," according to Jess R. Lord, of the University of Texas at Arlington.

541.
MARIJUANA IMPAIRS NORMAL FUNCTIONING

"As far as the effect of marijuana on behavior of normal individuals is concerned," Dr. Phillip Zeidenberg stated, "there is no doubt that it impairs normal functioning.

"In our work we have found it to interfere with memory, speech, and pain perception. Numerous other studies, more extensive than ours, and involving other parameters, show that much normal behavior in our society is not possible under the agent. Drive or performance, for example, is significantly impaired. . . .

"We found that marijuana interferes with the immediate memory and thereby directly interferes with the flow of speech giving the characteristic marijuana speech which is so well known."

542.
NATIONAL COMMISSION REPORTS ON ADVERSE CONSEQUENCES

According to The Official Report of the National Commission on Marihuana and Drug Abuse: "Marijuana's alleged criminogenic role is not always limited to violent or aggressive behavior. Some commentators also postulate that marijuana leads to or causes nonviolent forms of criminal or delinquent conduct, ranging from sexual promiscuity to grand larceny . . . marijuana frequently impairs judgment, distorts reality and diminishes, at least temporarily, the user's sense of personal and social responsibility. Regular or heavy use over an extended period of time is felt to interfere, perhaps irreversibly, with the orderly development of psychosocial and moral maturity."

543.
CAUSES "LOSS OF SELF-CONTROL"

One known hazard arising from the use of marijuana is the "loss of self-control, in which an individual might do things he would not ordinarily do in his sober state," stated Dr. Sidney Cohen, as Director of the Division of Narcotic Addiction and Drug Abuse of the National Institute of Mental Health.

544.
A DOCTOR'S QUESTION

"Often I ask marijuana users, would you like your surgery done by somebody who is high? They all say, 'Are you crazy?' They know that they're not trustworthy."

545.
PERSONALITY CHANGES THAT MAY FOLLOW MARIJUANA USE

Jack H. Mendelson et al., "The Effects of Marihuana Use on Human Operant Behavior: Individual Data," in *Pharmacology of Marihuana*, vol. 2., eds. M.C. Braude and S. Szara (New York: Raven Press, 1976), p. 643.

Some of the personality changes that may follow marijuana use are an inability to follow routines, reduced drive and ambition and a diminished capacity to endure frustration.

546.
THAT MARIJUANA WORSENS PSYCHOLOGICAL PROBLEMS HAS BEEN KNOWN FOR LONG TIME

"Some campus health officials have reported a number of (marijuana) users whose existing psychological problems have been seriously accentuated, often disabling the person, and a lesser number whose psychological difficulties have been precipitated by the use of the drug," reported Professor Stuart L. Hills.

547.
HEAVY USE INCREASES HOSTILITY IN SOME PEOPLE

"Hashish," stated Dr. Sidney Cohen, "has been used to work up the courage needed to perform a dangerous act. Studies of heavy users of marijuana reveal that such individuals have significantly greater feelings of hostility than a comparable group of non-users."

548.
NATIONAL COMMISSION CONCERNED ABOUT BEHAVIOR EFFECTS

"An extreme form (of amotivational syndrome) has been reported in populations of lower socioeconomic makes in several developing nations. These reports describe lethargy, instability, social deterioration, a loss of interest in virtually all activities other than drug use. This state of social and economic disability also results in precipitation and aggravation of psychiatric disorders (overt psychotic behavior) and possible somatic complications among very heavy and very long term users of high potency cannabis products," stated the National Commission of Marihuana and Drug Abuse.

549.
MARIJUANA CAN BREAK DOWN "CONTROLS OF CONSCIENCE"

The use of drugs "can break down the ordinary controls of conscience that limit one's behavior, and alcohol and marijuana are among these so-called disinhibiting agents," commented Dr. Leo E. Hollister, Medical Investigator for the Veteran's Administration Hospital in Palo Alto, California.

550.
USERS PERSISTENTLY SHOW ALTERED MENTAL FUNCTIONS

Dr. Hardin B. Jones reported that: "I have found that cannabis users while not acutely intoxicated persistently show a pattern of undesirably altered mental functions." Some of these include the use of *non sequitur* in speech, susceptibility to unusual and often foolish behavior, narrowing of facial expression, abrupt transitions in expressing thought and an inability to remember facts and details from one minute to another.

551.
EFFECTS OF MARIJUANA INCLUDE WITHDRAWAL, PHOBIAS AND COMPULSIVE BEHAVIOR

"While there is agreement among all sources concerning manifestations of breaks with reality, the present study, in addition, reports that during the drug's (marijuana) use the effects also include increased withdrawal, phobias, and compulsive behavior," stated Jess R. Lord, reviewing the findings of his research.

552.
NATIONAL INSTITUTE ON DRUG ABUSE REPORTS ON ONE YEAR MONKEY STUDY

Sassenrath and Chapman studied the effects of marijuana on the social behavior of monkeys. "Given oral doses equivalent to very heavy human cannabis use the monkeys responded much like humans. They slept and rested more frequently; active social interaction such as grooming of others was reduced. Over more extended periods of administration, the monkeys gradually showed fewer and fewer of these effects. While aggression was initially reduced, after receiving THC for weeks or months during the year-long study the monkeys became irritable and aggressive . . ." summarized the National Institute on Drug Abuse.

553.
RESEARCH SHOWS DEPRESSANT EFFECT ON ACTIVITY LEVEL

Cannabis seems to have a depressant effect on the activity of animals in research studies conducted by Drs. Loren Miller and William Drew. This effect is measured in terms of activity levels; the animals become less active and quieter under the influence of marijuana. A period of excitement and stimulation often preceded this period of depressed activity.

554.
DUAL ACTION OF POT

"Marijuana has a biphastic action, with an initial period of stimulation (anxiety, heightened perceptions, euphoria) followed by a later period of sedation (sleepiness, dreamlike states). With higher doses definite psychotomimetic effects are observed: difficulty with thinking, concentrating or speaking, and depersonalization."

555.
CREATES WEIRD BUT ELUSIVE CHANGES IN PEOPLE

Dr. Franz E. Winkler, formerly a New York City physician, and staff member of Clinical Medicine at the New York Medical College, suggested that people look at the personalities of their friends and relatives whom they knew before they started using marijuana. He said that by comparing their present personalities with their former selves, the difference should be obvious. "Unfortunately," Dr. Winkler added, "people are not observant enough to notice the weird but elusive changes in themselves or others unless their attention is directed to them."

556.
MANY ADVERSE EFFECTS FOUND

Tart describes the common emotional reactions to marijuana intoxication as distortion of the perception of time and space, euphoria, relaxation, lack of inhibition, feelings of well-being. Commonly experienced cognitive effects are impaired such as immediate memory, fragmentation of thought, altered sense of identity, increased suggestibility, a feeling of enhanced insight and decreased concentration ability. Less common effects are dizziness, nausea, hunger, a feeling of lightness and exaggerated laughter.

557.
GREEK STUDY REPORTS ON USERS

Tharp, Paul, "Cannabis Conference: The Latest Word From Science," *The Village Voice*, February 9, 1976.

Marijuana "users tend to avoid military service, are more likely to be unemployed, and have fewer skilled jobs, and tend to suffer from paranoid schizophrenia more than nonusers," found a group of investigators in various studies from the University of Athens Medical School in Greece.

558.
WARNING TO INEXPERIENCED USERS

"In the inexperienced user, it (cannabis) may induce panic or one state may quickly follow another. In addition, the user experiences perceptual changes and what seems to him to be a slowing of time."

559.
THE HYPNOTIC EFFECT OF MARIJUANA

Marijuana is a hypnotic drug with a long lasting hypnotic spell. Often the user is talked into many situations that he would avoid otherwise. It is the opinion of Dr. Hardin B. Jones that "the hypnotic effects of marijuana are . . . largely responsible for the acceptance of the hazardous consequences of more powerful drugs . . . and overly generous compliance with unreasonable requests by friends."

560.
PEOPLE AND MARIJUANA INTERACT . . . SOMETIMES IN UNEXPECTED WAYS

Dr. Robert C. Peterson stated that "it should be kept in mind that, like other psychoactive drugs, marijuana's effects are heavily dependent on dosage as well as the set and setting of use. None of this is intended to deny that large numbers in any given culture may agree on a particular effect—it is only to emphasize that psychoactive drugs, including marijuana, do not simply have effects on people, but that people and drugs interact, sometimes in unexpected ways."

561.
CALIFORNIA ASSEMBLYMAN REPORTS ADVERSE EFFECTS

From his observations of reports by various authorities, California Assemblyman William Campbell compiled the following list of adverse effects produced by marijuana:

"1. Marijuana distorts time and space relationships and makes it difficult to relate to reality.

"2. Marijuana causes the user to exhibit antisocial behavior normally controlled by religious or social inhibitions.

"3. Marijuana alters perception and makes visual, auditory, gustatory, olfactory and touch sensitivity more acute.

"4. When a large dose of the drug is ingested, the user tends to misjudge his own capabilities regarding relationships with other people.

562.
DISTURBING EFFECTS GREATER AMONG HIGHER EDUCATED

"On the basis of excellent, extensive research sponsored by the Egyptian government, it looks as though the more intelligent the individual and the higher his educational level, the more disturbing the effects of marijuana."

563.
SMOKERS MORE MOODY AND UNHAPPY IN COLLEGE SURVEY

Marijuana smokers rate themselves more unhappy and moody than nonsmokers according to a survey of drug use among college students conducted by Robbins et al.

564.
PERFORMANCE OF INEXPERIENCED USERS WORSE THAN EXPERIENCED USERS

As a result of the many experiments conducted to determine the effects of marijuana on users, it has been observed that naive users react differently than experienced smokers of the drug. "Naive subjects commonly report less marked subjective effects than those reported by experienced users. However, naive subjects demonstrate greater decrement in actual performance."

565.
MARIJUANA IS AN INTOXICANT . . .

Excerpt from THE SEEKERS by Jess Stearn. Copyright © 1968, 1969 by Jess Stearn. Used by permission of Doubleday & Company, Inc.

"Marijuana is an intoxicant which in some cases has a slight and, in others, a great effect on the behavior of individuals. The users of marijuana maintain a muscular coordination, so marijuana users continue to function, and when under the influence of marijuana, the likelihood of getting involved in dangerous and delinquent behavior is greater." This summarizes the testimony of the parole chief at the California Rehabilitation Center, Dr. Victor H. Vogel.

566.
HASHISH CAN LEAD TO SERIOUS PERSONALITY CHANGES

Hashish smoking precipitating severe insanity is a familiar phenomenon in many Arab countries. There is also an increase in the number of hashish psychoses in Sweden. Dr. Nils Bejerot stated: "I have seen several young people who, following a single hashish psychosis, have suffered from very serious personality changes which will probably be permanent and lead to life-long incapacity."

567.
MARIJUANA WORSENED USER'S DEPRESSION

From THE DRUG SCENE by Donald B. Louria. Copyright 1968 by Donald B. Louria. Used with permission of McGraw-Hill Book Company.

Dr. Dana Farnsworth of Harvard University reported the following case: "A nineteen year old man became depressed, used marijuana to combat an acute depressive episode, experienced 'black despair' and then obtained sedative pills from a friend which he took in an attempt at suicide."

567.
MARIJUANA WORSENED USER'S DEPRESSION

From THE DRUG SCENE by Donald B. Louria. Copyright 1968 by Donald B. Louria. Used with permission of McGraw-Hill Book Company.

Dr. Dana Farnsworth of Harvard University reported the following case: "A nineteen year old man became depressed, used marijuana to combat an acute depressive episode, experienced 'black despair' and then obtained sedative pills from a friend which he took in an attempt at suicide."

568.
WHAT HAPPENS WHILE YOU'RE SMOKING

Dr. Roy H. Hart asked a 26-year-old user, "What happens to you while you're actually smoking?" His response was, "I can't think or concentrate. It affects my memory. So many things I can't remember . . . I make idiotic decisions . . . I wind up loafing around doing absolutely nothing. I sleep all day and don't want to get down to the cab station (where he works from 4:30 P.M. until 1:30 A.M. or 2:30 A.M.). I get irritable and paranoid as hell." Dr. Hart then asked him what paranoid meant: "I'm suspicious. I'm depressed. I get a very bad feeling. A very insecure feeling . . . It's a feeling of emptiness, insecurity, impermanence. Of being afraid . . ."

569.
USER ACTS LIKE AGED PERSON

"The habitual marijuana user reacts physiologically and behaviorally like an aged person whose brain is shrunken."

570.
EFFECTS OF WITHDRAWAL AFTER LONG-TERM USE

"The Perils Of 'Pot' Start Showing Up." *U.S. News & World Report*, June 10, 1974, p. 58. Copyright 1974 U.S. News & World Report, Inc.

". . . Dr. M.I. Soueif, of the Department of Psychology at Cairo University in Egypt, said withdrawal after long-term use results in the individual's becoming 'quarrelsome, anxious, impulsive, easily upset and difficult to please' . . ."

571.
COMPLEXITIES OF MARIJUANA AND AGGRESSION

Abel found that "with animals under stress . . . marijuana tended to increase aggression. This suggests that the relationship between marijuana and aggression may be more complex than was earlier supposed," stated the report of the National Institute on Drug Abuse.

572.
MARIJUANA MAY CONTRIBUTE TO CRIME

As long ago as 1958, it was discovered that marijuana may contribute to the incidence of premeditated crime when used to "bolster courage" before the crime is actually committed.

573.
MARIJUANA USERS UNABLE TO "SEE" ITS HARMFUL EFFECTS

Marijuana's "early use is beguiling. Pot smokers are so enraptured by the illusion of warm feelings that they are unable to sense the deterioration of their own mental and physiological processes," reported Dr. D. Harvey Powelson.

"Its continued use leads to delusional thinking. And along with the delusions comes the strong need to seduce others into using drugs. I have rarely seen a regular marijuana user who didn't actively attempt to influence friends to use the drug."

As director of the Department of Psychiatry in the Student Health Center at the University of California at Berkeley, he has observed and counseled some 200 students who used marijuana regularly. "The patients who used pot told us that it heightened their 'awareness' of particular experiences and made them feel mellow and peaceful, with real insights about the world. These self-observations were simply not true. They were part of what we have come to recognize as the marijuana illusion."

574.
MARIJUANA AND SCHOOL DROPOUTS

There is no guarantee that because one marijuana user experiences no adverse effects, another user will be as fortunate. There is evidence to show that individuals who become dependent on it exhibit similar characteristics and behavioral patterns. These characteristics fit dropouts, not the top students.

575.
ALTERS MENTAL INTERPRETATION OF VISUAL SIGHTS

In an extensive two year research study, characteristic effects of marijuana on vision included: "seeing forms and meaningful patterns in visual material that normally is ambiguous, and finding visual imagery more vivid than usual."

576.
MARIJUANA HAZARDS GREATER FOR "HIGH-RISK" PERSONS

The American Medical Association reported that for certain high risk persons, the hazards of marijuana use are greater. "Although such persons do not constitute the majority of users, the personal and societal implications of their involvement, given current usage patterns, are of a magnitude to warrant concern."

577.
INVESTIGATIONS FIND SEDATIVE ACTION

"Aggressiveness (as judged by questionnaires) usually declines, perhaps from the sedative action of cannabis, but nevertheless suicidal actions and fighting occur," summarized Drs. Paton and Pertwee.

578.
THC MAKES RHESUS MONKEYS PASSIVE

Tetrahydrocannabinol (THC), the active component in cannabis can be synthesized. Extremely small doses can cause an immediate psychotic condition. In laboratory studies, THC was administered to rhesus monkeys and their behavior was markedly altered. They sat still under the influence of THC while normally they are active and aggressive. It was even possible to put a finger in a monkey's mouth without evoking any reaction.

579.
AMA WARNING TO PEOPLE WHO ARE IMMATURE, UNSTABLE OR ALREADY ILL

"Marijuana is potentially damaging to health in a variety of ways, but it can be especially harmful when used by a person who is immature, unstable, or already ill."

Chapter XXII

AFFECTS MENTAL HEALTH

580.
USERS EXPERIENCE INCREASED PARANOID SYMPTOMS

"The present research," reported Jess R. Lord of the University of Texas, "appears to support current clinical reports of mental confusion and rather terrifying paranoid thoughts. While rather pure type paranoid reactions appear relatively rare in clinical reporting, the findings of this study lead us to wonder whether there is rather broadly experienced shifts, though usually not often large, to increased paranoid symptoms as marijuana is used."

581.
IRREVERSIBLE EFFECTS

"There are mind-altering effects of marijuana, some of which are reversible, but many of which are irreversible."

582.
REPORTED CASES OF PSYCHOSIS FROM MARIJUANA USE AT SOCIALLY ACCEPTABLE LEVELS

Gabriel G. Nahas, *Marihuana: Deceptive Weed* (New York: Raven Press, 1973), p. 236, citing H.S. Kaplan, "Psychosis Associated with Marijuana," *N.Y. State J. Med.* 71 (1971): 433;435.

Dr. H.S. Kaplan reported "5 cases of psychosis associated with marijuana use at dose levels that are generally socially acceptable in the New York area. She states that this reaction, marked by symptoms of paranoia, depersonalization, and hallucinations that rarely last more than 1 week, is distinguishable from an acute schizophrenia reaction. . . . Most of the patients . . . recover from this frightening experience without damage in a few days. However, occasionally the psychotic episode is prolonged, and some of the mental problems . . . persist."

583.
CAN CAUSE THOSE WITH PSYCHIATRIC PROBLEMS TO AVOID NEEDED TREATMENT

Dr. Stanley F. Yolles believes that "those users who already have significant psychiatric problems might readily be led (by the use of marijuana) to avoid obtaining necessary psychiatric treatment . . . only to wind up as one of the group of users whose entire life becomes absorbed in the drug culture."

484.
TENDENCY TOWARD PARANOIA AND SCHIZOPHRENIA IN USERS

In the words of Dr. Hardin B. Jones, the average marijuana user "is likely to have a tendency toward paranoia or schizophrenia, or both. This may be caused by chronic disturbance of the neural mechanisms by which sensations received through two or more organs are synthesized into a composite interpretation of the physical cause. Such a disturbance, which occurs in both psychotic persons and those using marijuana, can lead to completely inaccurate interpretations of the real world."

585.
INCREASED DEPRESSION AND REDUCED MORALE AMONG TEST SUBJECTS

"While the present study found a significant increase in depression, users report feelings of euphoria, self-confidence, self-satisfaction, well-being, and a sense of one's own worth as being dominant." However, what the users actually experience is "reduced morale, feelings of uselessness, inability to view the future with optimism, reduced self-confidence, increased worry, and introversion," reported Jess R. Lord.

586.
CAN CAUSE ACUTE ANXIETY STATE

Dr. Lester Grinspoon, Harvard University psychiatrist, feels that marijuana can cause "an acute anxiety state" or a psychosis in a person whose psychological state is unstable. He feels that the altered state of consciousness and the distortion of perception and body image may be enough to precipitate a schizophrenic reaction in a person who already demonstrates anxiety.

587.
CHRONIC USE FOUND TO CAUSE DEPRESSION AND APATHY

"Chronic cannabis use in heavy doses affects the central nervous system. The changes are related to the type of dose and the setting in which the dose is taken. Overall, the picture is one of depression and apathy, but continued repeatedly higher doses sometimes may produce . . . aggressive behavior."

588.
EVERY USE PRODUCES TOXIC STATE

Every use of cannabis produces a toxic state. Dr. Roy H. Hart stated: "I have yet to meet anyone, patient or otherwise, whose aim with cannabis is a state short of intoxication. In the acute state the minimum that is observed is impairment of orientation (temporal distortion), impairment of memory (registration defect), and altered affect (some degree of euphoria or dysphoria). Impairment of intellectual functions and impairment of judgment also occur, in some degree, in the acute state. The non-acute state, that is, repetitions of acute usage of a frequency which lead to a subchronic condition, are also characterized by deficits or impairments in the 5 functions used to measure OBS, whether they be large or small, whether or not we have the clinical or scientific/technological skills and paraphernalia to assess them with accuracy and precision as is done so splendidly in analytical chemistry, where what is to be measured can be isolated so much more effectively."

589.
REACTIONS OF 11 MARIJUANA USERS

At a meeting of the American Psychiatric Association in 1967, Dr. Martin H. Keeler reported the adverse effects of marijuana he observed in 11 users of the drug. Most common symptoms were confusion and disorientation, panic, fear, and paranoia. Two of the subjects experienced alterations in their behavior and lifestyle attributed to the use of marijuana.

590.
MAY PRECIPITATE PSYCHOTIC EPISODES

On the basis of a two year detailed study, involving more than 37,000 marijuana smokers, Dr. I. R. Rosengard stated that "marijuana may precipitate psychotic episodes in persons who have a pre-existing borderline personality or psychotic disorder."

591.
CAN TRIGGER PSYCHOTIC EPISODE IN SOME PEOPLE

"In persons with a history of psychosis, marijuana can trigger a psychotic episode. Such episodes can also be triggered in these people by other drugs, such as alcohol, amphetamines, and LSD."

592.
". . . WOULD APPEAR TO BE A DANGEROUS DRUG"

Doris H. Milman, "The role of marihuana in patterns of drug abuse by adolescents," *The Journal of Pediatrics* vol. 74, no. 2. (February 1969): 283-290.

Dr. Doris H. Milman of the Department of Pediatrics, State University of New York, Downstate Medical Center, wrote in a recent article "that marijuana, as used by young people with unstable personalities, is capable of precipitating acute psychoses, may contribute to the production of chronic psychoses, disrupts the young person's way of life, and is associated with multiple drug usage. On these bases, marijuana would appear to be a dangerous drug requiring governmental control."

593.
DEPRESSION, PANIC, PARANOIA

Dr. Martin Keeler, Professor of Psychiatry at the University of North Carolina, studied in detail 11 student users of marijuana. Cases of depression, panic, paranoia, and disorientation were found. He contends marijuana "can initiate destructive alterations in personality and life style."

594.
MARIJUANA DANGEROUS FOR SCHIZOPHRENICS

Dr. Martin H. Keeler reported that the "dissolution of ordinary adaptive and defensive psychological structure that occurs during the marijuana reaction is potentially dangerous for individuals with a predisposition to schizophrenia."

595.
RELATIONSHIP BETWEEN MARIJUANA AND MENTAL HEALTH

Excerpt from THE SEEKERS by Jess Stearn. Copyright © 1968, 1969 by Jess Stearn. Used by permission of Doubleday & Company, Inc.

Marijuana, according to Dr. Martin H. Keeler, can adversely affect the unstable and even the stable if the dosage is large enough. He continued: "Perhaps all investigators would agree . . . that marijuana cannot produce functional psychopathology but can only precipitate it in individuals so predisposed. Many would interpret this as an exoneration of the drug. Others would hold that the occurrence of psychopathology in an individual at a given time requires many factors and that many more people have predisposition to mental illness than develop it. In this sense marijuana usage might precipitate trouble that would not have otherwise occurred. . . . The use of the drug can initiate changes in style of life. . . ."

596.
IN ILLINOIS STUDY "FREAK-OUTS" OCCURRED IN 20% OF SUBJECTS

In a substantial study conducted by doctors at the Illinois Research Hospital in Chicago, the most common emotional mood from marijuana use was a pleasant emotional state. "Occasional 'freak-outs,' that is, temporarily overwhelming negative emotions, occurred, however, in 20 percent of users." Dr. Rosengard of the above research group noted that because all of the users in the study were continuous users by their own choice, "the negative, unpleasant effects probably are under-represented."

597.
ADVERSE REACTIONS IN INEXPERIENCED USERS

". . . It seems clear that marijuana can precipitate certain less-serious adverse reactions, such as simple depressive and panic reactions, particularly in inexperienced users," stated physician and psychologist Dr. Rosengard.

598.
PARANOID THINKING IS COMMON REACTION AMONG REGULAR CANNABIS USERS

Paranoid thinking has been noted in 28 out of 40 cases of continuing cannabis users by Keeler and found in 10 out of 12 in the cases of Talbott and Teague.

599.
MARIJUANA PRODUCES FALSE SENSE OF SECURITY

The marijuana smoker can derive a feeling of self-confidence from the effects of the drug. He can feel powerful, secure, and on top of the world at one moment; however, a single negative factor can destroy the entire illusion and produce feelings of anxiety and paranoia.

600.
IMMEDIATE AND REMOTE DANGERS OF MARIJUANA

"What are the immediate and remote dangers of marijuana use?" The immediate dangers, according to Dr. L.E. Hollister, "are almost identical with those from LSD, probably because at higher doses many of the same mental and emotional reactions are obtained. Manic or elated excitement, panic, stress states, precipitation of schizophrenia-like or depressive illnesses, and frank deliriums have been encountered among users.

What is more disturbing are reports of subtle effects on the personality associated with prolonged use: loss of a desire to work, loss of motivation, and loss of judgment and intellectual functions. . . .

"In view of the fact that many drug users are recruited from segments of our youth favored with intelligence and opportunity, the future loss of a large number of these individuals from productive society may be of considerable social consequence."

601.
PARANOID DELUSIONS

In a study by F.T. Melges, a cigarette containing 20 milligrams of THC, (a common dose) was smoked for ten minutes by six subjects. Four of the six, none of whom had a previous history of delusions, experienced paranoid delusions.

602.
OVERT ANXIETY IS SIGNIFICANT SYMPTOM OF MARIJUANA USE

"With the exception of repression tendencies, the syndrome of overt anxiety was significantly increased as marijuana was used. Thus, instead of being a subordinate reaction as the literature reports, anxiety is a very dominant aspect of the marijuana experience," reported Jess R. Lord.

603.
EFFECTS ON NOVICE USERS

"The complications of acute marijuana intoxication are infrequent, and usually consist of anxiety or paranoid states. Any individual, especially a novice, may become confused about the changes that he experiences. The loss of ego controls can result in delusional thinking, usually of a suspicious, paranoid nature. The patient may panic and injure himself or others. Spontaneous recurrences of the marijuana state (flashbacks) have been described," stated Dr. Jess L. Steinfeld.

604.
ACUTE PANIC ANXIETY REACTION IS COMMON

"Probably the most common adverse psychological reaction to marijuana use among American users is the acute panic anxiety reaction. It represents an exaggeration of the more usual marijuana response in which the individual loses perspective and becomes acutely anxious."

Although this response usually occurs with relatively inexperienced smokers of the drug, an unexpectedly large dose of marijuana may cause the more experienced user to become acutely anxious also, according to a report by the National Institute on Drug Abuse.

605.
DOCTOR WARNS CHRONIC SMOKERS

Some of the results of chronic cannabis use are pathological forms of thinking resembling paranoia, deterioration of mental functioning, lack of motivation and a progressive and chronic passivity, reported Dr. Gabriel G. Nahas.

606.
ORAL DOSE CAUSED PSYCHOTIC REACTION IN MENTALLY HEALTHY INDIVIDUALS

Dr. Phillip Zeidenberg reported that: "There is no doubt that a single dose of tetrahydrocannabinol can cause an acute psychotic reaction in mentally healthy individuals. One of our subjects in a small pilot study with oral delta-9-tetrahydrocannabinol had an acute paranoid break lasting several hours. This young man is of unquestionably sound mental health. Marijuana use is also associated with longer lasting and even chronic psychoses. Many of these individuals, but not all, are found to have a previous history of serious mental illness."

607.
ANOTHER POTENTIAL DANGER

"Cannabis opponents consider the psychotomimetic quality of the drug another potential danger. Physicians and psychiatrists, especially, feel that marijuana is capable of precipitating powerful, though temporary, psychotic episodes—or, more generally, disturbing psychic adverse reactions."

608.
THREE ADVERSE REACTIONS

"In persons who have no history of mental illness and who have never taken a hallucinogen, three adverse reactions to marijuana have been observed. . . .

"The first, a depressive reaction, most often occurs in obsessive-compulsive persons.

"The second, a panic reaction, frequently occurs in novice users and older persons, usually those who have ambivalent feelings about marijuana. . . . Such panic reactions account for about 75 percent of all adverse reactions to marijuana.

"The third, a temporary toxic psychosis, never occurs following smoking, because the user falls asleep before the required dose can be smoked. The psychosis follows oral ingestion of high doses of marijuana or hashish."

609.
PRODUCES AN INTOXICATION

According to Alexander R.K. Mitchell, cannabis "produces an intoxication after some preliminary stimulation. Gradually the subject experiences pleasant sopor in which there is uncontrolled gaiety. There is some distortion of perception. It intensifies the prevailing mood but can induce sudden panics or profound depression."

610.
MARIJUANA'S MENTAL AFTER-EFFECTS

"Mentally, it (marijuana) has . . . after-effects: panic, gross confusion, impulsive and aggressive behavior, depersonalization, hallucinations, depression, and indolence," stated Max Rafferty.

611.
"ACUTE PSYCHOTIC REACTION" FROM ONE-TIME USE

From MARIJUANA AND YOUR CHILD by Jules Saltman. Copyright © 1970 by Jules Saltman. Used by permission of Grosset & Dunlap, Inc.

A case of "acute psychotic reaction" including panic and dissociation after a one-time use of marijuana has been reported by a young man with a previous personality disorder by Dr. Doris Milman of the Downstate Medical Center.

612.
MARIJUANA FRIGHT

From THE DRUG SCENE by Donald B. Louria. Copyright 1968 by Donald B. Louria. Used with permission of McGraw-Hill Book Company.

". . . I have been called by several physicians reporting cases of marijuana fright observed in their own practices. It is abundantly clear that such reactions may occur after smoking a single marijuana cigarette," reported Donald B. Louria.

613.
"PRECIPITATES MORE SERIOUS PSYCHOPATHOLOGY"

Various reports in the United States state that marijuana use may cause chronic disturbances. It is difficult to evaluate the exact role of marijuana in such cases, "although it may have precipitated more serious psychopathology."

614.
ACUTE TOXIC PSYCHOSES

"Acute toxic psychoses often occur primarily after heavy usage greater than that to which the individual is accustomed. These psychoses have some characteristics of an acute brain syndrome."

615.
MULTIPLE BAD EFFECTS

"I think I'm coming down with schizophrenia," stated a 26 year old nursing student who began to smoke pot during the final year of her training program. In the beginning she smoked only on weekends with friends, but eventually began smoking once or twice during the week with or without a companion. Under the pressure of final exams, she smoked one or two joints a night while attempting to study.

"She noticed that she was not thinking so clearly anymore, had difficulty concentrating, suffered memory lapses, and was alarmed and depressed over the precipitious decline in her once staunch grade-point average. Most frightening to her were several episodes of depersonalization, when she would experience an identical self standing apart from her. During one of these experiences, she was aware that she had a severe headache but suffered no pain. She was frightened recalling the moment because 'the other me had the headache.'"

616.
"PERCEPTION OF THE EXTERNAL ENVIRONMENT IS CHANGED. . ."

In an extensive study conducted by Dr. I.R. Rosengard at the Illinois Research Hospital in Chicago, "150 experienced marijuana users—estimated to cover the effects of about 37,000 occasions of use—'were analyzed to discover common reactions to marijuana in non-laboratory situations. The researchers found that' perception of the external environment is changed in virtually all sensory modalities."

617.
PSYCHOTIC-LIKE RESPONSE SIMILAR BETWEEN THC AND HASHISH

Excerpt from THE SEEKERS by Jess Stearn. Copyright © 1968, 1969 by Jess Stearn. Used by permission of Doubleday & Company, Inc.

". . . Tests with THC have shown as little as 18 milligrams of THC, (one/ two-thousandth part of an ounce) given to an average-sized male, brought on the psychotic-like responses of the strongest hashish, a form of marijuana whose potency hardly anybody questions."

618.
REVERSIBLE PSYCHOSIS DEVELOPS OCCASIONALLY

Alexander R.K. Mitchell reports "that occasionally a reversible psychosis develops with prolonged and excessive use" of cannabis.

619.
1939 REPORT ON ACUTE INTOXICATION

From THE DRUG SCENE by Donald B. Louria. Copyright 1968 by Donald B. Louria. Used with permission of McGraw-Hill Book Company.

Back in 1939 Dr. Walter Bromberg studied the relationship between smoking marijuana cigarettes and acute intoxication. Fourteen of his patients developed acute intoxication after only smoking a single cigarette. Acute intoxication is characterized by mental confusion, hunger, talkativeness, disorientation, excitement, visual hallucinations, a feeling of intellectual brilliancy, euphoria, anxiety, hysteria, panic states, changes in time perception, depressions, crowding of sensations and recklessness. Some of the patients even had suicidal and assaultive urges.

620.
FEELINGS OF PARANOIA COMMON AMONG CANNABIS USERS

"A paranoia state is common . . . a transient paranoia is familiar to most users with feelings of persecution, of being watched and talked about, of betrayal, of distrusting the world with everyone an enemy."

621.
HIGH DOSES CAN CAUSE PSYCHOTIC REACTIONS

In 1967 Dr. H. Isbell, a West German pharmacologist conducted the first experimental study with pure delta-9-THC. He found that the hallucinogenic properties of THC are dependent on dosage, confirming the earlier findings of Jacques Moreau. Dr. Isbell said that sufficiently high doses (15-20 mg. smoked) "can cause psychotic reactions in any individual."

622.
CANNABIS MAY PRODUCE DEPRESSION

In 12 out of 100 regular cannabis users, researchers Chopra and Chopra have found that cannabis produces depression.

623.
6-MONTH STUDY OF CHRONIC USERS IN JAMAICA

Gabriel G. Nahas, *Marihuana: Deceptive Weed* (New York: Raven Press, 1973), p. 242, citing D.J. Spencer, "Cannabis Induced Psychosis," *W. Indian Med. J.* 19 (1970): 228-230.

Dr. D.J. Spencer reported that over a 6-month period he observed nine men aged 18-24 in Jamaica. All were chronic marijuana smokers, who had to be hospitalized in the psychiatric ward for periods of 4-8 weeks. None of them reported previous psychiatric problems. Their acute psychotic episode was sudden and marked by aggressive behavior, gross psychomotor activity, disturbance of sleep, delusions of grandeur, and symptoms of amnesia at the onset. They were treated with medication, hypnotics, and in 4 cases, electroshock therapy. Following the acute phase of their illness, they still showed signs of amnesia, dull emotional responses, poor motivation and thought fragmentation.

624.
ADVERSE PSYCHOTIC REACTIONS IN INDIA

Gabriel G. Nahas, *Marihuana: Deceptive Weed* (New York: Raven Press, 1973), p. 237.

In 1971, Chopra reported his study of 200 adverse psychotic reactions among cannabis users in Calcutta over a 5-year period. "Sixty-eight of these patients (37%) were in good health, had no personality problems and no history of mental problems. . . . The toxic episodes lasted from a few hours to a few days, and were followed by a '90% recovery rate' after the drug was withdrawn."

625.
CANNABIS-INDUCED PSYCHOSIS

"Another study documented nine cases of cannabis-induced psychosis observed within a six month period on the island of Jamaica; these were 18-24 years old with no previous personal nor family history of mental illness."

626.
STUDY COMPARES PARANOID PSYCHOSIS FROM LONG TERM MARIJUANA USE WITH PARANOID SCHIZOPHRENIA

A 1976 clinical study of 25 patients conducted in India by V.R. Thacore and S.R.P. Shukla, compared the characteristics of paranoid psychosis resulting from long-term marijuana use with that of paranoid schizophrenia. The subjects with cannabis psychosis were found to be more bizarre in their behavior, more violent and panicky.

627.
TOXIC PSYCHOSIS FROM CANNABIS REPORTED IN AFRICA

Gabriel G. Nahas, *Marihuana: Deceptive Weed* (New York: Raven Press, 1973), p. 237.

Dr. Gabriel G. Nahas reported that: "In all African countries where cannabis is used extensively, toxic psychosis attributed to the use of the drug is reported. In South Africa, mental hospitals have reported that 2 to 3% of their admissions were due to 'da-ga' smoking. In Nigeria, researchers Asuni and Lambo reported that 14% of the psychotic admissions were users, and one half of these admissions were related directly to cannabis intoxication. . . . Recovery was not always rapid, requiring in some cases up to 12 months."

628.
REACTIONS AMONG CANNABIS-USERS IN VIETNAM

Among the adverse reactions found in cannabis users in Vietnam, there were 12 cases that appeared to be acute toxic psychosis. The doctors "also reported seeing many less-serious reactions, such as anxiety states, depression, dissociation, depersonalization, disorientation, paranoid thoughts, and hallucinations," reported Dr. I.R. Rosengard.

629.
DESCRIPTION OF THE ACUTE TOXIC STATE

The acute toxic state "is characterized by acute or subacute onset, confusion, visual and auditory hallucinations, paranoid ideation, excitation or aggression, and amnesia for the period of onset. The syndrome usually is self-limited and lasts a few days to a few weeks. . . . The most frequent picture described in the Eastern reports seems to be the acute toxic state."

Chapter XXIII
PSYCHOLOGICAL DEPENDENCE

630.
USED AS AN ESCAPE

Perhaps marijuana is not physically addictive; however, users of the drug often become addicted to the pleasure associated with it, to the freedom from responsibility obtained from its use. Frequently young marijuana users have no desire to do anything other than smoke and get "high." The reality of their drug world has no problems, reported Dr. James Wall of New York Hospital.

631.
DOCTOR WARNS OF PSYCHOLOGICAL DEPENDENCY

"Without doubt, a psychological dependency is created in the repeated use of the drug," reported Dr. I.R. Rosengard.

632.
HEAVY MARIJUANA USE LINKED TO MANY PROBLEMS

Mirin concluded that the heavy use of marijuana appeared to be linked to the following: "psychological dependence, search for insight or meaningful experience, multiple-drug use, poor work adjustment, diminished goal

183

directed activity and ability to master new problems, poor social adjustment, and poor heterosexual relationships."

633.
NATIONAL INSTITUTE OF MENTAL HEALTH REPORTS ON PSYCHOLOGICAL DEPENDENCE

In reporting to the 91st Congress, the National Institute of Mental Health stated that while marijuana does not lead to physical dependence or true addiction, psychological dependence on marijuana is well known. Some people prefer to function in an intoxicated rather than a sober state.

634.
AS IT IS USED REGULARLY LESS IS NEEDED TO PRODUCE A DANGEROUS TOXIC EFFECT

"The Perils of 'Pot' Start Showing Up," *U.S. News & World Report*, June 10, 1974, p. 58. Copyright 1974 U.S. News & World Report, Inc. Reprinted from 'U.S. News & World Report':

". . . Regular users of cannabis develop a tolerance for the drug, thus requiring greater levels of its use to get a 'high,'" Professor Paton reported. "This increased intake may be a serious factor," he added, "since preliminary tests on animals indicate that as the drug is used regularly, less of it is needed to produce a dangerous toxic effect. . . ."

635.
EXTENSIVE REVIEW FINDS MARIJUANA "A DANGEROUS DRUG"

Excerpt from THE SEEKERS by Jess Stearn. Copyright (c) 1968, 1969 by Jess Stearn. Used by permission of Doubleday & Company, Inc.

Even in 1968, the American Medical Association and the National Research Council described marijuana as a "dangerous drug which could cause psychological dependence and lead to psychosis." Evidence and claims were reviewed by 16 scientists for two years before this report was made.

636.
PSYCHOLOGICAL DEPENDENCE IN MODERATE USERS

The Official Report of the National Commission on Marihuana and Drug Abuse states: "Some moderate users evidence a degree of psychological dependence which increases in intensity with prolonged duration of use. Behavioral effects are less in stable personalities but greater in those with emotional instability. Prolonged duration of use does increase the probability of some behavioral and organic consequences including the possible shift to a heavy use pattern."

637.
PSYCHOLOGICAL AND BEHAVIORAL DEPENDENCE DOCUMENTED

"It is well documented," stated Dr. Gabriel G. Nahas, "that cannabis may create a state of psychological dependence or behavioral dependence which is an important obstacle to discontinued usage."

638.
IS MARIJUANA HABIT FORMING?

Chronic marijuana users will go to great lengths to insure that they will not be without the drug. Dr. David P. Ausubel notes that deprivation may result in "anxiety, restlessness, irritability, or even a state of depression with suicidal fantasies, sometimes self-mutilating actions, or actual suicidal attempts."

639.
PSYCHOLOGICAL DEPENDENCY SEEN BY DOCTORS

"Without question the danger most commonly seen by physicians and psychiatrists in marijuana is its power to engender a kind of psychological dependence in the user."

640.
POSITION OF THE NEW YORK STATE OFFICE OF DRUG ABUSE SERVICES

The New York State Office of Drug Abuse Services has taken the official position that marijuana may cause psychological dependence in chronic users, and that the psychological effects of marijuana are quite variable.

641.
PSYCHIC DEPENDENCE MAKES IT DIFFICULT TO STOP USING

Professor M.I. Soueif of Egypt, stated that "the majority of cannabis takers—78.5 percent—expressed a desire, but inability to get rid of the habit, and about one-fourth of this discontented majority had made actual though unsuccessful attempts to stop the habit completely. According to their own reports, takers, when deprived of the drug, tend to become quarrelsome, anxious, impulsive, easily upset, and difficult to please. . . . Their productivity deteriorates in quantity and quality. Such changes, combined with what seems to be an overpowering urge to continue taking the drug, constitutes some aspects of . . . psychic dependence."

642.
COMPULSIVE PSYCHOLOGICAL DEPENDENCE IN FOREIGN COUNTRIES

"The very heavy users, found in countries where the use of cannabis has been indigenous for centuries, have a compulsive psychological dependence on the drug, most commonly used in the form of hashish. Clear-cut behavioral changes and a greater incidence of associated biological injury occur as duration of use increases," reported The National Commission on Marihuana and Drug Abuse.

Chapter XXIV

COMPARISON WITH OTHER DRUGS

643.
A STRONG PSYCHEDELIC

"Research suggests that THC . . . is a psychedelic drug and a powerful one. By weight it may be stronger than any psychedelic except LSD," commented Dr. Allen Cohen.

644.
CANNABIS PSYCHOSIS

According to Dr. Roy H. Hart: "If parallels must be drawn, cannabis psychosis should be more appropriately compared to amphetamine psychosis or cocaine psychosis, both brain syndromes, rather than to schizophrenia, a functional disorder of unknown etiology."

645.
DANGERS OF HEAVY USE

From MARIJUANA AND YOUR CHILD by Jules Saltman. Copyright © 1970 by Jules Saltman. Used by permission of Grosset & Dunlap, Inc.

According to Dr. Harris Isbell, the effects of large doses of marijuana can be "psychotomimetic" or imitative of insanity. The "marked distortion in visual and auditory perception, depersonalization, derealization and hallucinations, both auditory and optical" are very much like the sensations of an LSD 'trip.'

646.
"SHOULD BE PLACED LOWER ON THE LIST FOR LEGALIZATION THAN SOME OTHER DRUGS"

Dr. W.D.M. Paton, Professor of Pharmacology at Oxford University, testified before the United States Subcommittee on Internal Security that "there is no rational dividing line between cannabis and other drugs such as LSD or some opiates." He explains that the reactions produced from a large dose of marijuana overlap with those from a small dose of LSD or the less active opiates. Reactions in both cases are hallucinatory, and with the less active opiates, analgesia (absence of pain), euphoria, and 'day dreaming' occur. He said that because of the unique cumulative action of cannabis, and its ability to produce prolonged cognitive impairment in a young person, it should be placed lower on the list for legalization than some other drugs.

647.
A SENATOR'S WARNING

The "dangers of cannabis are much closer to the dangers of heroin, in scope and quality, than they are to the admitted but far more limited dangers of coffee or tobacco—or, for that matter, alcohol," commented Senator James O. Eastland in his introduction to the hearings before the United States Senate Internal Security Subcommittee in 1974.

648.
SIMILARITY TO DRUGS

In a study by Dr. E.R. Sinnett, experienced drug users rated marijuana as similar to hypnotic, sedative and depressant drugs rather than to psychedelic drugs such as LSD.

649.
MARIJUANA SOMETIMES RESEMBLES THE PSYCHOTOMIMETIC DRUGS

"With the availability of standardized doses of the psychoactive principle, delta-9-THC, a number of studies have been done with the experimental administration of marijuana. Some report auditory and visual hallucinations in subjects at high dosages, thus suggesting that marijuana may resemble the psychotomimetic drugs under some circumstances," stated Dr. I.R. Rosengard.

650.
MAKES OTHER DRUGS MORE DEPRESSANT

The interaction of delta-9-THC with 13 other drugs was researched by Pryor in a behavioral study in 1976. There were 3 physiological and 13 behavioral tests used. "The principal effect is that when THC is added to any of these drugs the resultant effect either shifts to the depressant side or becomes more depressant."

651.
THC'S DEPRESSANT EFFECT

Gordon T. Pryor, "Acute and Subacute Behavioral and Pharmacological Interactions of delta-9-Tetrahydrocannabinol with Other Drugs," in *Pharmacology of Marihuana*, vol. 2., eds. M.C. Braude and S. Szara (New York: Raven Press, 1976), p. 553.

Gordon T. Pryor concludes that the depressant effects of delta-9-THC dominate when THC is given along with other drugs. If the other drug has a depressant effect, the result is a combined depressant effect of the two drugs, even if the other drug is given in such quantities that are normally inactive. If the other drug has stimulant properties, they are cancelled by the depressant properties of THC. In no instance were any of the thirteen drugs Pryor evaluated able to offset the strong depressant effects of delta-9-THC.

Chapter XXV

CAN LEAD TO USING OTHER DRUGS

652.
LARGE MAJORITY OF HEROIN ADDICTS BEGAN WITH POT

Excerpt from THE SEEKERS by Jess Stearn. Copyright © 1968, 1969 by Jess Stearn. Used by permission of Doubleday & Company, Inc.

"While not everybody smoking marijuana went on to heroin, a diversity of reports indicated that the majority of addicts had begun with heroin. Of 2213 narcotics addicts examined at the Public Health Service hospital in Lexington, 70.4 percent had used marijuana prior to their addiction, reported Gene R. Haslip of the Bureau of Narcotics. It is true that not all persons who ever smoked a marijuana cigarette have gone on to the use of heroin, but a large majority of addicts began their drug-taking with marijuana."

653.
WHY MARIJUANA SMOKERS USE MORE AND MORE

". . . There's no question that people who use marijuana regularly over a significant period of time are clearly in a state of not being interested in anything but feeling good. There are physiological explanations for that.

"Marijuana contains a chemical which affects the pleasure center. You get the illusion of feeling good. Then this illusion becomes more important than really feeling good. At the same time the effect of the drug is wearing off as you become tolerant to it. So you use more of it. And as that goes on, you either have to use stronger drugs or get another high."

654.
THE HEROIN CONNECTION

From MARIJUANA AND YOUR CHILD by Jules Saltman. Copyright © 1970 by Jules Saltman. Used by permission of Grosset & Dunlap, Inc.

Seventy percent of several thousand drug patients examined by John C. Ball at the Lexington and Fort Worth federal hospitals reported they had used marijuana before becoming heroin addicts.

655.
26% OF HEAVY SMOKERS SURVEYED WENT ON TO HARDER DRUGS

Dr. Nahas discussed the results of a survey done by Columbia University among 5,500 high school students in New York State. The results published in December 1975 "clearly states that marijuana is a crucial stepping-stone toward the use of heroin or other dangerous drugs. The statistics show that among those students who were heavy marijuana users, 26 percent went on to use heroin or other destructive drugs. This does not allow a scientist to say categorically that marijuana leads to heroin, because 74 percent of heavy marijuana users did not go on to use heroin, but it seems to me that 26 percent is a high percentage. I want to add, by contrast only 1% of the students who did not use marijuana or any other drugs went directly to heroin—1 percent versus 26 percent. So, the statistics are significant."

656.
STUDENTS DISCOVER MARIJUANA MIXED WITH BLACK OPIUM

In an experiment at Georgia Tech, several students bought marijuana in Atlanta. They then tested their purchases in a laboratory and found the marijuana also contained black opium, which could lead marijuana users to a more dangerous addiction.

657.
MARIJUANA MAY BE LACED WITH HEROIN

It was discovered in Lakewood, Ohio that drug dealers were mixing heroin in the marijuana. They sprayed heroin on the cannabis in order to cause addiction and thus raise the demand for heroin.

658.
MARIJUANA SPRAYED WITH HEROIN CAN CAUSE ADDICTION

One of the risks involved with using marijuana is the difficulty in determining whether the substance being used is pure marijuana or something more dangerous and addictive. Drug pushers sometime spray heroin on marijuana. Eventually, people who smoke the tainted marijuana can become addicted to heroin. The dealer will have succeeded in increasing the demand for the hard drug.

659.
PROBLEM WHEN USED WITH OTHER DRUGS

Multiple drug use is a serious problem that is in need of more attention. Manno et al. reported that delta-9-THC acts synergistically with caffeine and amphetamines. A depressant action is potentiated with ethanol and barbiturates by delta-9-THC.

660.
CONNECTION BETWEEN MARIJUANA AND NARCOTICS FOUND IN LATE 1960's

"A large majority of persons addicted to narcotic drugs have a history of marijuana use," reported Fred Dick of the previous Bureau of Narcotics in San Francisco.

661.
HOW MARIJUANA USERS MOVE ON TO OTHER DRUGS

"Drug users who eventually get into serious emotional difficulty have to start somewhere. They become part of a 'drug subculture' by using allegedly 'safe' drugs like marijuana. Then they go on to hashish (a more potent form of marijuana), LSD, mescaline, amphetamines, etc. It is easy to float along and try the next drug when the 'pot' fails to produce its desired effect. When most of the crowd is using drugs and one of the group is one step ahead of another, it is quite natural to want to go along. It is disturbing to observe this pattern in Scarsdale among youngsters who just one or two years ago said, 'We're too smart to try stuff like acid or mescaline.' Every addict presents the same story," explained Dr. Marvin Moser, Chairman of the 1969 Scarsdale Drug Abuse Committee.

662.
LOS ANGELES REPORT: 90% OF ALL NARCOTICS ADDICTS STARTED WITH MARIJUANA

"Our experience has proved," stated the Los Angeles County Sheriff's office, "that well in excess of 90 percent of all narcotics addicts in this country have graduated to the use of heroin through the use of marijuana."

663.
HEAVY USERS TEND TO USE HARDER DRUGS

"Heavy marijuana users tend to use amphetamines, LSD and opiates more than persons who use marijuana infrequently or not at all," wrote the editors of *Psychology Today*.

664.
AS PEOPLE GET USED TO MARIJUANA THEY MOVE ON TO HASHISH

"The usual pattern, I would say, is using low-grade quality (marijuana), and then as people become tolerant, they are looking for more and more highs, and they are moving gradually from better quality marijuana to hashish. But some people immediately jump from one to the other," testified Dr. Harvey Powelson before a Congressional Committee.

665.
MARIJUANA EXPERIMENTERS MAY ALSO TRY HEROIN

"What we have witnessed in a very short period of time is the same type of person, the white middle and upper-middle-class citizen of Greater Boston, who was a rampant experimenter with marijuana in the early and mid-1960's, now turning up with needle marks and in the heroin category in increasing numbers," said Richard Callahan, as regional director of the Bureau of Narcotics and Dangerous Drugs in Boston in a 1970 report to the 91st Congress.

666.
1969 FINDING LINKS MARIJUANA TO HEROIN USE

How valid is the assumption that there is a progression from marijuana to harder drug use? Daniel Glaser, James A. Inciardi and Dean V. Babst, studied the records of the New York City Health Department's Narcotic Registry. They found that "while half of the male adolescent heroin users had a heroin record 5 or 10 years later, about 40 percent of the marijuana users also acquired a heroin record in this follow-up period." The researchers concluded that "among New York City male adolescents apprehended for relatively unadvanced delinquency, marijuana use is almost as portentous of adult heroin use as is actual use of heroin as an adolescent."

667.
EVEN 10 YEARS AGO REPORTS STATED MARIJUANA LEADS TO HARD DRUGS

Geller and Boas report that,"a growing number of youngsters from affluent areas have been moving from marijuana to heroin." While "disadvantaged" students are under stronger pressure in this respect because they live in areas where heroin addiction is an adult problem, the advantaged students to whom pot is a cheap, easy escape from school boredom may find the more potent drugs a temptation (although those who do advance to more dangerous drugs are generally plagued by psychological problems)."

668.
STUDIES SHOW INCREASED MARIJUANA USE OFTEN LEADS TO LSD

In 1974, Dr. Donald B. Louria of the New Jersey Medical School was particularly interested in seeing whether there is a relationship between the frequency of marijuana use and subsequent use of LSD.

He points out that his group carried out three epidemiologic studies, all of which show similar results. It may be seen that the more often marijuana is used, the more likely it is that an individual will experiment at least once with LSD.

"In one of the three studies . . . the infrequent user of marijuana had a 4 percent likelihood of using LSD; for the monthly user, the chance of using LSD increased to 9 percent; the weekly marijuana user had a 22 percent likelihood of experimenting with LSD, and among those who used marijuana more than once per week, the likelihood of trying LSD increased to 44 percent."

The "daily marijuana user in the studies we performed, and in various studies across the country that were performed, has a likelihood of using LSD somewhere between 65 and 85 percent."

669.
USERS DEVELOP A DEPENDENCY

According to Richard Callahan, regional director of the Bureau of Narcotics and Dangerous Drugs in Boston, a percentage of marijuana users develop a dependency on the drug, as alcoholics depend on alcohol. The difference, he said, is that alcoholics stick with alcohol, but some marijuana users frequently progress to LSD, speed, and heroin.

670.
DOCTOR FINDS MOST LSD AND HEROIN USERS START WITH POT

". . . Marijuana is at the center of the pattern of multi-drug usage. Only rarely have I come onto cases of young people using heroin or LSD where the preceding step wasn't marijuana. . . . I am willing to say this is the pattern in nearly 100 percent of the cases."

671.
CONTRIBUTES TO GROWTH OF MULTI-USE DRUGS

The Le Dain reports that "cannabis must be reckoned as a potent factor contributing to the growth of multi-use drugs."

672.
USERS TWICE AS LIKELY TO HAVE USED ILLICIT DRUGS

"Current marijuana users are about twice as likely to have used any illicit drugs than are those who have ceased using marijuana," according to The Official Report of the National Commission on Marihuana and Drug Abuse.

673.
LEADS TO DRUG-ORIENTED LIFE

"The heavy marijuana user presents the greatest potential concern to the public health." It is the opinion of the National Commission on Marijuana and Drug Abuse that "these heavy marijuana users constitute a source of contagion within American society. They actively proselytize others into a drug-oriented way of life."

674.
"FROM MARIJUANA TO HEROIN . . ."

Tony J., a student in his senior year in high school, describes how he and his friends got involved with marijuana: "They all, like I, started off with marijuana, figured like everybody else they could handle it. Just would get high once in a while. They would try it and try it until the effect wore off. Although they would smoke more and more and more, still nothing would happen. Around where I lived, there weren't any pills like phenobarb and things like that. So our progression went directly from marijuana to heroin. . . . And after that, just like everybody else, marijuana didn't do me any more good either, but I had to break off because I couldn't take those side effects. I just couldn't make it with 'grass' so I went to heroin."

675.
USERS HAVE TENDENCY TO USE TOBACCO, ALCOHOL, ETC.

"The tendency to drink alcohol increases as one uses marijuana. The tendency to smoke tobacco increases as one uses marijuana. The use of marijuana increases his tendency to use tobacco, alcohol, LSD, cocaine and heroin—anything that is available."

676.
MARIJUANA LINKED TO THE CONTROL OF OPIUM AND COCAINE

Dr. Nahas reported that the 1961 Single Convention of the United Nations stated "marijuana is linked to the control of opium and cocaine. If one loosens the control on marijuana, one will have a social escalation up to cocaine and heroin. Once marijuana is taken out of the category of a forbidden drug, there will be pressure to free the others. This is the reason why I think there's still a chance that marijuana may not be legalized; it would create too many social problems in this country."

Chapter XXVI
HARMFUL EFFECTS CAN RETURN

677.
CANNABIS ABUSE CAUSES REACTIONS SIMILAR TO LSD

"Flashbacks or echo effects, so common in abuse of strong hallucinogens such as LSD, occasionally occur also in cannabis abuse, and the addicts call them 'clean trips,'" according to Dr. Nils Bejerot. These effects may be experienced as long as weeks and even months after the last dose of marijuana.

678.
SELF-DIAGNOSED MARIJUANA FLASHBACKS

Drs. Alan Brown and Arthur Stickgold of the University of California, Los Angeles, Psychiatry Department, discussed 13 cases of self-diagnosed marijuana flashbacks. "These are spontaneous recurrences of feelings and perceptions similar to those previously induced in the subjects following their use of marijuana." These cases were divided into descriptive categories, including: "1) prolonged anxiety reactions, 2) precipitation of psychotic reactions, 3) hallucinosis, 4) enhanced appreciation of environmental stimuli. . . ."

679.
CASE STUDY: HARMFUL EFFECTS REMAIN LONG AFTER USER STOPS SMOKING

"John, a young graduate student, was typical of many patients who used marijuana every day. He couldn't sleep regular hours and had trouble concentrating. He spoke in all the current cliches and was unable to focus his attention. He had followed me out of a lecture where I had talked about marijuana. He came to see me regularly to argue about pot. It was a year before he gave it up. But the effects of smoking so much marijuana over so long a period remained. Even today, John has to consciously focus his attention before he can do what other people do spontaneously," reported Dr. D. Harvey Powelson.

680.
EXPERIENCES INTERMITTENT HALLUCINATIONS

A 21 year-old marijuana smoker said that after ingesting more than the usual amount of the drug he lost track of what time it was and where he was, and had trouble coordinating his body. He claimed that the symptoms remained for a couple of weeks and that he experienced intermittent hallucinations.

681.
FLASHBACK REACTION TO CANNABIS

Gabriel G. Nahas, *Marihuana: Deceptive Weed* (New York: Raven Press, 1973), p. 240.

". . . The effects called flashbacks or abreaction syndrome may occur days, weeks, or even months after administration of a single dose of the drug and in the absence of any new intoxication. They are characterized by the sudden reappearance of the symptoms of the *Cannabis* intoxication, such as euphoria, anxiety, or hallucinations. In addition, marijuana smokers who try other hallucinogens, such as LSD or mescaline, recapture the effects of these drugs when they take *Cannabis*."

682.
USER REPORTS AFTER-EFFECT OF MARIJUANA USE

C.A. Tassinari et al., "The Neuropsychiatric Syndrome of delta-9-Tetrahydrocannabinol and Cannabis Intoxication in Naive Subjects: A Clinical and Polygraphic Study during Wakefulness and Sleep," in *Pharmacology of Marihuana*, vol. 1., eds. M.C. Braude and S. Szara (New York: Raven Press, 1976), p. 361.

A subject in the study of marijuana conducted by Tassinari, et al. reported that on the evening following the study, he experienced an intense feeling of anxiety for approximately one hour. This subject complained that "the effects were back again."

683.
FLASHBACKS CAN OCCUR WITHOUT ADDITIONAL USE

"A 21 year-old man smoked more than four marijuana cigarettes. He experienced confusion, disorientation, panic, and the sensation of loss of control of his hands; he could not talk and hallucinated colored spots and designs during the drug reaction.

"For 3 weeks thereafter he experienced confusion and disorientation and hallucinated designs similar to those that appeared during the marijuana experience. This took place most often when he was attempting to go to sleep.

"These events precipitated anxiety which required hospitalization. There was no evidence of schizophrenia or affective disorder. His symptoms gradually subsided during the next week."

684.
"BAD TRIP" CAN RETURN

From MARIJUANA AND YOUR CHILD by Jules Saltman. Copyright © 1970 by Jules Saltman. Used by permission of Grosset & Dunlap, Inc.

According to Jules Saltman, "One of the most troubling possibilities of LSD use is that the extreme sensations of a 'bad trip' can return without warning weeks or months after the original experience, even when the first trip was a 'good one.' A few indications have been seen that this may also happen after a single strong episode with marijuana. Four cases in which the sensations felt under the drug recurred intermittently for some days and even up to three weeks afterward have been reported by scientists of the University of North Carolina.

Chapter XXVII

WARNINGS FROM EXPERTS ALL OVER THE WORLD

685.
CAUTIONARY EVIDENCE AVAILABLE BUT HAS NOT REACHED PUBLIC

"The sad truth is that highly important and cautionary evidence has been available for years in the literature and in the experience of prominent medical men who have treated cannabis habitues. But it has not reached our youth and the public in any effective way as yet. . . ." This is the personal view of Keith Cowan, governmental advisor to the Canadian Province of Prince Edward Island.

686.
UNITED NATIONS COMMISSION REPORTS CANNABIS IS HARMFUL

The text of a resolution adopted February 24, 1975 by the United Nations Commission on Narcotic Drugs includes the statement that, "in view of the numerous findings of scientific research on cannabis, there can be no doubt as to the harmful nature of cannabis."

687.
⅓ OF MARIJUANA USERS IN STUDY SUFFERED ADVERSE REACTIONS

From a random sampling of a patient load of 50,000 young people, the medical director of the Haight-Ashbury Free Clinic reports that "fully one-third of those who used marijuana had adverse reactions at one time or another," stated Dr. Roy H. Hart.

688.
FORMER "PRO-MARIJUANA" PSYCHIATRIST NOW FINDS POT VERY DANGEROUS

"LSD and mescaline, I thought, were very dangerous. But marijuana was different," reported Dr. D. Harvey Powelson, who was the director of the University of California's student psychiatric clinic for five years. "I had tried it myself two times—once in the 1950s and again in the early 1960s—without noticing any ill effects. I had read the medical literature which, although sparse and out-of-date, indicated that it was non-addictive and produced no harmful effects. Within five years I knew I was totally wrong. What caused me to change my mind? It was the consequence of observing some 200 students whom I counseled."

689.
PSYCHOACTIVE PROPERTIES COVER A WIDE RANGE

Gabriel G. Nahas, *Marihuana: Deceptive Weed* (New York: Raven Press, 1973), pp. 77-78.

"*Cannabis sativa*, or marijuana, is not a single uniform plant like many of those encountered in nature, but a rather deceptive weed with several hundred variants. The intoxicating substances prepared from *Cannabis* vary considerably in potency according to the nature of the plant (fiber or drug type), according to the varying mixtures of different parts of the plant, and according to the techniques of fabrication. As a result, the psychoactive properties of *Cannabis* cover a very wide range of activity, from nonexistent for the fiber type, to hallucinogenic for the well-prepared, non-extracted drug type. Such a basic botanical fact has been overlooked by physicians and educators, who have spoken and written about marijuana as if it were a simple, single substance, 'mild intoxicant,' similar to beer or coffee, which uniformly yield a low concentration of psychotoxic substances. Such a view is at variance with all of the experimental data that we have . . . reviewed."

690.
LARGE NUMBER OF SCIENTISTS REGARD IT AS EXCEEDINGLY DANGEROUS DRUG

In his introduction to the published report of the hearings to investigate the Administration of the Internal Security Act and other Internal Security Laws, Senator James O. Eastland writes, "Part of the purpose of our recent hearing was . . . to present the 'other side' of the story—to establish the essential fact that a large number of highly reputable scientists today regard marijuana as an exceedingly dangerous drug."

691.
PSYCHOLOGICAL & ORGANIC CONSEQUENCES OF MARIJUANA AND HASHISH

According to the U.S. National Commission on Marijuana and Drug Abuse, "The heavy users show strong psychological dependence on marijuana and often hashish. Organic injury, especially diminution of pulmonary function, is possible. Specific behavioral changes are detectable."

492.
WILL TAKE 15 YEARS TO FIND OUT IF MARIJUANA IS TERATOGENIC IN HUMANS

According to Dr. Morton A. Stenchever, "it is going to take ten or fifteen years to begin to find out whether marijuana is teratogenic in humans."

693.
DATA FROM HOSPITAL EMERGENCY ROOMS SHOWS PEOPLE "BEING HURT"

"Data . . . collected from 790 hospital emergency rooms around the country reveal a 20 percent rise in emergency room episodes involving marijuana from the first quarter of 1974, to the fourth quarter. In about 40 percent of these episodes, the only drug determined to be involved was marijuana alone; 60 percent of the cases involved marijuana and other substances. . . . Thus, from both the law enforcement and medical treatment viewpoints we have evidence that people are being hurt by their association with cannabis," stated Jerry Jenson as Deputy Administrator of the Drug Enforcement Administration.

694.
CONVINCING EVIDENCE THAT 2 MAJOR FUNCTIONS OF MAN ARE SERIOUSLY IMPAIRED BY USE

"The survival of a society which strives to provide world leadership in the most critical time of human history is predicated on the integrity of two major functions of man," stated Dr. Gabriel G. Nahas. "The first one to be preserved is his brain function, the second is his reproductive capacity, for creating healthy offspring, the wave of the future. There is convincing evidence that both of these functions are seriously and perhaps irretrievably impaired by chronic marijuana use."

695.
PUBLIC NOT TOLD OF DANGEROUS FINDINGS

Dr. George K. Russell contends "that a substantial body of medical evidence exists" which shows "that marijuana is a dangerous substance . . . (yet) this information has not been communicated to the public in an effective way . . . Any move toward decriminalization (or outright legalization) must give serious consideration to the medical findings "

696.
DANGEROUS DELUSION THAT POT IS HARMLESS

"The most dangerous illusion of our time is the comforting, security-blanket image of marijuana as a harmless tranquilizer. In actual fact, "marijuana is a start down the long, downhill road. A first step. But it's more than that; it's bad in itself. . . ." writes Max Rafferty.

"Wrecked lives. Weakened kidneys. Damaged lungs. Riddled upper respiratory systems. These are some of marijuana's 'mild and nonaddictive' physical consequences. For the medically knowledgeable among the eager readers of these words, try these pot-products on for size: postural hypotension, mydriasis, conjunctival congestion, hypothemia, Raynaud Syndrome, and photophila. Good old loveable, harmless pot!"

697.
MARIJUANA PROBLEM GROWS WORSE

"The traffic in, and abuse of, marijuana products has taken a more serious turn in the last two or three years than either the courts, the news media, or the public is aware. The shift is clearly toward the abuse of stronger, more dangerous forms of the drug which renders much of what has been said in the 1960s about the harmlessness of its use obsolete." This is the statement of Mr. Andrew C. Tartaglino, then Deputy Administrator of the Drug Enforcement Administration at the opening of the hearings before the Senate Subcommittee to Investigate the Administration of the Internal Security Act and Other Internal Security Laws, May 9, 1974.

698.
"MAY BE MORE HARMFUL THAN PREVIOUSLY THOUGHT"

"Marijuana may be more harmful than previously thought," said Dr. William Pollin, as director of the National Institute of Drug Abuse. Possible effects could range from lowering a person's resistance to disease to birth defects.

699.
MOST SOCIETIES FIND MARIJUANA A PUBLIC HEALTH HAZARD

The American Medical Association and the National Research Council state that: "Cannabis is a dangerous drug and is a public health hazard. Practically all societies in which it has been extensively used have found it necessary to impose legal and social sanctions on users and distributors."

700.
FRENCH OFFICIALS AGREE MARIJUANA SHOULD BE BANNED

Upon returning to Paris after conducting experiments with African tribes, Professor M. Mabileau, pharmacologist and consultant to the French government on dangerous drugs, stated in 1970 that, "Every public health official in France is agreed that marijuana products are damaging to the health of the individual and should be banned just as opium and coca leaf derivatives are banned."

701.
EVIDENCE AGAINST MARIJUANA STEADILY INCREASES

In an article in *Human Events,* William A. Rusher stated: ". . . The steady accumulation of subsequent medical evidence—as reported in the respected British medical Journal *Lancet,* by the United Nations in Geneva, and by a subcommittee of the U.S. Senate—is that such use of marijuana is not only gravely but permanently harmful to the human body."

702.
NOT A "HARMLESS WEED"

"There are apocryphal stories going around that marijuana is a harmless weed," stated Dr. Stanley F. Yolles, as director of the National Institute of Mental Health.

Dr. Yolles stated that marijuana is "not an innocuous drug," and added that in some people it can cause "toxic psychoses lasting from one to 11 days." This could bring about "disruptions in thought processes and speech and loss of memory."

703.
EMERGING CONSENSUS IS THAT MARIJUANA IS A SERIOUSLY DANGEROUS AND DEBILITATING DRUG

". . . Prudence suggest(s) that we ought to go slow before we embark on any major revisions in our policy towards marijuana—because any changes we may make now in the light of incomplete knowledge may prove difficult if not impossible to reverse if future scientific evidence should reinforce what appears to be an emerging consensus that marijuana is a seriously dangerous and debilitating drug," testified Dr. Robert L. DuPont.

704.
IT IS DEFINITELY NOT AN INNOCUOUS DRUG

"The Perils Of 'Pot' Start Showing Up," U.S. News & World Report, June 10, 1974, p. 58. Copyright 1974 U.S. News & World Report, Inc. Reprinted from 'U.S. News & World Report.':

". . . It (cannabis) is definitely not an innocuous drug . . ." stated E. M. Steindler, as secretary of the Committee on Drug Abuse of the American Medical Association.

705.
NON-SMOKERS SUFFER HARMFUL EFFECTS JUST BY BEING IN THE SAME ROOM AS SMOKERS

David V. Forrest, James H. Ryan and Phillip Zeidenberg, of the New York State Psychiatric Institute, discovered that during a test involving marijuana-smoking subjects and a group of controls (who received a placebo), the controls and investigators became "distracted, irritable, and nauseated." When a urine sample was taken from a control subject, traces of the marijuana's active ingredient was found. Just by being in the same room where the group was smoking, the controls and the investigators received a passive high. Additionally, "numerous staff members who observed the patients smoking complained of subject discomfort and showed nausea, tachycardia, and conjunctival injection."

706.
PART OF RISK IS THAT USERS MAY BE UNAWARE OF WARNING SYMPTOMS

"The risk is great for the persistent marijuana user, and part of the risk is that he may harm himself before he can recognize the warning symptoms," reported Dr. Hardin B. Jones.

707.
CATHOLIC CONFERENCE WARNS: "SERIOUS ADVERSE . . . EFFECTS"

In April 1977, the New York State Catholic Conference issued a memorandum. It said in part, "the use of marijuana for other than medical prescription is harmful and should be prohibited. We hold this view because the available research to date regarding the use of marijuana indicates that there are significant grounds that its use will have serious and adverse physical and psychological effects."

708.
"POT IS NOT A SAFE DRUG"

"If you want to do it once for a kick, you might get away with it. But remember, you take chances. Pot is not a safe drug—psychologically, physically, or legally," reported Dr. Paul A. Walters, Jr., a staff psychiatrist at Harvard University.

709.
NO MEDICAL GROUP IN THE WORLD SAYS MARIJUANA IS HARMLESS

"No reputable medical group anywhere in the world has sanctioned the use of cannabis or declared it to be as innocuous or harmless as its advocates maintain."

710.
LEARNING THE HARD WAY

It appears that America will have to experiment with marijuana in order to find out what every other major nation in the world has discovered; that marijuana should be outlawed because its effects are harmful.

711.
NOBEL PRIZE WINNER FINDS CHRONIC USE HAZARDOUS

Dr. Andre F. Cournand, 1956 Nobel Prize Winner in Medicine and Physiology, stated that: "There is no question in my mind that chronic use of marijuana . . . is hazardous, both to the user and also to the society that is exposed to the consequences of the user's judgment during his 'high.'"

712.
"SERIOUS AND GROWING DANGER IN MANY COUNTRIES"

A report issued by the 11-member International Narcotics Control Board, appointed by the United Nations Economic and Security Council stated that the international controls aimed at eliminating the consumption of marijuana should not be relaxed. The 1972 report stated:

"On the contrary, present indications are that cannabis represents a serious and growing danger in many countries, both in its inherent potential for harm and in its association with other forms of drug abuse."

Findings of the UN Board lead to the conclusion that the consumption of marijuana is expanding at a "disquieting rate."

713.
"ALL OF THE UNANSWERED QUESTIONS ABOUT THE POSSIBLE ADVERSE EFFECTS . . . BECOME VITAL"

According to Dr. Robert L. DuPont, "we have learned more about marijuana in recent years. But I now want to emphasize what we still do not know about the effects of chronic marijuana use—especially daily use—in American populations. All of the unanswered questions about the possible adverse effect of marijuana on the body's immune response, basic cell metabolism, and other areas of functioning become vital here. So, too, do the continuing concerns about the impact of the use of the drug on reproductive functions."

714.
"THE MOST DANGEROUS DRUG . . ."

"There is NO argument FOR marijuana," reported Phyllis Schlafly. "In the opinion of many scientific experts, marijuana is actually 'the most dangerous drug with which we must contend today.'"

715.
DANGERS ARE BECOMING MORE APPARENT

In May 1974, Mr. Andrew Tartaglino, acting Deputy Administrator of the Drug Enforcement Administration said: "My own view is that it (marijuana) is a potentially harmful substance which we should not permit to become an accepted part of our society. Those of us in law enforcement have felt that the dangers inherent in this drug would become more apparent with increasing research; and we believe this is in fact now occurring."

716.
MORE RESEARCH IS NEEDED

In the conclusion of his recent study on the effects of marijuana on the human body, Dr. Rosengard concluded that ". . . many years of study are likely before the full story on possible physical effects from chronic use of marijuana will be complete."

717.
SCIENTIFIC FACTS POINT TO POTENTIAL DANGERS

"Among the scientists working in the field, it would seem that there is a general consensus that cannabis is dangerous. Opinions differ, however, on the degree of the danger to the individual and to society. In my opinion, it seems that, as progressively more scientific facts are discovered about cannabis, the more one becomes aware of its potential dangers," testified Dr. Olav J. Braenden, director of the United Nations Narcotics Laboratory, before the United States Senate Internal Security Subcommittee.

718.
RISKS INCREASE WITH POTENCY

"The data now indicate that some (marijuana) users are showing a preference for more potent preparations," stated Dr. Robert L. DuPont. "I would speculate that the risks to individual health and functioning will increase directly with the potency of the substance consumed."

719.
MARIJUANA SCIENTIFICALLY ESTABLISHED AS DANGEROUS TO MIND, BODY & SPIRIT

Excerpt from THE SEEKERS by Jess Stearn. Copyright © 1968, 1969 by Jess Stearn. Used by permission of Doubleday & Company, Inc.

"Far from being the harmless drug that its followers insisted it was, marijuana has been scientifically established as dangerous to body, mind and spirit," stated Jess Stearn.

720.
"LARGE-SCALE MARIJUANA USE IS SOCIALLY DESTRUCTIVE"

Dr. G. Nahas reported that it is evident from seeing what happened in many countries—India, Egypt, Morocco—that one reason that marijuana was made illegal is for social reasons. "Responsible political leaders see that the heavy use of marijuana among their people shuts them out of the mainstream of society. This is what seems to be forgotten in America—there is ample evidence that large-scale marijuana use is socially destructive."

721.
DIRECTOR OF THE NATIONAL ORGANIZATION FOR THE REFORM OF MARIJUANA LAWS CAUTIONS YOUNG NOT TO TRY POT

When asked what he would tell young people who think it's OK to try marijuana, Keith Stroup, as director of the National Organization for the Reform of Marijuana Laws, answered: "I would say don't. There are enough unanswered medical questions to warn against its use."

722.
"NO SCIENTIFIC EVIDENCE THAT MARIJUANA IS SAFE"

Dr. Hardin B. Jones stated that: "The fact is no scientific evidence has been found that marijuana is safe; we have only the personal testimonies of short-term users."

723.
ROLE OF MARIJUANA IN THE ALIENATED SUBCULTURE

"From the clinical point of view we had observed that the drug hindered maturation and retarded recovery from psychiatric illness. I had most particularly suggested that it appeared to play some part in the creation and diffusion of the alienated subculture," reported Dr. Andrew Malcolm.

724.
IMPAIRS THINKING AND BEHAVIOR

One conclusion that Dr. Gabriel G. Nahas reached is: "The derivatives of Cannabis contain substances which impair thinking and behavior. They do not have any therapeutic application. Adolescents who use these compounds frequently tend to become apathetic, to lose individual ambition and social responsibility, without the benefit of solving their emotional problems. For certain adolescents, Cannabis intoxication is the first step towards the regular use of drugs."

725.
A DOCTOR'S WARNING ABOUT DOCTORS WHO USE CANNABIS

In his testimony before the United States Senate Subcommittee on Internal Security, Dr. Hardin B. Jones stated his concern about the number of doctors who began smoking marijuana in medical school and are now practicing physicians and still smoking the drug: "In view of the life-and-death responsibilities of physicians, impairment of their judgment by cannabis use must be regarded as a major threat to the public welfare," he testified.

726.
DOCTOR CALLS ON MEDIA TO HELP PUBLICIZE HARMFUL EFFECTS

In a letter to the Editor of the New York Times, Dr. Nicholas A. Pace wrote: "Perhaps it is time for the media to interview reputable scientists, physicians and patients in drug rehabilitation centers concerning the harmful effects of marijuana before a whole generation of our youth is severely damaged because of ignorance."

727.
EVEN OPTIMISTIC OBSERVERS DISTURBED BY WIDER USE OF MARIJUANA

Dr. Robert L. DuPont, Director of the National Institute on Drug Abuse, testified before the Committee of the Judiciary, United States Senate, that "there appears to be a large and growing minority who use the drug more frequently, at a higher potency, and at a younger age. These trends disturb even the most optimistic observers of the contemporary marijuana scene in this country."

728.
MAJORITY OF 1800 PAPERS CONDEMN MARIJUANA

Several years ago one marijuana authority mentioned that Dr. Oliver Byrd of Stanford University was reviewing more than 1,800 published papers, "the overwhelming majority of which condemn cannabis as a dangerous weed."

729.
JUDGE SAYS IT IS HARMFUL AND DANGEROUS

"The normal brain function is altered or suspended, making the user more susceptible to the influence of others. The use of the drug also tends to accentuate any tendency toward improper conduct. In addition, it induces an abnormally subjective concentration on trivia. In short, marijuana produces a state which is analogous to a temporary mental aberration. Its prolonged and excessive use may induce a psychotic state, especially in those individuals with pre-existing psychological problems," wrote Superior Court Justice G. Joseph Tauro in 1967. He also said that it "is my opinion . . . that marijuana is a harmful and dangerous drug."

730.
HEALTH AND LEGAL FRATERNITY AGAINST POT

It has been pointed out by Dr. Robert L. DuPont that "there are virtually no public spokesmen for a truly 'pro pot' position on either the health or the legal sides of this issue in the United States today (1974). The contemporary disagreements about marijuana policy relate to the means rather than the ends. The question is, how best to discourage cannabis use without producing excessive social costs?"

731.
NOT ENOUGH KNOWN ABOUT MARIJUANA TO JUSTIFY LEGALIZATION

Responding to the prevalent question of whether marijuana should be legalized, Dr. L.E. Hollister stated that "we must realize that compared to our body of scientific knowledge about alcohol, what we know about marijuana is meager indeed. It is doubtful that even the number of subacute and chronic toxicity studies in several animal species required for certification for the repeated use of a drug by the Food and Drug Administration has ever been accomplished in the case of cannabis."

732.
74 NATIONS SEEK TO OUTLAW USE

A little known fact about the legalization of marijuana is that the United States is a signatory of the Single Conventions Treaty of 1961, which provides for the prohibition of dangerous drugs including cannabis. Seventy-three other member nations of the World Health Organization have signed the treaty. The treaty's aim is to eliminate the use of cannabis in the participating countries within the next 25 years.

733.
EPIDEMIC POTENTIAL OF CANNABIS

The 1974 Senate Subcommittee Hearings reported that the epidemic potential of cannabis is enormous. Several reasons were given:

1. Unlike an intoxicated alcoholic, the marijuana users appears "normal." Detection of use is difficult.

2. It is easily concealed and transported.

3. Users tend to actively urge others to use marijuana; peer pressure is greater than with alcohol.

4. There is a rapid escalation rate from occasional social use to chronic abuse if the drug is readily available.

734.
LARGE BODY OF RESEARCH PERTAINING TO CRIMINOGENIC EFFECTS

"Despite the inherent complexities of the issue and the difficulties in securing reliable and valid evidence," reports The National Commission on Marihuana and Drug Abuse, "a relatively large body of research is now available pertaining to the criminogenic effects of marijuana upon the individual and the nature and extent to which the drug constitutes a danger to public safety."

735.
"PRO-MARIJUANA" FORCES IGNORE EVIDENCE THAT POT IS DESTRUCTIVE

Excerpt from THE SEEKERS by Jess Stearn. Copyright © 1968, 1969 by Jess Stearn. Used by permission of Doubleday & Company, Inc.

"In the great marijuana debate . . . swarms of new upper-class smokers, educators and psychologists arbitrarily presented marijuana as a harmless drug, blandly ignoring mounting evidence that marijuana transcended alcohol, with all its alcoholics, as an unpredictably pernicious influence on contemporary living," reported Jess Stearn.

736.
1975 REPORT TO THE PRESIDENT: MARIJUANA IS FAR FROM HARMLESS

Although in its 1975 Annual Report to the President the Domestic Council Drug Abuse Task Force described marijuana as having the least serious consequences of all sensual drugs, it cautioned: "Recent research indicates that marijuana is far from harmless, and . . . chronic use can produce adverse psychological and physiological effects. Therefore, its use should be strongly discouraged as a matter of national policy."

737.
CHIEF WHITE HOUSE EXPERT ON DRUG ABUSE TESTIFIES

The chief White House expert on drug abuse testified at Senate Subcommittee hearings that removal of penalties for marijuana use and possession would result in the erroneous conclusion that the drug was safe. Dr. Robert L. Dupont, director of the White House's Special Action Office for Drug Abuse Prevention said that in fact, he felt "there was a great deal of evidence that using marijuana was harmful."

738.
A LAWYER'S POINT OF VIEW

"Another complication," stated lawyer Michael P. Rosenthal, "is that the drug (marijuana) may turn out to be more dangerous than some of us now believe—witness the example of cigarette smoking."

739.
OLD BUREAU OF NARCOTICS' VIEW OF MARIJUANA

The "official" view of marijuana held by police departments across the country, as stated by the former Commissioner of the old Bureau of Narcotics, Henry L. Giordano, is:

"From my studies and experience, one theme emerges—that marijuana is capable of inducing acts of violence, even murder. The drug frees the unconscious tendencies of the individual user, the result being reflected in frequent quarrels, fights and assaults."

740.
INSURANCE COMPANY WILL NO LONGER COVER USERS

In 1970, in addition to their policy of not insuring hard drug users, Occidental Life Insurance Company decided that the company would no longer issue life or health insurance to marijuana or LSD users. A company spokesman said that users might be psychologically unstable and the company was unable to measure the risk of users of these drugs.

741.
EVIDENCE TO SUGGEST LONG-TERM USE DANGEROUS

There is "evidence to suggest that heavy long-term use of the drug (cannabis), particularly in its most potent, laboratory grown, experimental strains, is hazardous."

742.
"IT'S *NOT* BENIGN"

According to Dr. William J. Messinger, internist and cardiologist at New York University, the real danger with marijuana is that the user cannot possibly know if he will be able to control himself after he has started smoking the drug. There are those who are not affected, but then there are those who cannot leave it alone. "No matter what you hear, it's *not* benign and it *does* matter," he said.

743.
PROBABLY DAMAGED 20 MILLION PEOPLE

"After 11 years of meaningful, longitudinal drug and alcohol studies, we have concluded that the smoking of pot is one of the major factors responsible for the polarization and alienation of our country," stated Alfred Miliman, as director of the Maryland Drug Abuse and Research Treatment Foundation.

He added that he has seen "the introversion, mystical and 'magical' thinking, the anti-motivational state, regression and other changes that have probably damaged 20 million people to date. All this without their awareness."

744.
SOCIETY ALREADY HARMED BY MARIJUANA

"I have seen personally a society in which de facto legalization of this drug (marijuana) has created a large number of people with the amotivational syndrome," commented Dr. Phillip Zeidenberg.

745.
DONNY AND MARIE OSMOND SPEAK OUT AGAINST POT

"Donny & Marie Osmond Tell: Why We're Opposed to Pot," *The NATIONAL ENQUIRER*, p. 42.

"We've seen people who have been hurt by marijuana," stated famous star Marie Osmond. Her brother Donny added, "We've seen people in the business—people we've looked up to because of their great musical abilities—begin using marijuana and ruin themselves. . . .

"We've seen musicians staggering around at performances because they were using marijuana, and they couldn't play the music right." THE NATIONAL ENQUIRER.

746.
WRONG TO SAY CANNABIS IS HARMLESS

"To say that cannabis is harmless is tantamount to saying that a man who cannot swim is totally safe from drowning as long as he keeps his head above water," wrote Edward Bloomquist.

747.
POTENTIAL HARM

The Official Report of the National Commission on Marihuana and Drug Abuse stated that "any psychoactive drug is potentially harmful to the individual, depending on the intensity, frequency and duration of use. Marijuana is no exception."

748.
LITTLE OR NO PUBLICITY FOR WRITINGS OR RESEARCH ON SERIOUS ADVERSE CONSEQUENCES

Concerned about the fact that there has been more "publicity for writings and research advocating a more tolerant attitude towards marijuana, while there has been little or no publicity for writings or research which point to serious adverse consequences," Dr. Henry Brill, as regional director of the New York State Department of Mental Hygiene stated: "I must admit that the favorable side for marijuana is more heavily presented than the unfavorable side. I can't agree with this kind of emphasis; I think it needs more balance. There have been both sides presented in many cases, but overall I am afraid that the statement is quite correct."

749.
DIFFICULTIES IN RESEARCHING MARIJUANA

Dr. Stanley F. Yolles, as director of the National Institute of Mental Health, spoke at a joint meeting of the Queens County Medical Society and the Queens County Psychiatric Society on the problems of researching marijuana. He first pointed out that there are actually many problems involved; the quality of marijuana varies from region to region; we have no long-term studies on the effects of marijuana; and investigators in the United States do not have access to such a population.

750.
MARIJUANA ONLY APPEARS TO BE HARMLESS

"Marijuana is a special drug because it appears to be harmless. This leads many to believe that it *is* harmless in fact, and therefore all right to use frequently, even daily," reported one of the nation's leading experts on drug abuse.

751.
PRESIDENT OF CANADIAN PSYCHIATRIC ASSOCIATION SAYS MARIJUANA IS HARMFUL TO HEALTH

According to Dr. Keith Yonge, President of the Canadian Psychiatric Association, all drugs which affect the mind, including marijuana, are detrimental to health.

752.
WORLD HEALTH ORGANIZATION FINDS CANNABIS HARMFUL IN 1961

As long ago as 1961, experts from the World Health Organization agreed that cannabis constitutes a danger to health and a hazard to society. At that time 500 delegates, including the best pharmacologists and toxicologists from 74 nations, met at the Single Convention on Narcotic Drugs. They recommended the limitation of cannabis in all its forms "to medical and scientific purposes."

753.
MANY NATIONS ARE CONCERNED ABOUT CANNABIS USE

The United States is among the nations supporting the agreement made at the United Nations Single Convention in 1961, and confirmed by the Geneva Conference of the International Narcotics Control Commission in 1975 to limit exclusively to medical and scientific purposes, the production, manufacture, export, import, distribution of, trade in, use and possession of drugs," including cannabis.

754.
WHY NATIONS BAN MARIJUANA

According to Dr. Pablo Wolff civilized countries have banned the use of marijuana for enjoyment because of the social and criminal threats it holds.

755.
UNFAVORABLE REPORTS FROM ALL OVER THE WORLD

As of 1970 cannabis had been the subject of many studies and experiments including 936 articles in English, 386 in French, 206 in German, 106 in Portuguese, 74 in Spanish, 45 in the Slavic languages, 33 in Italian, 12 in Latin, 8 in Dutch, 8 in Turkish, 7 in Russian, 3 in Greek, 3 in Norwegian, 2 in Swedish, and 31 in various other languages. One feature that stands out about this material is the fact that very few of the studies have anything favorable to say about marijuana.

756.
SWEDISH PROFESSOR WARNS AGAINST LEGALIZATION

"The demand for legalizing cannabis has been strongest in those countries which have had the shortest experience and the weakest forms of the drug. Correspondingly, I consider that as a psychiatrist one's attitude to cannabis becomes more negative the more one sees of its effects," stated Swedish Professor Nils Bejerot.

"If cannabis were legalized in the United States, this would probably be an irreversible process not only for this country and this generation, but perhaps for the whole of Western civilization. As far as I can see, another result would be a breakdown of the international control system regarding narcotics and dangerous drugs," he added.

757.
DRUG IS TABOO AMONG EDUCATED CLASSES IN EGYPT

At the age of eight, when living in Egypt, Dr. Gabriel G. Nahas said that he "already knew that in Egyptian society (and this also holds true for most other Middle Eastern countries where hashish is used) there is an unwritten law that makes the drug taboo among the educated classes."

758.
WHITE HOUSE POSITION ON PARAQUAT

Dr. Peter Bourne, White House Special Assistant for Health Issues, discussed the issue of Mexican grown marijuana that has been sprayed with paraquat being consumed in the United States. He felt that although something should be done about it—perhaps the Mexicans should switch to a non-toxic spray—that does not mean that marijuana that has not been sprayed with paraquat is harmless.

SOURCES

1. "New Evidence on Marijuana," *The Phyllis Schlafly Report*, vol. 8, no. 10, section 1, May 1975, p. 1.
2. U.S., Congress, Senate, Committee On The Judiciary, *Marihuana-Hashish Epidemic And Its Impact On United States Security, Hearings Before The Subcommittee To Investigate The Administration Of The Internal Security Act and Other Internal Security Laws*. Part 2. 93 Cong., 2d sess., 1974, p. 462.
3. National Institute on Drug Abuse, *Marijuana and Health, 6th Annual Report to the U.S. Congress*, 1976, p. 15.
4. Francis A. Soper, review of *Sensual Drugs*, by Hardin Jones and Helen Jones, in *Listen*, July 1977, p. 5.
5. "U.S. Study in Jamaica: No Serious Pot Effects Found," *The Tennessean*, 8 July 1975, p. 18.
6. W. Blanc et al., Letters, *The New York Times*, 1 July 1975. © Copyright 1971 by The New York Times Company. Reprinted by permission.
7. Harold Pascal, *The Marijuana Maze* (Canfield, Ohio: Alba House Communications, 1976), p. 104.
8. Tharp, Paul, "Cannabis Conference: The Latest Word From Science," *The Village Voice*, February 9, 1976.
9. Gabriel G. Nahas, "Medical Aspects of Marihuana Use." Testimony before the U.S. House of Representatives Select Committee on Narcotics Abuse, March 16, 1977, p. 6.
10. Gabriel G. Nahas, *Keep Off The Grass* (New York: Reader's Digest Press, 1976), p. 54.
11. Gabriel G. Nahas, *Keep Off The Grass* (New York: Reader's Digest Press, 1976), p. 151.
12. U.S., Congress, Senate, Committee On The Judiciary, *Marihuana-Hashish Epidemic And Its Impact On United States Security, Hearings Before The Subcommittee To Investigate The Administration Of The Internal Security Act And Other Internal Security Laws*. 93 Cong., 2d sess., 1974, p. 54.
13. Hardin B. Jones and Helen C. Jones, *Sensual Drugs* (Cambridge, England: Cambridge University Press, 1977), p. 227.
14. Excerpt from THE SEEKERS by Jess Stearn. Copyright © 1968, 1969 by Jess Stearn. Used by permission of Doubleday & Company, Inc.
15. Gabriel G. Nahas, "Medical Aspects of Marihuana Use." Testimony before the U.S. House of Representatives Select Committee on Narcotics Abuse, March 16, 1977, p. 6.
16. Hardin B. Jones and Helen C. Jones, *Sensual Drugs* (Cambridge, England: Cambridge University Press, 1977), p. 263.
17. Gabriel G. Nahas, *Keep Off The Grass* (New York: Reader's Digest Press, 1976), p. 65.
18. Excerpt from THE SEEKERS by Jess Stearn. Copyright © 1968, 1969, by Jess Stearn. Used by permission of Doubleday & Company, Inc.
19. Western Electric Company, *Drug Facts* (pamphlet).
20. John Kaplan, *Marijuana—The New Prohibition* (New York: Thomas Y. Crowell Company, 1970; Apollo Edition, 1975), pp. 59-60, citing Donald E. Miller, "What Policemen Should Know About the Marijuana Controversy," address before the International Narcotic Enforcement Officers Association at Louisville, Ky. 22-26 October 1967, pp. 7-8.
21. U.S., Congress, Senate, Committee On The Judiciary, *Marihuana-Hashish Epidemic And Its Impact On United States Security, Hearings Before The Subcommittee To Investigate The Administration Of The Internal Security Act and Other Internal Security Laws*. 93 Cong., 2d sess., 1974, p. 45.
22. Leo E. Hollister, "Human Pharmacology of Marihuana (Cannabis)," in *Drug Dependence* eds. Robert T. Harris, William M. McIsaac and Charles R. Schuster, Jr. (Austin, Texas: University of Texas Press, 1970), p. 75. Copyright © 1970 by the University of Texas Press. All rights reserved.
23. Reese T. Jones and Neal Benowitz, "The 30 Day Trip—Clinical Studies of Cannabis Tolerance and Dependence," in *Pharmacology of Marihuana*, vol. 2., eds. M.C. Braude and S. Szara (New York: Raven Press, 1976), pp. 631-632.
24. W.D.M. Paton and R.G. Pertwee, "The Actions of Cannabis In Man," in *Marijuana: Chemistry, Pharmacology, Metabolism and Clinical Effects*, ed. Raphael Mechoulam (New York: Academic Press, Inc., 1973), p. 311.
25. Smith Kline, French Laboratories and the National Education Association, "Drugs of Abuse and Their Effects," in *Drug Awareness: Key Documents on LSD, marijuana and the drug culture*, eds. Richard E. Horman and Allan M. Fox (New York: Avon Books, 1970), p. 37.
26. Gabriel G. Nahas, "Is Marijuana Really All That Bad," Selections from *Listen* (Washington, D.C.: Narcotics Education, Inc., 1977).
27. New York State Narcotic Addiction Control Commission, *Marijuana* (pamphlet).
28. Excerpt from THE SEEKERS by Jess Stearn. Copyright © 1968, 1969 by Jess Stearn. Used by permission of Doubleday & Company, Inc.
29. Gabriel G. Nahas, *Keep Off the Grass*, (New York: Reader's Digest Press, 1976), p. 53.
30. Harris Rosenkrantz, "Cellular, Immunological, and Hormonal Effects," in *Pharmacology of Marihuana* vol. 1., eds. M.C. Braude and S. Szara (New York: Raven Press, 1976), p. 141.
31. George K. Russell, *Marihuana Today*, rev. ed. (New York: The Myrin Institute, Inc. for Adult Education, 1976), p. 42, citing C. Barnes et al., "Tolerance of Delta-9-THC in Adult Rats with Differential Delta-9-THC Exposure When Immature or During Early Adulthood," *Psychopharmacologia* 34 (1974): 181-190.
32. Reprinted with the permission of the American Medical Association, from HEALTH ASPECTS OF MARIHUANA USE, a report of the AMA Council on Scientific Affairs, December 6, 1977.
33. U.S., Congress, Senate, Committee On The Judiciary, *Marihuana-Hashish Epidemic And Its Impact On United States Security, Hearings Before The Subcommittee To Investigate The Administration Of The Internal Security Act and Other Internal Security Laws*. 93 Cong., 2d sess., 1974, p. 293.
34. Edward F. Domino et al., "Short-Term Neuropsychopharmacological Effects of Marihuana Smoking in Experienced Male Users," in *Pharmacology of Marihuana*, vol. 1., eds. M.C. Braude and S. Szara (New York, Raven Press, 1976), p. 411.
35. Vera Rubin and Lambros Comitas, *Ganja in Jamaica* (Garden City, New York: Anchor Press/Doubleday, 1976: originally published in hardcover by Mouton & Co., Publishers, 1975), p. 91.
36. Weldon L. Witters and Patricia Jones-Witters, *Drugs & Sex* (New York: Macmillan Publishing Co., Inc., 1975), Copyright © 1975, Weldon L. Witters and Patricia Jones-Witters, p. 141, citing L.E. Hollister, "Marihuana in man: Three years later," *Science* 172 (1971) 21-24. Copyright 1971 by the American Association for the Advancement of Science.
37. E.R. Bloomquist, *Marijuana* (Beverly Hills: Glencoe Press, The Macmillan Company, 1968), p.11. © Copyright, Edward R. Bloomquist, 1968.
38. U.S. Congress, House, First Report by the Select Committee on Crime, *Marihuana*, H.R. 91-978, 91st Cong., 2d sess., 1970, p. 5.
39. Gabriel G. Nahas, *Keep Off The Grass* (New York: Reader's Digest Press, 1976), p. 159.
40. Leo E. Hollister, "Human Pharmacology of Marihuana (Cannabis)," in *Drug Dependence* eds. Robert T. Harris, William M. McIsaac, and Charles R. Schuster, Jr. (Austin, Texas: University of Texas Press, 1970), p. 72. Copyright © 1970 by the University of Texas Press. All rights reserved.
41. National Institute on Drug Abuse, *Marijuana and Health, 6th Annual Report to the U.S. Congress*, 1976, p. 25.
42. I.R. Rosengard, "Marijuana," *Science Digest*, May 1978, pp. 71-72.
43. E.R. Bloomquist, *Marijuana* (Beverly Hills: Glencoe Press, The Macmillan Company, 1968), p. 180. © Copyright, Edward R. Bloomquist, 1968.
44. Thomas Weisman, *Drug Abuse and Drug Counseling* (New York: Jason Aronson, 1972), p. 141, citing "Characteristics of Tetrahydrocannabinol Tolerance," *Marijuana: Chemistry, Pharmacology and Patterns of Social Usage* (Annals of the New York Academy of Sciences 191, 1971).

45. S. Allentuck, "Medical Aspects," in *The Marijuana Problem in the City of New York* (Mayor's Committee on Marijuana), 1944.
46. Hardin B. Jones, "What the Practicing Physician Should Know About Marijuana," *Private Practice*, January 1976, pp. 34-40.
47. I.R. Rosengard, "Marijuana," *Science Digest*, April 1978, p. 72.
48. Harris Rosenkrantz, "Cellular, Immunological, and Hormonal Effects," in *Pharmacology of Marihuana*, vol. 1., eds. M.C. Braude and S. Szara (New York: Raven Press, 1976), p. 141.
49. Ronald Bruce, ed., *The Pot Report* (New York: Universal-Award House, Inc. 1971), p. 89, citing J.E. Hughes et al., "Marijuana and the diabetic coma," *Journal of the American Medical Association* vol. 214, no. 6, (November 1970): 1113-1114. Copyright 1970, American Medical Association.
50. I.R. Rosengard, "Marijuana," *Science Digest*, May 1978, p. 71.
51. I.R. Rosengard, "Marijuana," *Science Digest*, May 1978, p. 69.
52. Department of Health, Education, and Welfare, National Institute of Mental Health, Marijuana Research Program, *Marihuana and Health—A Preliminary Report*, p. 8, (pamphlet).
53. Hardin B. Jones and Helen C. Jones, *Sensual Drugs* (Cambridge, England: Cambridge University Press, 1977), p. 255.
54. Dr. D. Harvey Powelson (as told to Ted Torkelson and Leon Cornforth), "Our Most Dangerous Drug," Selections from *Listen* (Washington, D.C.: Narcotics Education, Inc., n.d.).
55. Nicholas A. Pace, "The Marijuana Cover-Up," Op-Ed piece submitted to *The New York Times*, February 24, 1976.
56. U.S., Congress, Senate, Committee On The Judiciary, *Marihuana-Hashish Epidemic And Its Impact On United States Security, Hearings Before The Subcommittee To Investigate The Administration Of The Internal Security Act And Other Internal Security Laws*. 93 Cong., 2d sess., 1974, p. 27.
57. Ned Rosinsky, "Marijuana Linked to Brain Damage, Scientists Disclose at Symposium," *Spotlight*, 27 February 1978, p. 9.
58. M. Stanton Evans, "The Myths of Marijuana," *Human Events*, 19 October 1974, p. 14.
59. Dr. D. Harvey Powelson (as told to Ted Torkelson and Leon Cornforth), "Our Most Dangerous Drug," Selections from *Listen* (Washington, D.C.: Narcotics Education, Inc., n.d.).
60. Hardin B. Jones and Helen C. Jones, *Sensual Drugs* (Cambridge, England: Cambridge University Press, 1977), p. 256.
61. Harold Pascal, *The Marijuana Maze* (Canfield, Ohio: Alba House Communications, 1976), p. 23, citing "Temporal Disorganization and Delusional-like Ideation, Processes Induced by Hashish and Alcohol," *Archives of General Psychiatry* 23 (1970): 204.
62. New York State Conservative Party, 14 March 1978.
63. Franz Winkler, *About Marijuana* (New York: The Myrin Institute, Inc., 1970).
64. Nicholas A. Pace, "The Marijuana Health Hazard," May 1977, p. 3.
65. Reprinted with the permission of the American Medical Association, from HEALTH ASPECTS OF MARIHUANA USE, a report of the AMA Council on Scientific Affairs, December 6, 1977.
66. U.S., Congress, House, First Report by the Select Committee on Crime, *Marihuana*, H.R. 91-978, 91st Cong., 2d sess., 1970, p. 10.
67. U.S., Congress, Senate, Committee On The Judiciary, *Marihuana-Hashish Epidemic And Its Impact On United States Security, Hearings Before The Subcommittee To Investigate The Administration Of The Internal Security Act And Other Internal Security Laws*, Introduction by Senator James O. Eastland. 93 Cong., 2d sess., 1974, p. XIV.
68. Excerpt from THE SEEKERS by Jess Stearn. Copyright © 1968, 1969 by Jess Stearn. Used by permission of Doubleday & Company, Inc.
69. Stanley F. Yolles, "The Psychiatrist Looks At Drug Abuse," in *Drug Abuse In Industry*, eds. Pasquale A. Carone and Leonard W. Krinsky (Springfield: Charles C. Thomas, 1973), p. 71. Courtesy of Charles C. Thomas, Publisher.
70. From MARIJUANA AND YOUR CHILD by Jules Saltman. Copyright © 1970 by Jules Saltman. Used by permission of Grosset & Dunlap, Inc.
71. From MARIJUANA AND YOUR CHILD by Jules Saltman. Copyright © 1970 by Jules Saltman. Used by permission of Grosset & Dunlap, Inc.
72. Nicholas A. Pace, "The Marijuana Health Hazard," May 1977, p. 2.
73. U.S., Congress, Senate, Committee On The Judiciary, *Marihuana-Hashish Epidemic And Its Impact On United States Security, Hearings Before The Subcommittee To Investigate The Administration Of The Internal Security Act And Other Internal Security Laws*, Introduction by Senator James O. Eastland. 93 Cong., 2d sess., 1974, p. X.
74. Hardin B. Jones and Helen C. Jones, *Sensual Drugs* (Cambridge, England: Cambridge University Press, 1977), p. 228.
75. Cecile Leuchtenberger and Rudolf Leuchtenberger, "Cytological and Cytochemical Studies of the Effects of Fresh Marihuana Cigarette Smoke on Growth and DNA Metabolism of Animal and Human Lung Cultures," in *Pharmacology of Marihuana*, vol. 2., eds. M.C. Braude and S. Szara (New York: Raven Press, 1976), p. 609.
76. U.S., Congress, Senate, Committee On The Judiciary, *Marihuana-Hashish Epidemic And Its Impact On United States Security, Hearings Before The Subcommittee To Investigate The Administration Of The Internal Security Act And Other Internal Security Laws*. 93 Cong., 2d sess., 1974, p. 70.
77. U.S., Congress, Senate, Committee On The Judiciary, *Marihuana-Hashish Epidemic And Its Impact On United States Security, Hearings Before The Subcommittee To Investigate The Administration Of The Internal Security Act And Other Internal Security Laws*. 93 Cong., 2d sess., 1974, p. 79.
78. Cecile Leuchtenberger and Rudolf Leuchtenberger, "Cytological and Cytochemical Studies of the Effects of Fresh Marihuana Cigarette Smoke on Growth and DNA Metabolism of Animal and Human Lung Cultures," in *Pharmacology of Marihuana*, vol. 2., eds. M.C. Braude and S. Szara (New York: Raven Press, 1976), p. 598.
79. Nicholas A. Pace, "The Marijuana Health Hazard," May 1977, p. 2.
80. *National Review Magazine*, 6 June 1975.
81. Hardin B. Jones and Helen C. Jones, *Sensual Drugs* (Cambridge, England: Cambridge University Press, 1977), p. 229, citing C. Leuchtenberger et al., "Cytological and cytochemical effects of whole smoke and the gas vapour phase of marihuana cigarettes on growth and nuclear protein metabolism of cultured mammalian cells," *Marihuana: Chemistry, Biochemistry, and Cellular Effects* (New York: Springer Verlag, 1976).
82. "Higher Cancer Risk Found In Marijuana Than In Tobacco," *The New York Times*, 3 December 1975. © 1975 by The New York Times Company. Reprinted by permission.
83. Dr. D. Harvey Powelson (as told to Ted Torkelson and Leon Cornforth), "Our Most Dangerous Drug," Selections from *Listen* (Washington, D.C.: Narcotics Education, Inc., n.d.)
84. Dr. Hardin B. Jones, "What Marijuana Really Does," Selections from *Listen* volume 30 (Washington, D.C.: Narcotics Education, Inc., n.d.).
85. Nicholas A. Pace, "The Marijuana Health Hazard," May 1977, p. 6.
86. Gabriel G. Nahas, *Keep Off the Grass* (New York: Reader's Digest Press, 1976), p. 50.
87. Gabriel G. Nahas, "Is Marijuana Really All That Bad?" Selections from *Listen* (Washington, D.C.: Narcotics Education, Inc., 1977).
88. "Is Marijuana Safe?" *The Phyllis Schlafly Report*, vol. 11, no. 10, section 1, May 1978, p. 1.
89. U.S., Congress, Senate, Committee On The Judiciary, *Marihuana-Hashish Epidemic And Its Impact On United States Security, Hearings Before The Subcommittee To Investigate The Administration Of The Internal Security Act And Other Internal Security Laws*. 93 Cong., 2d sess., 1974, pp. 201-202.
90. David Chandler, "Pot Is Safe, Right? Wrong, Says A Doctor: It Can Cause Brain Damage," *People Weekly*, December 9, 1974, pp. 12-13.

91. Hardin B. Jones, "Problems Executives Must Anticipate With The Growth of Marijuana Smoking," *Executive Health* (P.O. Box 589, Rancho Santa Fe, California 92067), October 1977.
92. Gurbakhsh S. Chopra and Balwant S. Jandu, "Psychoclinical Effects Of Long Term Marijuana Use in 275 Indian Chronic Users. A Comparative Assessment of Effects in Indian and USA Users," *Chronic Cannabis Use* (New York Annals of the New York Academy of Sciences, vol. 282, 1976), p. 106.
93. Kenneth McKenna, "Marijuana Kills," in *Marijuana: Teenage Killer*, ed. Norman Hill (New York: Webster's Red Seal Publications, Inc., 1971), p. 23. Copyright © 1971 by Webster's Red Seal Publications Inc.
94. Gabriel G. Nahas, *Keep Off the Grass* (New York: Reader's Digest Press, 1976), p. 149.
95. Nils Bejerot, *Addiction: An Artificially Induced Drive* (Springfield, Illinois: Charles C. Thomas, 1972), p. 23. Courtesy of Charles C. Thomas, Publisher.
96. Dr. Hardin B. Jones, "What Marijuana Really Does," Selections from *Listen* volume 30 (Washington, D.C.: Narcotics Education, Inc. n.d.).
97. Hardin B. Jones and Helen C. Jones, *Sensual Drugs* (Cambridge, England: Cambridge University Press, 1977), p. 224, citing M. Evans, "Cannabis and cerebral atrophy," *R. Soc. Health J.* 94, pp. 15-18.
98. Dr. Hardin B. Jones, "What Marijuana Really Does," Selections from *Listen* volume 30 (Washington, D.C.: Narcotics Education, Inc., n.d.).
99. George K. Russell, *Marihuana Today* rev. ed. (New York: The Myrin Institute for Adult Education, 1976), p. 41, citing A.M.G. Campbell et al., "Cerebral Atrophy in Young Cannabis Smokers," *Lancet* 7736 (1971), pp. 1219-1224.
100. U.S., Congress, Senate, Committee on the Judiciary, *Marihuana-Hashish Epidemic and Its Impact on United States Security, Hearings Before The Subcommittee To Investigate The Administration Of The Internal Security Act And Other Internal Security Laws*. 93 Cong., 2d sess., 1974, p. 60.
101. Nicholas A. Pace, "The Marijuana Health Hazard," May 1977, p. 6.
102. Gabriel G. Nahas, "Medical Aspects of Marihuana Use," Testimony before the U.S. House of Representatives Select Committee on Narcotics Abuse, March 16, 1977, p. 21.
103. Hardin B. Jones, "Problems Executives Must Anticipate With The Growth of Marijuana Smoking," *Executive Health* (P.O. Box 589, Rancho Santa Fe, California 92067), October, 1977.
104. I.R. Rosengard, "Marijuana," *Science Digest*, May 1978, p. 71.
105. U.S., Congress, Senate, Committee On The Judiciary, *Marihuana-Hashish Epidemic And Its Impact On United States Security, Hearings Before The Subcommittee To Investigate The Administration Of The Internal Security Act And Other Internal Security Laws*. 93 Cong., 2d sess., 1974, p. 62.
106. "New Study Reveals Marijuana Danger," *Human Events*, 16 October 1971.
107. Gabriel G. Nahas, "Medical Aspects of Marihuana Use," Testimony before the U.S. House of Representatives Select Committee on Narcotics Abuse, March 16, 1977, pp. 21-22.
108. T.H. Maugh, II, "Marihuana (II): Does It Damage The Brain?" *Science* 185 (August 1974): 775-776. Copyright 1974 by the American Association for the Advancement of Science.
109. T.H. Maugh, II, "Marihuana (II): Does It Damage the Brain?" *Science* 185 (August 1974): 775-776. Copyright 1974 by the American Association for the Advancement of Science.
110. "New Study Reveals Marijuana Danger," *Human Events*, 16 October 1971.
111. National Institute on Drug Abuse, *Marijuana and Health, 6th Annual Report to the U.S. Congress*, 1976, p. 22.
112. U.S. Congress, Senate, Committee On The Judiciary, *Marihuana-Hashish Epidemic And Its Impact On United States Security, Hearings Before The Subcommittee To Investigate The Administration Of the Internal Security Act And Other Internal Security Laws*, Introduction by Senator James O. Eastland. 93 Cong., 2d Sess., 1974, pp. IX-X.
113. Dr. D. Harvey Powelson (as told to Ted Torkelson and Leon Cornforth), "Our Most Dangerous Drug," Selections from *Listen* (Washington, D.C.: Narcotics Education, Inc., n.d.).
114. U.S. Congress, House, First Report by the Select Committee on Crime, *Marihuana*, H.R. 91-978, 91st Cong., 2d sess., 1970, p. 51.
115. Hardin B. Jones, "What the Practicing Physician Should Know About Marijuana," *Private Practice*, January 1976, pp. 34-40.
116. A. Michael Rossi and John O'Brien, "Memory and Time Estimation," in *The Use of Marihuana: A Psychological and Physiological Inquiry*, eds. Jack H. Mendelson, A. Michael Rossi and Roger E. Meyer (New York: Plenum Press, 1974), p. 106, citing M.C. Braude et al., "Some pharmacological correlates to marihuana use," *Seminars in Drug Therapy I* (1971).
117. T.H. Maugh, II, "Marihuana (II): Does it Damage the Brain?" *Science* 185 (August 1974): 775-776. Copyright 1974 by the American Association for the Advancement of Science.
118. E.R. Bloomquist, *Marijuana* (Beverly Hills: Glencoe Press, The Macmillan Company, 1968), p. 102 © Copyright, Edward R. Bloomquist, 1968.
119. Dr. D. Harvey Powelson (as told to Ted Torkelson and Leon Cornforth), "Our Most Dangerous Drug," Selections from *Listen* (Washington D.C.: Narcotics Education, Inc., n.d.).
120. Dr. Hardin B. Jones, "What Marijuana Really Does," Selections from *Listen* volume 30 (Washington, D.C.: Narcotics Education, Inc., n.d.).
121. Nicholas A. Pace, "The Marijuana Health Hazard," May 1977, p. 2.
122. T.H. Maugh, II, "Marihuana (II) Does It Damage the Brain?" *Science* 185 (August 1974): 775-776. Copyright 1974 by the American Association for the Advancement of Science.
123. Gabriel G. Nahas, *Keep Off the Grass* (New York: Reader's Digest Press, 1976), p. 149.
124. U.S., Congress, Senate, Committee On the Judiciary, *Marihuana-Hashish Epidemic and Its Impact on United States Security, Hearings Before The Subcommittee To Investigate The Administration of the Internal Security Act and Other Internal Security Laws*. 93 Cong. 2d Sess., 1974, p. 65.
125. U.S., Congress, Senate, Committee On The Judiciary, *Marihuana-Hashish Epidemic and Its Impact on United States Security, Hearings Before the Subcommittee To Investigate The Administration of the Internal Security Act and Other Internal Security Laws*. 93 Cong. 2d Sess., 1974, p. 58.
126. T.H. Maugh, II, "Marihuana (II) Does It Damage the Brain?" *Science* 185 (August 1974): 775-776. Copyright 1974 by the American Association for the Advancement of Science.
127. Paul R. Robbins, *Marijuana: A Short Course* (Boston: Branden Press, Inc., 1976), p. 40, citing "Marijuana and ethanol: Effects on Sleep," *Psychiatry in Medicine* 4 (1973): 201-212.
128. Gabriel G. Nahas, *Marihuana: Deceptive Weed* (New York: Raven Press, 1973), p. 249.
129. Weldon L. Witters and Patricia Jones-Witters, *Drugs & Sex* (New York: Macmillan Publishing Co. Inc., 1975), p. 141, citing J. Volavka et al., "Marijuana: EEG and behavior," *Ann. N.Y. Acad. Sci.* 191 (1971): 206-215. Copyright © 1975, Weldon L. Witters and Patricia Jones-Witters.
130. Hardin B. Jones, "What the Practicing Physician Should Know About Marijuana," *Private Practice*, January 1976, pp. 34-40.
131. Reproduced by permission of the National Research Council of Canada from the Canadian *Journal of Physiology and Pharmacology*, volume 51, pp. 401-403, 1973.
132. U.S., Congress, Senate, Committee on the Judiciary, *Marihuana-Hashish Epidemic and Its Impact on United States Security, Hearings Before The Subcommittee To Investigate The Administration Of The Internal Security Act And Other Internal Security Laws*. 93 Cong., 2d sess., 1974, p. 160.
133. Hardin B. Jones, "What the Practicing Physician Should Know About Marijuana," *Private Practice*, January 1976, pp. 34-40.

134. U.S., Congress, Senate, Committee On The Judiciary, *Marihuana-Hashish Epidemic And Its Impact On United States Security, Hearings Before The Subcommittee To Investigate The Administration Of The Internal Security Act And Other Internal Security Laws*. 93 Cong., 2d sess., 1974, p. 137.
135. George K. Russell, *Marihuana Today* rev. ed. (New York: The Myrin Institute, Inc. for Adult Education, 1976), p. 43, citing F.S. Tennant et al., "Medical Manifestations Associated with Hashish," *Journal American Medical Association* 216 (1971): 1965-1969, © Copyright 1971, American Medical Association; and F.S. Tennant Jr., Testimony before the Senate Subcommittee on Internal Security," May 1974, ref. 48, pp. 288-314.
136. Cecile Leuchtenberger and Rudolf Leuchtenberger, "Cytological and Cytochemical Studies of the Effects of Fresh Marihuana Cigarette Smoke on Growth and DNA Metabolism of Animal and Human Lung Cultures," in *Pharmacology of Marihuana*, vol. 2., eds. M.C. Braude and S. Szara (New York: Raven Press, 1976), p. 609.
137. Cecile Leuchtenberger and Rudolf Leuchtenberger, "Cytological and Cytochemical Studies of the Effects of Fresh Marihuana Cigarette Smoke on Growth and DNA Metabolism of Animal and Human Lung Cultures," in *Pharmacology of Marihuana*, vol. 2., eds. M.C. Braude and S. Szara (New York: Raven Press, 1976), p. 609.
138. George K. Russell, *Marihuana Today*, rev. ed. (New York: The Myrin Institute, Inc. for Adult Education, 1976), p. 47.
139. Excerpt from "Marijuana: More Dangerous Than You Know" by Dr. Harvey Powelson, *The Reader's Digest*, December 1974.
140. U.S., Congress, Senate, Committee On The Judiciary, *Marihuana-Hashish Epidemic And Its Impact On United States Security, Hearings Before The Subcommittee To Investigate The Administration Of The Internal Security Act And Other Internal Security Laws*. 93 Cong., 2d sess., 1974, p. 79.
141. Gabriel G. Nahas, "Is Marijuana Really All That Bad?" Selections from *Listen* (Washington, D.C.: Narcotics Education, Inc., 1977).
142. Nicholas A. Pace, "The Marijuana Health Hazard," May 1977, p. 3.
143. George K. Russell, "Critique of Dr. Norman E. Zinberg's Article on Marihuana in Psychology Today," [Written testimony submitted to the March 14-17 1977 hearings of the House Select Committee on Narcotics Abuse (Rep. Lester L. Wolff, Chairman)].
144. Nicholas A. Pace, "The Marijuana Health Hazard," May 1977, p. 7.
145. Excerpt from "Marijuana: More Dangerous Than You Know" by Dr. Harvey Powelson, *The Reader's Digest*, December 1974.
146. National Institute on Drug Abuse, *Marijuana And Health, 6th Annual Report to the U.S. Congress*, 1976, p. 16.
147. "Hashish Damages Body Cells, U.S. Research Group Finds," *Paris Herald Tribune*, 29 September 1973.
148. Hardin B. Jones, "What the Practicing Physician Should Know About Marijuana," *Private Practice*, January 1976, pp. 34-40.
149. National Institute on Drug Abuse, *Marijuana and Health, 6th Annual Report to the U.S. Congress*, 1976, p. 16.
150. George K. Russell, *Marihuana Today* rev. ed. (New York: The Myrin Institute, Inc. for Adult Education, 1976), p. 47, citing S. Grupta, "Impairment of Rosette-Forming T-Lymphocytes in Chronic Marihuana Smokers," *New England Journal of Medicine* 219 (1974): 874-876. Reprinted, by Permission From The New England Journal of Medicine.
151. Albert E. Munsen, "Marijuana and Immunity," in *Marijuana and Health Hazards*, ed. Jared R. Tinklenberg (New York: Academic Press, Inc., 1975), p. 40, citing S.S. Lefkowitz et al., "Effects of certain highly abused drugs on antibody production," *J. Reticuloendothel. Soc.* 16 (1974): 25a.
152. George K. Russell, *Marihuana Today* rev. ed. (New York: The Myrin Institute, Inc. for Adult Education, 1976), p. 47 citing H. Rosenkrantz, "The Immune Response and Marihuana," ref. 61 (1976) 441-456.
153. George K. Russell, *Marihuana Today* rev. ed. (New York: The Myrin Institute, Inc. for Adult Education, 1976), p. 46, citing G.G. Nahas et al., "Inhibition of Cellular Mediated Immunity In Marihuana Smokers," *Science* 183 (1974): 419-420. Copyright 1974 by the American Association for the Advancement of Science.
154. Gabriel G. Nahas, *Keep Off The Grass*, (New York: Reader's Digest Press, 1976), p. 51.
155. Hardin B. Jones and Helen C. Jones, *Sensual Drugs* (Cambridge, England: Cambridge University Press, 1977), p. 237, citing G.G. Nahas in U.S. Senate Hearings, 1974.
156. Gabriel G. Nahas, *Keep Off The Grass* (New York: Reader's Digest Press, 1976), p. 155.
157. Dr. D. Harvey Powelson (as told to Ted Torkelson and Leon Cornforth), "Our Most Dangerous Drug," Selections from *Listen* (Washington, D.C.: Narcotics Education, Inc., n.d.).
158. "The Perils of 'Pot' Start Showing Up," *U.S. News & World Report*, June 10, 1974, p. 58.
159. National Institute on Drug Abuse, *Marijuana and Health, 6th Annual Report to the U.S. Congress*, 1976, p. 17.
160. Kenneth McKenna, "Marijuana Kills," in *Marijuana: Teenage Killer*, ed. Norman Hill (New York: Webster's Red Seal Publications, Inc., 1971), p. 24. Copyright © 1971 by Webster's Red Seal Publications, Inc.
161. U.S., Congress, Senate, Committee on the Judiciary, *Marihuana-Hashish Epidemic and Its Impact on United States Security, Hearings Before The Subcommittee To Investigate The Administration Of The Internal Security Act and Other Internal Security Laws*. 93 Cong., 2d sess., 1974, p. 210.
162. Excerpt from "Marijuana: More Dangerous Than You Know" by Dr. Harvey Powelson, *The Reader's Digest* December 1974.
163. Dr. Hardin B. Jones, "Sex, Marijuana, and the Unborn Child," Selections from *Listen* volume 30 (Washington, D.C.: Narcotics Education, Inc., n.d.).
164. "Hashish Damages Body Cells, U.S. Research Group Finds," *Paris Herald Tribune*, 29 September 1973.
165. George K. Russell, *Marihuana Today* rev. ed. (New York: The Myrin Institute, Inc. for Adult Education, 1976), p. 46, citing G.G. Nahas, et al., *Marihuana: Chemistry, Biochemistry and Cellular Effects* (New York: Springer-Verlag, 1976).
166. Gabriel G. Nahas, *Keep Off The Grass* (New York: Reader's Digest Press, 1976), p. 170.
167. U.S., Congress, Senate, Committee on the Judiciary, *Marihuana-Hashish Epidemic and Its Impact on United States Security, Hearings Before The Subcommittee To Investigate The Administration Of The Internal Security Act And Other Internal Security Laws*. 93 Cong., 2d sess., 1974, p. 114.
168. Gabriel G. Nahas, *Keep Off The Grass* (New York: Reader's Digest Press, 1976), pp. 155-156.
169. Gabriel G. Nahas, *Keep Off The Grass* (New York: Reader's Digest Press, 1976), p. 170.
170. Gabriel G. Nahas, "Is Marijuana Really All That Bad?" Selections from *Listen* (Washington, D.C.: Narcotics Education Inc., 1977).
171. U.S., Congress, Senate, Committee on the Judiciary, *Marihuana-Hashish Epidemic and Its Impact on United States Security, Hearings Before The Subcommittee To Investigate The Administration Of The Internal Security Act and Other Internal Security Laws*. 93 Cong., 2d sess., 1974, p. 137.
172. U.S., Congress, Senate, Committee on the Judiciary, *Marihuana-Hashish Epidemic and Its Impact on United States Security, Hearings Before The Subcommittee To Investigate The Administration Of The Internal Security Act And Other Internal Security Laws*, Introduction by Senator James O. Eastland. 93 Cong., 2d sess., 1974, p. IX.
173. U.S., Congress, Senate, Committee on the Judiciary, *Marihuana-Hashish Epidemic and Its Impact on United States Security, Hearings Before The Subcommittee To Investigate The Administration Of The Internal Security Act And Other Internal Security Laws*. 93 Cong., 2d sess., 1974, pp. 86-89.
174. George K. Russell, "Critique of Dr. Norman E. Zinberg's Article on Marihuana in Psychology Today," [Written testimony, submitted to the March 14-17, 1977 hearings of the House Select Committee on Narcotics Abuse (Rep. Lester L. Wolff, Chairman)].
175. George K. Russell, *Marihuana Today* rev. ed. (New York: The Myrin Institute, Inc. For Adult Education, 1976), "Effects of Chronic Cannabis Use In Man," ref. 61 (1976): 533-550.
176. Gabriel G. Nahas, "Is Marijuana Really All That Bad?" Selections from *Listen* (Washington, D.C.: Narcotics Education, Inc., 1977).

177. Nicholas A. Pace, "The Marijuana Health Hazard," May 1977, p. 7.
178. Gabriel G. Nahas, *Keep Off The Grass* (New York: Reader's Digest Press, 1976), p. 148.
179. National Institute on Drug Abuse, *Marijuana and Health, 6th Annual Report to the U.S. Congress*, 1976, p. 17, citing A. Morishima et al., "Effects of Marihuana Smoking, Cannabinoids, and Olivetol on Replication of Human Lymphocytes: Formation of Micronuclei," in *Pharmacology of Marihuana*, vol. 2, eds. M.C. Braude and S. Szara (New York: Raven Press, 1976), pp. 711-722.
180. George K. Russell, *Marihuana Today* rev. ed. (New York: The Myrin Institute, Inc. for Adult Education, 1976), p. 47, citing B.H. Paterson et al., "Studies of the Immune Response in Chronic Marihuana Smokers," *Pharmacologist* 16 (1974): 259.
181. Gabriel G. Nahas, "Medical Aspects of Marihuana Use," Testimony before the U.S. House of Representatives Select Committee on Narcotics Abuse, March 16, 1977, p. 6.
182. Hardin B. Jones and Helen C. Jones, *Sensual Drugs* (Cambridge, England: Cambridge University Press, 1977), p. 236.
183. Morton A. Stenchever, "Observations on the Cytogenetic Effects of Marijuana," in *Marijuana and Health Hazards*, ed. Jared R. Tinklenberg (New York: Academic Press, Inc., 1975), p. 25.
184. Hardin B. Jones and Helen C. Jones, *Sensual Drugs* (Cambridge, England: Cambridge University Press, 1977), p. 238, citing G.G. Nahas et al., "Inhibition of cellular mediated immunity in marijuana smokers," *Science* 183 (1974): 419-420.
185. National Institute On Drug Abuse, *Marijuana and Health, 6th Annual Report to the U.S. Congress*, 1976, p. 17.
186. Gabriel G. Nahas, *Keep Off The Grass* (New York: Reader's Digest Press, 1976), p. 134.
187. Gabriel G. Nahas, *Keep Off The Grass* (New York: Reader's Digest Press, 1976), p. 136.
188. Reproduced by permission of the National Research Council of Canada from the *Canadian Journal of Physiology and Pharmacology*. volume 51, pp. 401-403, 1973.
189. "Effects of Opium Alkaloids and Cannabinoids on Replication of Lymphocytes," *Bulletin of the New York Academy of Medicine*, vol. 51, no. 10 (November 1975) 1177-1178.
190. Harold Pascal, *The Marijuana Maze* (Canfield, Ohio: Alba House Communications, 1976), pp. 58-59.
191. Hardin B. Jones and Helen C. Jones, *Sensual Drugs* (Cambridge, England: Cambridge University Press, 1977), p. 306, citing D.K. Lawrence and E.W. Gill, "The Effects of delta-1-tetrahydrocannabinol and other cannabinoids on spin-labeled liposomes and their relationship to mechanisms of general anesthesia," *Mod. Pharmacol*. 11 (1975): 595-602.
192. George K. Russell, *Marihuana Today* rev. ed. (New York: The Myrin Institute, Inc. for Adult Education, 1976), p. 46, citing G.G. Nahas, Testimony before the Senate Subcommittee on Internal Security, May 1974, ref. 48, p. 108: and G.G. Nahas, *Keep Off The Grass* (New York: Reader's Digest Press, 1976; and G.G. Nahas et al., "Inhibitory Effects of Delta-9-Tetrahydrocannabinol on Nucleic Acid Synthesis and Proteins in Cultured Lymphocytes," ref. 61 (1976) pp. 299-312.
193. Steve S. Matsuyama, "Cytogenetic Studies of Marijuana," in *Marijuana and Health Hazards*, ed. Jared R. Tinklenberg (New York: Academic Press, Inc., 1975), p. 20, citing S. Kumar et al., "Chromosome abnormalities in Cannabis addicts," *J. Assoc. Physicians Indic*. 19 (1972): 193-195.
194. Robert C. Kolodny, "Research Issues in the Study of Marijuana and Male Reproductive Physiology in Humans," in *Marijuana and Health Hazards*, ed. Jared R. Tinklenberg (New York: Academic Press, Inc., 1975), p. 76, citing V.P. Dixit, "The Effect of chronically administered cannabis extract on the testicular function of mice," *Eur. J. Pharm*. 26 (174): 111-114.
195. U.S., Congress, Senate, Committee On The Judiciary, *Marihuana-Hashish Epidemic And Its Impact On United States Security, Hearings Before The Subcommittee To Investigate The Administration Of The Internal Security Act and Other Internal Security Laws*, Introduction by Senator James O. Eastland. 93 Cong., 2d sess., 1974, p. X.
196. Hardin B. Jones and Helen C. Jones, *Sensual Drugs* (Cambridge, England: Cambridge University Press, 1977), p. 241, citing C. Leuchtenberger et al., "Cytological and cytochemical effects of whole smoke and the gas vapor phase of marihuana cigarettes on growth and nuclear protein metabolism of cultured mammalian cells," *Marihuana: Chemistry, Biochemistry, and Cellular Effects* (New York: Springer-Verlag, 1976).
197. Gabriel G. Nahas, *Keep Off the Grass* (New York: Reader's Digest Press, 1976), p. 149.
198. Hardin B. Jones and Helen C. Jones, *Sensual Drugs* (Cambridge, England: Cambridge University Press, 1977), p. 232.
199. Excerpt from "Marijuana: More Dangerous Than You Know" by Dr. Harvey Powelson, *The Reader's Digest*, December 1974.
200. Hardin B. Jones and Helen C. Jones, *Sensual Drugs* (Cambridge, England: Cambridge University Press, 1977), p. 231, citing W.C. Hembree, "Marihuana effects upon human gonadal function," *Marihuana: Chemistry, Biochemistry and Cellular Effects* (New York: Springer-Verlag, 1976).
201. Robert C. Kolodny et al., "Depression of Plasma Testosterone Levels After Chronic Intensive Marihuana Use," *New England Journal Of Medicine*, vol. 290, no. 16 (April 1974): 874. Reprinted, By Permission From The New England Journal of Medicine.
202. Niles Bejerot, *Addiction and Society* (Springfield, Illinois: Charles C. Thomas, 1970), p. 57. Courtesy of Charles C. Thomas, Publisher.
203. Hardin B. Jones and Helen C. Jones, *Sensual Drugs* (Cambridge, England: Cambridge University Press, 1977), p. 230, citing R.C. Kolodny, "Depression of plasma testosterone levels after chronic internal marijuana use," *Marijuana and Health Hazards* (New York: Academic Press, 1975).
204. Robert C. Kolodny et al., "Depression of Plasma Testosterone with Acute Marihuana Administration," in *Pharmacology of Marihuana*, vol. 1., eds. M.C. Braude and S. Szara (New York: Raven Press, 1976), pp. 219-221.
205. Jane E. Brody, "Male Sex Debility Is Traced To Marijuana," *The New York Times*, 16 September 1975, p. 1. © 1975 by The New York Times Company. Reprinted by permission.
206. Gabriel G. Nahas, "Is Marijuana Really All That Bad," Selections from *Listen* (Washington, D.C.: Narcotics Education, Inc., 1977).
207. Robert C. Kolodny, "Research Issues in the Study of Marijuana and Male Reproductive Physiology in Humans," in *Marijuana and Health Hazards*, Jared R. Tinklenberg (New York: Academic Press, Inc., 1975), p. 79.
208. Hardin B. Jones, "What the Practicing Physician Should Know About Marijuana," *Private Practice* January 1976, pp. 34-40.
209. Jane E. Brody, "Male Sex Debility Is Traced to Marijuana," *The New York Times*, 16 September 1975, p. 1. © 1975 by The New York Times Company. Reprinted by permission.
210. Gabriel G. Nahas et al., Letter to the Editor, *The New England Journal of Medicine*, vol. 291, no. 6 (August 1974): 309. Reprinted by Permission From the New England Journal of Medicine.
211. Tharp, Paul, "Cannabis Conference: The Latest Word from Science," *The Village Voice*, February 9, 1976.
212. Robert C. Kolodny, "Research Issues in the Study of Marijuana and Male Reproductive Physiology in Humans," in *Marijuana and Health Hazards*, ed. Jared R. Tinklenberg (New York: Academic Press, Inc., 1975), p. 76, citing A. Merari et al., "Effects of delta-1 tetrahydrocannabinol on copulation in the male rat," *Psychopharmacologia* 28 (1973): 243-246.
213. Hardin B. Jones and Helen C. Jones, *Sensual Drugs* (Cambridge, England: Cambridge University Press, 1977), p. 241, citing C.N. Stefanis and M.R. Issidorides, "Cellular effects of chronic cannabis use in man," *Marihuana: Chemistry, Biochemistry and Cellular Effects* (New York: Springer-Verlag, 1976).
214. Hardin B. Jones, "What the Practicing Physician Should Know About Marijuana," *Private Practice*, January 1976, pp. 34-40.
215. Jolane Solomon and Douglas X. Shattuck, Letter To The Editor, *New England Journal of Medicine*, vol. 291, no. 3 (August 1974): 309. Reprinted By Permission From The New England Journal of Medicine.
216. Gabriel G. Nahas, *Keep Off the Grass* (New York: Reader's Digest Press, 1976), p. 160.

217. Harris Rosenkrantz, "Cellular, Immunological and Hormonal Effects," in *Pharmacology of Marihuana,* vol. 1., eds. M.C. Braude and S. Szara (New York: Raven Press, 1976), p. 141.
218. Robert C. Kolodny, "Research Issues in the Study of Marijuana and Male Reproductive Physiology in Humans," in *Marijuana and Health Hazards* ed. Jared R. Tinklenberg (New York: Academic Press, Inc., 1975), p. 76 citing H. Rosenkrantz et al., "Comparative chronic toxicities of delta-9-THC administered by inhalation or orally in rats," *Pharmacology of Marihuana* (New York: Raven Press.
219. Dr. Hardin B. Jones, "Sex, Marijuana, and the Unborn Child," Selections from *Listen* volume 30 (Washington, D.C.: Narcotics Education, Inc., n.d.).
220. Harold Pascal, *The Marijuana Maze* (Canfield, Ohio: Alba House Communications, 1976), pp. 65-66.
221. M.C. Braude and S. Szara eds., *Pharmacology of Marijuana,* vol. 1., (New York: Raven Press, 1976), p. 226.
222. Gabriel G. Nahas, "Medical Aspects of Marihuana Use," Testimony before the U.S. House of Representatives Select Committee on Narcotics Abuse, March 16, 1977, pp. 7-8.
223. Hardin B. Jones and Helen C. Jones, *Sensual Drugs* (Cambridge, England: Cambridge University Press, 1977), p. 232.
224. Nicholas A. Pace, "The Marijuana Health Hazard," May 1977, p. 7.
225. Robert C. Kolodny et al., "Depression Of Plasma Testosterone Levels After Chronic Intensive Marihuana Use," *New England Journal of Medicine,* vol. 290, no. 16 (April 1974): 872. Reprinted, By Permission From the New England Journal of Medicine.
226. Charles Peterson, "Marijuana and the Male," *Parade Magazine,* 13 May 1973, p. 18.
227. Excerpt from THE SEEKERS by Jess Stearn. Copyright © 1968, 1969 by Jess Stearn. Used by permission of Doubleday & Company, Inc.
228. W.D.M. Paton and R.G. Pertwee, "The Actions of Cannabis in Man," in *Marijuana: Chemistry, Pharmacology, Metabolism and Clinical Effects,* ed. Raphael Mechoulam (New York: Academic Press Inc., 1973), p. 315, citing E. Marcovitz and H.J. Myers, *War Med.,* 6 (1944): 382.
229. Erich Goode, "Sex and Marijuana," *Sexual Behavior,* May 1972, p. 49.
230. Erich Goode, "Sex and Marijuana," *Sexual Behavior,* May 1972, p. 46.
231. *Marijuana: A Short Course* (Boston: Branden Press, Inc., 1976), p. 47, citing "Drug use and the sexual behavior of college women," *Journal of Sex Research* 9 (1973): 21-29.
232. Paul R. Robbins, *Marijuana: A Short Course* (Boston: Branden Press, Inc. 1976), p. 47, citing "Chronic marijuana use and psycho-social adaptation," *American Journal of Psychiatry* 130 (1973): 132-140. Copyright 1973, the American Psychiatric Association. Reprinted by permission.
233. Hardin B. Jones and Helen C. Jones, *Sensual Drugs* (Cambridge, England: Cambridge University Press, 1977), p. 232.
234. Steven S. Matsuyama, "Cytogenetic Studies of Marijuana," in *Marihuana and Health Hazards,* ed. Jared R. Tinklenberg (New York: Academic Press, Inc., 1975), p. 17.
235. M. Stanton Evans, "The Myths of Marijuana," *Human Events,* 19 October 1974, p. 14.
236. *Human Events,* August 20, 1977.
237. Gabriel G. Nahas, "Medical Aspects of Marihuana Use," Testimony before the U.S. House of Representatives Select Committee on Narcotics Abuse, March 16, 1977, pp. 9-10.
238. "Is Marijuana Safe?" *The Phyllis Schlafly Report,* vol. 11, no. 10, section 1, May 1978, p. 1.
239. Dr. W.D.M. Paton
240. U.S., Congress, Senate, Committee On The Judiciary, *Marihuana-Hashish Epidemic And Its Impact on United States Security, Hearings Before The Subcommittee To Investigate The Administration Of The Internal Security Act And Other Internal Security Laws.* 93 Cong., 2d sess., 1974, p. 125.
241. Kenneth McKenna, "Marijuana Kills," in *Marijuana: Teenage Killer,* ed. Norman Hill (New York: Webster's Red Seal Publications, Inc., 1971), p. 23. Copyright © 1971 by Webster's Red Seal Publications, Inc.
242. Dr. Hardin B. Jones, "Sex, Marijuana, and the Unborn Child," Selections from *Listen* volume 30 (Washington, D.C.: Narcotics Education, Inc., n.d.)
243. New York State Narcotic Addiction Control Commission, *Marijuana* (pamphlet).
244. Hardin B. Jones, "Problems Executives Must Anticipate With The Growth of Marijuana Smoking," *Executive Health* (P.O. Box 589, Rancho Santa Fe, California 92067), October, 1977.
245. Hardin B. Jones, "Problems Executives Must Anticipate With The Growth of Marijuana Smoking," *Executive Health* (P.O. Box 589, Rancho Santa Fe, California 92067), October 1977.
246. Hardin B. Jones and Helen C. Jones, *Sensual Drugs* (Cambridge, England: Cambridge University Press, 1977), pp. 240-241, citing R.D. Harbison and B. Mantilla-Plata, "Prenatal toxicity, maternal distribution, and placental transfer of tetrahydrocannabinol," *J. Pharmacol. Exp. Ther.* 180 (1972): 446-453.
247. George K. Russell, *Marihuana Today,* rev. ed. (New York: The Myrin Institute, Inc. for Adult Education, 1976), p. 42, citing P.A. Fried, "Short and Long-Term Effects of Pre-Natal Cannabis Inhalation Upon Rat Offspring," *Psychopharmacologia* 50 (1976) 255-91.
248. Bernard Mantilla-Plata and Raymond D. Harbison, "Influence of Alteration of Tetrahydrocannabinol Metabolism on Tetrahydrocannabinol-Induced Teratogenesis," in *Pharmacology of Marihuana,* vol. 2, eds. M.C. Braude and S. Szara (New York: Raven Press, 1976), p. 733.
249. Bernardo Mantilla-Plata and Raymond D. Harbison, "Influence of Alteration of Tetrahydrocannabinol Metabolism on Tetrahydrocannabinol-Induced Teratogenesis," in *Pharmacology of Marihuana,* vol. 2., eds. M.C. Braude and S. Szara (New York: Raven Press, 1976), p. 733.
250. Robert C. Kolodny, "Research in the Study of Marijuana and Male Reproductive Physiology in Humans," in *Marijuana and Health Hazards,* ed. Jared R. Tinklenberg (New York: Academic Press, Inc., 1975), p. 78, citing R.C. Kolodny et al., unpublished data (1974).
251. Allen Geller and Maxwell Boas, *The Drug Beat* (Chicago: Cowles Book Company, Inc., 1969), p. 91.
252. Gabriel G. Nahas, "Is Marijuana Really All That Bad," Selections from *Listen* (Washington, D.C.: Narcotics Education, Inc., 1977).
253. Morton A. Stenchever, "Observations on the Cytogenetic Effects of Marijuana," in *Marijuana and Health Hazards,* ed. Jared R. Tinklenberg (New York: Academic Press, Inc., 1975), p. 28.
254. Dr. Hardin B. Jones, "Sex, Marijuana, and the Unborn Child," Selections from *Listen* volume 30 (Washington, D.C.: Narcotics Education, Inc., n.d.).
255. The Official Report Of The National Commission on Marihuana and Drug Abuse, *Marihuana: A Signal Of Misunderstanding,* with a foreword from Raymond P. Shafer, Chairman (New York: The New American Library, Inc., 1972), p. 104.
256. "Fate Of The Pot Smoker," *The Commercial Appeal,* 10 February 1974, sec. 6, p.4.
257. Weldon L. Witters and Patricia Jones-Witters, *Drugs & Sex* (New York: MacMillan Publishing Co., Inc., 1975), Copyright © 1975, Weldon L. Witters and Patricia Jones-Witters, pp. 140-141, citing G.S. Chopra, "Man and Marijuana," *Intern. J. Addict* 4 (1969): 755-759.
258. U.S., Congress, House, First Report by the Select Committee on Crime, *Marihuana,* H.R. 91-978, 91st Cong., 2d sess., 1970, p. 10.
259. Reprinted from DRUGS AND THE MIND, New Revised Edition, by Robert S. De Ropp. Copyright © 1957, 1976 by Robert S. De Ropp. Used by permission of the publisher, Delacorte Press/Seymour Lawrence.
260. I.R. Rosengard, "Marijuana," *Science Digest,* April 1978, p. 74.
261. Nils Bejerot, *Addiction: An Artificially Induced Drive* (Springfield, Illinois: Charles C. Thomas, 1972), p. 22. Courtesy of Charles C. Thomas, Publisher.

262. W.D.M. Paton and R.G. Pertwee, "The Actions of Cannabis in Man," in *Marijuana: Chemistry, Pharmacology, Metabolism and Clinical Effects*, ed. Raphael Mechoulam (New York: Academic Press, Inc., 1973), p. 320.
263. Leo E. Hollister, "Human Pharmacology of Marihuana (Cannabis)," in *Drug Dependence* eds. Robert T. Harris, William M. McIsaac, and Charles R. Schuster, Jr. (Austin, Texas: University of Texas Press, 1970), p. 74. Copyright © 1970 by the University of Texas Press. All rights reserved.
264. Erich Goode, *Drugs in American Society* (New York: Alfred A. Knopf, Inc., 1972), p. 7.
265. Ronald Bruce, ed., *The Pot Report* (New York: Universal-Award House, Inc.; Award Books, 1971), p. 70.
266. "Medical Aspects," in *The Marijuana Problem in the City of New York* (Mayor's Committee on Marijuana), 1944.
267. U.S., Congress, Senate, Committee on the Judiciary, *Marihuana-Hashish Epidemic and Its Impact on United States Security, Hearings Before The Subcommittee To Investigate The Administration Of The Internal Security Act And Other Internal Security Laws*, Introduction by Senator James O. Eastland, 93 Cong., 2d sess., 1974, p. X.
268. George K. Russell, *Marihuana Today* rev. ed. (New York: The Myrin Institute, Inc. for Adult Education, 1976), p. 47, citing A. Chari-Bitron, "Effect of Delta-9-Tetrahydrocannabinol on Red Blood Cell Membranes and on Alveolar Macrophages," ref. 61 (1968): 273-282.
269. Hardin B. Jones, "Problems Executives Must Anticipate With The Growth of Marijuana Smoking," *Executive Health* (P.O. Box 589, Rancho Santa Fe, California 92067), October 1977.
270. U.S., Congress, Senate, Committee on the Judiciary, *Marihuana-Hashish Epidemic and Its Impact on United States Security, Hearings Before The Subcommittee To Investigate The Administration Of The Internal Security Act And Other Internal Security Laws*, Introduction by Senator James O. Eastland. 93 Cong., 2d sess., 1974, p. X.
271. National Institute on Drug Abuse, *Marihuana and Health: Sixth Annual Report to the U.S. Congress* (Washington, D.C.: Government Printing Office, 1976): 14-15, citing D.P. Tashkin et al., "Subacute effects of heavy marihuana smoking on pulmonary function in healthy men," *New England Journal of Medicine*, vol. 294, no. 3 (January, 1976): 125-129. Reprinted, By Permission From The New England Journal of Medicine.
272. Jerrold G. Bernstein et al., "Physiological Assessments: Cardiopulmonary Function," in *The Use of Marihuana: A Psychological and Physiological Inquiry*, ed.. Jack H. Mendelson, A. Michael Rossi and Roger E. Meyer (New York: Plenum Press, 1974), p. 160.
273. I.R. Rosengard, "Marijuana," *Science Digest*, May 1978, p. 70.
274. U.S. Department of Health, Education and Welfare, HEW NEWS, March 10, 1977.
275. Jerrold G. Bernstein et al., "Physiological Assessments: Cardiopulmonary Function," in *The Use Of Marihuana: A Psychological And Physiological Inquiry*, eds. Jack H. Mendelson, A. Michael Rossi and Roger E. Meyer (New York: Plenum Press, 1974), p. 160.
276. Hardin B. Jones, "What the Practicing Physician Should Know About Marijuana," *Private Practice*, January 1976, pp. 34-40.
277. W.D.M. Paton and R.G. Pertwee, "The Actions of Cannabis in Man," in *Marijuana: Chemistry, Pharmacology, Metabolism and Clinical Effects*, ed. Raphael Mechoulam (New York: Academic Press, Inc., 1973), p. 321.
278. U.S., Congress, Senate, Committee on the Judiciary, *Marihuana-Hashish Epidemic and Its Impact on United States Security, Hearings Before The Subcommittee To Investigate The Administration Of The Internal Security Act And Other Internal Security Laws*. 93 Cong., 2d sess., 1974, p. 191.
279. U.S., Congress, Senate, Committee On The Judiciary, *Marihuana-Hashish Epidemic And Its Impact On United States Security, Hearings Before The Subcommittee To Investigate The Administration Of The Internal Security Act And Other Internal Security Laws*. 93 Cong., 2d sess., 1974, p. 94.
280. L. Vachon et al., "Bronchial Effect of Marihuana Smoke in Asthma," in *Pharmacology of Marijuana*, Vol.2., eds. M.C. Braude and S. Szara (New York: Raven Press, 1976), p. 783.
281. Carlton R. McCarthy et al., "The Effect of Marihuana on the In Vitro Function of Pulmonary Alveolar Macrophages," in *Pharmacology of Marijuana* vol. 1., eds. M.C. Braude and S. Szara (New York: Raven Press, 1976), p. 215.
282. From MARIJUANA AND YOUR CHILD by Jules Saltman. Copyright © 1970 by Jules Saltman. Used by permission of Grosset & Dunlap, Inc.
383. Hardin B. Jones and Helen C. Jones, *Sensual Drugs* (Cambridge, England: Cambridge University Press, 1977), p. 307, citing W.D.M. Paton and J. Crown eds., *Cannabis and Its Derivatives: Pharmacology and Experimental Psychology* (London: Oxford University Press, 1972).
284. W.D.M. Paton and R.G. Pertwee, "The Actions of Cannabis in Man," in *Marijuana: Chemistry, Pharmacology, Metabolism and Clinical Effects*, ed. Raphael Mechoulam (New York: Academic Press, Inc. 1973), p. 325, citing M.C. Kew et al., *Lancet* 1 (1969): 578.
285. National Institute on Drug Abuse, *Marijuana and Health, 6th Annual Report to the U.S. Congress*, 1976, pp. 12-13.
286. National Institute on Drug Abuse, *Marijuana and Health, 6th Annual Report to the U.S. Congress*, 1976, p. 14.
287. Paul R. Robbins, *Marijuana: A Short Course* (Boston: Branden Press, Inc., 1976), p. 36.
288. Jerrold G. Bernstein et al., "Physiological Assessments: Cardiopulmonary Function," in *The Use Of Marihuana: A Psychological Inquiry*, eds. Jack H. Mendelson, A. Michael Rossi and Roger E. Meyer (New York: Plenum Press, 1974), p. 160.
289. Wilbert S. Aronow and John Cassidy, "Effect of Marihuana and Placebo-Marihuana Smoking on Angina Pectoris," *New England Journal of Medicine*, vol. 291, no. 2 (July 1974): 65. Reprinted, By Permission From The New England Journal of Medicine.
290. Reprinted from DRUGS AND THE MIND, New Revised Edition, by Robert S. De Ropp. Copyright © 1957, 1976 by Robert S. De Ropp. Used by permission of the publisher, Delacorte Press/Seymour Lawrence.
291. I.R. Rosengard, "Marijuana," *Science Digest* April 1978, p. 73.
292. Edward F. Domino et al., Short Term Neuropsychopharmacological Effects of Marihuana Smoking in Experienced Male Users," in *Pharmacology of Marihuana*, vol. 1, eds. M.C. Braude and S. Szara (New York: Raven Press, 1976) p. 401.
293. Robert L. Dupont, "Marihuana: Our Next Step," February 4, 1977, (Washington, D.C.: Psychiatric Institute Foundation), p. 18.
294. Hardin B. Jones, "What the Practicing Physician Should Know About Marijuana," *Private Practice*, January 1976, pp. 34-40.
295. Paul R. Robbins, *Marijuana: A Short Course* (Boston: Branden Press, Inc., 1976), pp. 39-40, citing "The effects of marijuana on human sleep patterns," *Biological Psychiatry* 8 (1974): 47-54.
296. A. Michael Rossi, Jerrold G. Bernstein, and Jack H. Mendelson, "Sleep—Wakefulness Behavior," in *The Use of Marihuana: A Psychological and Physiological Inquiry*, eds. Jack H. Mendelson, A. Michael Rossi and Roger E. Meyer (New York: Plenum Press, 1974), p. 161.
297. Weldon L. Witters and Patricia Jones-Witters, *Drugs & Sex* (New York: Macmillan Publishing Co., Inc., 1975). Copyright © 1975, Weldon L. Witters and Patricia Jones-Witters, p. 141, citing Copyright © 1970, The Society for Psychophysiological Research. Quoted with permission of the publisher from "Marijuana intoxication: Reported effects on sleep," by C.T. Tart & H.J. Crawford, PSYCHOPHYSIOLOGY, 1970, 7, 348.
298. U.S. Congress, House, First Report by the Select Committee on Crime, *Marihuana*, H.R. 91-978 91st Cong., 2d Sess., 1970, p. 9.
299. A. Michael Rossi and John O'Brien, "Memory and Time Estimation," In *The Use of Marihuana: A Psychological and Physiological Inquiry*, eds. Jack H. Mendelson, A. Michael Rossi and Roger E. Meyer (New York: Plenum Press, 1974), p. 106.
300. W.D.M. Paton and R.G. Pertwee, "The Actions of Cannabis in Man," in *Marijuana: Chemistry, Pharmacology, Metabolism and Clinical Effects*, ed. Raphael Mechoulam (New York: Academic Press, Inc., 1973), p. 317.

301. Hardin B. Jones and Helen C. Jones, *Sensual Drugs* (Cambridge, England: Cambridge University Press, 1977), p. 215.
302. Harris Rosenkrantz, "Cellular, Immunological and Hormonal Effects," in *Pharmacology of Marihuana*, vol. 1., eds. M.C. Braude and S. Szara (New York: Raven Press, 1976), p. 146.
303. Hardin B. Jones and Helen C. Jones, *Sensual Drugs* (Cambridge, England: Cambridge University Press, 1977), pp. 229-230, citing P. Lomax, "The Effect of Marihuana on Pituitary-thyroid activity in the rat," *Agents Actions* 1 (1970): 252-257.
304. Stephen Szara, "Clinical Pharmacology of Cannabis: Scientific and Nonscientific Constraints," in *Pharmacology of Marihuana*, vol. 1., eds. M.C. Braude and S. Szara (New York: Raven Press, 1976), p. 28.
305. Hardin B. Jones and Helen C. Jones, *Sensual Drugs* (Cambridge, England: Cambridge University Press, 1977), p. 232, citing J. Solomon et al., "Uterotrophic effect on delta-9-tetrahydrocannabinol in ovarlectomized rats," *Science* 192 (1976): 550-561.
306. W.D.M. Paton and R.G. Pertwee, "The Actions of Cannabis in Man," in *Marijuana: Chemistry, Pharmacology, Metabolism and Clinical Effects* ed. Raphael Mechoulam (New York: Academic Press, Inc., 1973), p. 303, citing E.L. Abel, *Nature (London)* 231 (1971) 58 and *Science* 173 (1971) 1038.
307. I.R. Rosengard, "Marijuana," *Science Digest*, April 1978, p. 75.
308. I.R. Rosengard, "Marijuana," *Science Digest* April 1978, p. 76.
309. Paul R. Robbins, *Marijuana: A Short Course* (Boston: Branden Press, Inc., 1976), p. 42, citing "Residual effects of marihuana usage on learning and memory," *Psychological Record* 23 (1973): 169-178.
310. Edward F. Domino et al., "Short-Term Neuropsychopharmacological Effects of Marihuana Smoking in Experienced Male Users," in *Pharmacology of Marihuana* vol. 1., eds. M.C. Braude and S. Szara (New York: Raven Press, 1976), p. 406.
311. Stanley F. Yolles, "The Psychiatrist Looks At Drug Abuse," in *Drug Abuse in Industry*, eds. Pasquale A. Carone and Leonard W. Krinsky (Springfield, Illinois: Charles C. Thomas, 1973), pp. 71-72. Courtesy of Charles C. Thomas, Publisher.
312. Hardin B. Jones, "What the Practicing Physician Should Know About Marijuana," *Private Practice*, January 1976, pp. 34-40.
313. Simone Radouco-Thomas et al., "Effect of Chronic Administration of Delta-1-Tetrahydrocannabinol on Learning and Memory in Developing Mice," in *Pharmacology of Marihuana*, vol. 2, eds. M.C. Braude and S. Szara (New York: Raven Press, 1976), p. 487.
314. Ronald Bruce, ed., *The Pot Report* (New York: Universal-Award House, Inc.; Award Books, 1971), p. 77, citing C.T. Tart, "Marijuana intoxication, common experience," *Nature* 222 (1970): 701-704
315. Paul R. Robbins, *Marijuana: A Short Course* (Boston: Branden Press, Inc., 1976), pp. 41-42, citing "Marihuana and memory: Acquisition of retrieval," *Science* 173 (1971): 1038-1040.
316. W.D.M. Paton and R.G. Pertwee, "The Actions of Cannabis in Man," in *Marijuana: Chemistry, Pharmacology, Metabolism and Clinical Effects*, ed. Raphael Mechoulam (New York: Academic Press, Inc., 1973), p. 302, citing J.R. Tinklenberg, *Nature (London)* 226 (1970): 1171.
317. T.H. Maugh, II, "Marihuana (II): Does It Damage the Brain?" *Science* 185 (August 1974): 775-776. Copyright 1974 by the American Association for the Advancement of Science.
318. Ronald Bruce, ed., *The Pot Report* (New York: Universal-Award House, Inc.; Award Books, 1971), p. 78, citing L.D. Clark et al., "Behavioral effects of marijuana: Experimental studies," *Archives of General Psychiatry* 23 (1970): 193-198. Copyright 1970, American Medical Association.
319. George K. Russell, *Marihuana Today* rev. ed. (New York: The Myrin Institute, Inc. for Adult Education, 1976), p. 32, citing L.E. Hollister, "Marihuana in Man: Three Years Later," *Science* 172 (1971): 21-24.
320. Dr. Hardin B. Jones, "What Marijuana Really Does," Selections from *Listen* volume 30 (Washington, D.C.: Narcotics Education, Inc., n.d.).
321. Thomas Weisman, *Drug Abuse And Drug Counseling* (New York: Jason Aronson, 1972), p. 141, citing "Marihuana and Temporal Disintegration," *Science* 168 (1970): 1119.
322. Ronald Bruce, ed., *The Pot Report* (New York: Universal-Award House, Inc.; Award Books, 1971), pp. 77-78.
323. Excerpt from "Marijuana: More Dangerous Than You Know" by Dr. Harvey Powelson, *The Reader's Digest*, December 1974.
324. U.S., Congress, Senate, Committee On The Judiciary, *Marihuana-Hashish Epidemic And Its Impact On United States Security*, Hearings Before The Subcommittee To Investigate The Administration Of The Internal Security Act And Other Internal Security Laws. 93 Cong., 2d sess., 1974, p. 195.
325. Ian Campbell, "The Amotivational Syndrome And Cannabis Use With Emphasis On The Canadian Scene," *Chronic Cannabis Use* (New York: Annals of the New York Academy of Sciences, vol. 282, 1976), p. 35.
326. Gabriel G. Nahas, "Medical Aspects of Marihuana Use," Testimony before the U.S. House of Representatives Select Committee on Narcotics Abuse, March 16, 1977, pp. 22-23.
327. Hardin B. Jones, "Problems Executives Must Anticipate With The Growth of Marijuana Smoking," *Executive Health* (P.O. Box 589, Rancho Santa Fe, California 92067), October, 1977.
328. Harold Pascal, *The Marijuana Maze* (Canfield Ohio: Alba House Communications, 1976), pp. 71-72, citing *Marijuana—Deceptive Weed* (New York: Raven Press, 1973).
329. E.R. Bloomquist, *Marijuana* (Beverly Hills: Glencoe Press, The Macmillan Company, 1968, p. 73. © Copyright, Edward R. Bloomquist, 1968.
330. George K. Russell, *Marihuana Today* rev. ed. (New York: The Myrin Institute, Inc. for Adult Education, 1976), p. 42, citing K.A. Fehr et al., "Permanent Learning Impairment After Chronic Heavy Exposure to Cannabis or Ethanal in the Rat," ref. 61, pp. 495-505.
331. Gurbakhsh S. Chopra and Balwant S. Jandu, "Psycho-clinical Effects Of Long-Term Marijuana Use in 275 Indian Chronic Users. A Comparative Assessment of Effects In Indian and USA Users," *Chronic Cannabis Use* (New York: Annals of the New York Academy of Sciences, vol. 282, 1976), p. 105.
332. Leo E. Hollister, "Human Pharmacology of Marihuana (Cannabis)," in *Drug Dependence* eds. Robert T. Harris, William M. McIsaac, and Charles R. Schuster, Jr. (Austin, Texas: University of Texas Press, 1970), p. 75. Copyright © 1970 by the University of Texas Press. All rights reserved.
333. U.S., Congress, House, First Report by the Select Committee on Crime, *Marihuana*, H.R. 91-978, 91st Cong., 2d sess., 1970, p. 113.
334. W.D.M. Paton and R.G. Pertwee, "The Actions of Cannabis in Man," in *Marijuana: Chemistry, Pharmacology, Metabolism and Clinical Effects*, ed Raphael Mechoulam (New York: Academic Press, Inc., 1973), p. 306.
335. W.D.M. Paton and R.G. Pertwee, "The Actions of Cannabis in Man," in *Marijuana: Chemistry, Pharmacology, Metabolism and Clinical Effects*, ed. Raphael Mechoulam (New York: Academic Press, Inc., 1973), pp. 306-307, citing L.D. Clark et al., *Arch. Gen. Psychiat.* 23 (1970): 193.
336. Weldon L. Witters and Patricia Jones-Witters, *Drugs & Sex* (New York: Macmillan Publishing Co. Inc., 1975), Copyright © 1975, Weldon L. Witters and Patricia Jones-Witters, p. 142, citing L.E. Hollister, "Marihuana in man: Three years later," *Science* 172 (1971): 21-24 and L.D. Clark et al., "Experimental studies·of marijuana," *Amer. J. Psychiat.* 125(1968): 135-140. Copyright 1968, American Psychiatric Association, Reprinted by permission.
337. W.D.M. Paton and R.G. Pertwee, "The Actions of Cannabis in Man," in *Marijuana: Chemistry, Pharmacology, Metabolism and Clinical Effects*, ed. Raphael Mechoulam (New York: Academic Press, Inc., 1973), p. 303, citing E.L. Abel, *Nature (London)* 231 (1971): 58.
338. Harold Pascal, *The Marijuana Maze* (Canfield, Ohio: Alba House Communications, 1976), p. 74, citing "Adverse Reactions to Marijuana," *New England Journal of Medicine* 282 (1970): 997-1000. Reprinted by permission from The New England Journal of Medicine.

339. Weldon L. Witters and Patricia Jones-Witters, *Drugs & Sex* (New York: Macmillan Publishing Co. Inc., 1975), pp. 141-142. Copyright © 1975, Weldon L. Witters and Patricia Jones-Witters.
340. Gabriel G. Nahas, *Marihuana: Deceptive Weed* (New York: Raven Press, 1973), p. 22.
341. U.S., Congress, Senate, Committee On The Judiciary, *Marihuana-Hashish Epidemic And Its Impact On United States Security, Hearings Before The Subcommittee To Investigate The Administration Of The Internal Security Act And Other Internal Security Laws*. 93 Cong., 2d sess., 1974, p. 64.
342. U.S., Congress, Senate, Committee On The Judiciary, *Marihuana-Hashish Epidemic And Its Impact On United States Security, Hearings Before The Subcommittee To Investigate The Administration Of The Internal Security Act and Other Internal Security Laws*. 93 Cong., 2d sess., 1974, pp. 22-23.
343. Richard Golstein, "The College Scene in the U.S.A.," in *The Book of Grass: An Anthology of Indian Hemp* (New York: Grove Press, 1967), p. 217.
344. W.D.M. Paton and R.G. Pertwee, "The Actions of Cannabis in Man," in *Marijuana: Chemistry, Pharmacology, Metabolism and Clinical Effects*, ed. Raphael Mechoulam (New York Academic Press, Inc., 1973), p. 299.
345. E.R. Bloomquist, *Marijuana* (Beverly Hills: Glencoe Press, The Macmillan Company, 1968), pp. 183-184. © Copyright, Edward R. Bloomquist, 1968.
346. I.R. Rosengard, "Marijuana," *Science Digest*, May 1978, p. 68.
347. "Dangers of marijuana are cited by reader," letter to the editors, *Long Island Press*.
348. William M. McIsaac et al., "Distribution of Marihuana in Monkey Brain and Concomitant Behavioral Effects," *Nature* 230 (April 1970), p. 594.
349. Excerpt from THE SEEKERS by Jess Stearn. Copyright © 1968, 1969 by Jess Stearn. Used by permission of Doubleday & Company, Inc.
350. Jess R. Lord, *Marijuana and Personality Change* (Lexington, Massachusetts: D.C. Heath and Company, Lexington Books, 1971), p. 99.
351. W.D.M. Paton and R.G. Pertwee, "The Actions of Cannabis in Man," in *Marijuana: Chemistry, Pharmacology, Metabolism and Clinical Effects*, ed. Raphael Mechoulam (New York: Academic Press, Inc., 1973), p. 297.
352. Nils Bejerot, *Addiction: An Artifically Induced Drive* (Springfield, Illinois: Charles C. Thomas, 1972), p. 22. Courtesy of Charles C. Thomas, Publisher.
353. Weldon L. Witters and Patricia Jones-Witters, *Drugs & Sex* (New York: Macmillan Publishing Co. Inc., 1975), Copyright © 1975, Weldon L. Witters and Patricia Jones-Witters, p. 143, citing R.T. Jones, "Marihuana-induced 'high': Influence of expectation, setting and previous drug experience," *Pharmacol. Rev*. 23 (1971): 359-370, and A.A. Baker et al., "Some hospital admissions associated with cannabis," *Lancet* (1969): 148.
354. Gabriel G. Nahas, "Medical Aspects of Marihuana Use," Testimony before the U.S. House of Representatives Select Committee on Narcotics Abuse, March 16, 1977, p. 13.
355. Nils Bejerot, *Addiction: An Artificially Induced Drive* (Springfield, Illinois: Charles C. Thomas, 1972), p. 23. Courtesy of Charles C. Thomas, publisher.
356. U.S., Congress, Senate, Committee On The Judiciary, *Marihuana-Hashish Epidemic And Its Impact On United States Security, Hearings Before The Subcommittee To Investigate The Administration Of The Internal Security Act and Other Internal Security Laws*. 93 Cong., 2d sess., 1974, p. 183.
357. Nils Bejerot, Addiction and Society (Springfield, Illinois: Charles C. Thomas, 1970), pp. 57-58. Courtesy of Charles C. Thomas, Publisher.
358. W.D.M. Paton and R.G. Pertwee, "The Actions of Cannabis in Man," in *Marijuana: Chemistry, Pharmacology, Metabolism and Clinical Effects*, ed. Raphael Mechoulam (New York: Academic Press, Inc., 1973), p. 296.
359. Harold Pascal, *The Marijuana Maze* (Canfield, Ohio: Alba House Communications, 1976), pp. 64-65.
360. E.R. Bloomquist, *Marijuana* (Beverly Hills: Glencoe Press, The Macmillan Company, 1968), p. 87. © Copyright, Edward R. Bloomquist, 1968.
361. F. Ames, "A Clinical and Metabolic Study of Acute Intoxication with Cannabis Sativa and Its Role in Model Psychoses," *J. Mental Sci*. 104 (1958): 972-999.
362. George K. Russell, *Marihuana Today*, rev. ed. (New York: The Myrin Institute, Inc. for Adult Education, 1976), pp. 18-19, citing H. Isbell et al., "Effects of Delta-9-Tetrahydrocannabinol in Man," *Psychopharmacologia* 14 (1967): 115-123.
363. Andrew Malcolm, *The Tyrrany of the Group* (Totowa, New Jersey: Littlefield, Adams & Co., 1975; published first by Clark, Irwin & Co., 1973), pp. 20, 28.
364. W.D.M. Paton and R.G. Pertwee, "The Actions of Cannabis in Man," in *Marijuana: Chemistry, Pharmacology, Metabolism and Clinical Effects*, ed. Raphael Mechoulam (New York: Academic Press, Inc., 1973), p. 297, citing W. Grossman, *Ann. Intern. Med*. 70 (1969): 529, and A.A. Baker and E.G. Lucas, *Lancet* 1 (1969): 148.
365. Ronald Bruce, Ed., *The Pot Report* (New York: Universal-Award House, Inc., 1971), pp. 69, citing Report by the Advisory Committee on Drug Dependence, *Cannabis* (London: Her Majesty's Stationery Office, 1968).
366. Gabriel G. Nahas, *Keep Off the Grass* (New York: Reader's Digest Press, 1976), p. 16.
367. W.D.M. Paton and R.G. Pertwee, "The Actions of Cannabis in Man," in *Marijuana: Chemistry, Pharmacology, Metabolism and Clinical Effects*, ed. Raphael Mechoulam (New York: Academic Press, Inc., 1973), p. 308.
368. Excerpt from THE SEEKERS by Jess Stearn. Copyright © 1968, 1969 by Jess Stearn. Used by permission of Doubleday & Company, Inc.
369. Anne Kaufman, "Seducer of the Young," in *Marijuana: Teenage Killer*, ed. Norman Hill (New York: Webster's Red Seal Publications, Inc., 1971), pp. 103-111. Copyright © 1971 by Webster's Red Seal Publications, Inc.
370. Nicholas A. Pace, "The Marijuana Health Hazard," May 1977, pp. 4-5.
371. Lawrence K. Altman, "Scientists Intensify Research on Marijuana's Effects," *The New York Times*, 21 May 1971. © 1971 by The New York Times Company. Reprinted by permission.
372. Stanley Yolles, "An Expert Answers Teen-Agers Questions About Drugs," reprinted from *Family Weekly Magazine* (State of New York: Narcotic Addiction Control Commission, March 8, 1970).
373. U.S., Congress, Senate, Committee On The Judiciary, *Marihuana-Hashish Epidemic And Its Impact On United States Security, Hearings Before The Subcommittee To Investigate The Administration Of The Internal Security Act and Other Internal Security Laws*. 93 Cong., 2d sess., 1974, pp. 51-52.
374. From MARIJUANA AND YOUR CHILD by Jules Saltman. Copyright © 1970 by Jules Saltman. Used by permission of Grosset & Dunlap, Inc.
375. George K. Russell, *Marihuana Today*, rev. ed. (New York: The Myrin Institute, Inc. for Adult Education, 1976), p. 6.
376. From THE MARIHUANA SMOKERS, by Erich Goode, © 1970 by Basic Books, Inc., Publishers, New York.
377. Harold Pascal, *The Marijuana Maze* (Canfield, Ohio: Alba House Communications, 1976), pp. 74-75.
378. National Institute on Drug Abuse, *Marijuana and Health, 6th Annual Report to the U.S. Congress*, 1976, p. 10.
379. Dr. Hardin B. Jones, "What Marijuana Really Does," Selections from *Listen* volume 30 (Washington, D.C.: Narcotics Education, Inc., n.d.).
380. Roswell Johnson, in *Drugs: For & Against*, Harold Hart, ed. (New York: Hart Publishing Company, Inc., 1970), pp. 66-69.
381. From THE MARIJUANA SMOKERS, by Erich Goode, ©af171970 by Basic Books, Inc., Publishers, New York.
382. U.S., Congress, Senate, Committee On The Judiciary, *Marihuana-Hashish Epidemic And Its Impact On United States Security, Hearings Before The Subcommittee To Investigate The Administration Of The Internal Security Act And Other Internal Security Laws*, Introduction by Senator James O. Eastland. 93 Cong., 2d sess., 1974, p. XI.
383. Hardin B. Jones and Helen C. Jones, *Sensual Drugs* (Cambridge, England: Cambridge University Press, 1977), p. 221, citing J.D. Miliman et al., "The thought disorders of the cannabis syndrome," Paper presented at the National Drug Abuse Conference, March 29, 1976, New York.

384. Ian Campbell, "The Amotivational Syndrome and Cannabis Use With Emphasis On The Canadian Scene," *Chronic Cannabis Use* (New York: Annals of the New York Academy of Sciences, vol. 282, 1976), p. 35.
385. Excerpt from THE SEEKERS by Jess Stearn. Copyright 1968, 1969 by Jess Stearn. Used by permission of Doubleday & Company, Inc.
386. Franz Winkler, *About Marijuana* (New York: The Myrin Institute, Inc., 1970).
387. Franz Winkler, *About Marijuana* (New York: The Myrin Institute, Inc., 1970).
388. U.S., Congress, Senate, Committee On The Judiciary, *Marihuana-Hashish Epidemic And Its Impact On United States Security, Hearings Before The Subcommittee To Investigate The Administration Of The Internal Security Act And Other Internal Security Laws*, Introduction by Senator James O. Eastland. 93 Cong., 2d sess., 1974, p. XI.
389. U.S., Congress, Senate, Committee On The Judiciary, *Marihuana-Hashish Epidemic And Its Impact On United States Security, Hearings Before The Subcommittee To Investigate The Administration Of The Internal Security Act And Other Internal Security Laws*. 93 Cong., 2d sess., 1974, pp. 184-185.
390. T.H. Maugh, II, "Marihuana (II): Does It Damage the Brain?" *Science* 185 (August 1974): 775-776. Copyright 1974 by the American Association for the Advancement of Science.
391. U.S. Congress, House, First Report by the Select Committee on Crime, *Marihuana*, H.R. 91-978, 91st Cong., 2d sess., 1970, p. 11.
392. Roy H. Hart, "A Psychiatric Classification of Cannabis Intoxication," *J. Amer. Acad. Psychiat. Neurol.* vol. 1, no. 4 (1976): 90.
393. Hardin B. Jones, "What the Practicing Physician Should Know About Marijuana," *Private Practice*, January 1976, pp. 34-40.
394. The Official Report Of The National Commission on Marihuana And Drug Abuse, *Marihuana: A Signal Of Misunderstanding*, with a foreword from Raymond P. Shafer, Chairman (New York: The New American Library, Inc., 1972), p. 76.
395. Excerpt from THE SEEKERS by Jess Stearn. Copyright © 1968, 1969 by Jess Stearn. Used by permission of Doubleday & Company, Inc.
396. Hardin B. Jones, "What the Practicing Physician Should Know About Marijuana," *Private Practice*, January 1976, pp. 34-40.
397. U.S., Congress, House, First Report by the Select Committee on Crime, *Marihuana*, H.R. 91-978, 91st Cong., 2d sess., 1970, p. 12.
398. New York State Narcotic Addiction Control Commission, *Marijuana* (pamphlet).
399. Gurbakhsh S. Chopra and Balwant S. Jandu, "Psycho-clinical Effects Of Long-Term Marijuana Use in 275 Indian Chronic Users. A Comparative Assessment of Effects In Indian and USA Users," *Chronic Cannabis Use* (New York: Annals of the New York Academy of Sciences, vol. 282, 1976), p. 101.
400. Excerpt from THE SEEKERS by Jess Stearn. Copyright © 1968, 1969 by Jess Stearn. Used by permission of Doubleday & Company, Inc.
401. U.S., Congress, House, First Report by the Select Committee on Crime, *Marihuana*, H.R. 91-978, 91st Cong., 2d sess., 1970, p. 12.
402. The Official Report Of The National Commission on Marihuana And Drug Abuse, *Marihuana: A Signal Of Misunderstanding*, with a foreword from Raymond P. Shafer, Chairman (New York: The New American Library, Inc., 1972), p. 107.
403. Gabriel G. Nahas, "Is Marijuana Really All That Bad," Selections from *Listen* (Washington, D.C.: Narcotics Education, Inc., 1977).
404. Excerpt from THE SEEKERS by Jess Stearn. Copyright ©af301968, 1969 by Jess Stearn. Used by permission of Doubleday & Company, Inc.
405. Gurbaksh S. Chopra and Balwant S. Jandu, "Psycho-clinical Effects Of Long-Term Marijuana Use in 275 Indian Chronic Users. A Comparative Assessment of Effects in Indian and USA Users," *Chronic Cannabis Use* (New York: Annals of the New York Academy of Sciences, vol. 282, 1976), p. 101.
406. I.R. Rosengard, "Marijuana," *Science Digest*, April 1978, p. 72.
407. E.R. Bloomquist, *Marijuana* (Beverly Hills: Glencoe Press, The Macmillan Company, 1968), p. 186. © Copyright, Edward R. Bloomquist, 1968.
408. W.D.M. Paton and R.G. Pertwee, "The Actions of Cannabis in Man," in *Marijuana: Chemistry, Pharmacology, Metabolism and Clinical Effects*, ed. Raphael Mechoulam (New York: Academic Press, Inc., 1973), p. 316.
409. Dr. Hardin B. Jones, "What Marijuana Really Does," Selections from *Listen* volume 30 (Washington D.C.: Narcotics Education, Inc., n.d.).
410. Gabriel G. Nahas, *Marihuana: Deceptive Weed* (New York: Raven Press, 1973), p. 22.
411. Tharp, Paul, "Cannabis Conference: The Latest Word From Science," *The Village Voice*, February 9, 1976.
412. W.D.M. Paton and R.G. Pertwee, "The Actions of Cannabis in Man," in *Marijuana: Chemistry, Pharmacology, Metabolism and Clinical Effects*, ed. Raphael Mechoulam (New York: Academic Press, Inc., 1973), p. 298.
413. A. Michael Rossi and John O'Brien, "Memory and Time Estimation," in *The Use of Marihuana: A Psychological and Physiological Inquiry*, eds. Jack H. Mendelson, A. Michael Rossi and Roger E. Meyer (New York: Plenum Press, 1974), p. 90, citing L.D. Clark et al., "Behavioral effects of marihuana: experimental studies," *Arch. Gen. Psychiat.* 23 (1970): 193-198. Copyright 1970, American Medical Association.
414. A. Michael Rossi and John O'Brien, "Memory and Time Estimation," in *The Use Of Marihuana: A Psychological and Physiological Inquiry*, eds. Jack H. Mendelson, A. Michael Rossi and Roger E. Meyer (New York: Plenum Press, 1974), p. 99.
415. U.S., Congress, Senate, Committee on the Judiciary, *Marihuana-Hashish Epidemic and Its Impact on United States Security, Hearings Before The Subcommittee To Investigate The Administration Of The Internal Security Act And Other Internal Security Laws*. 93 Cong., 2d sess., 1974, pp. 21-22.
416. Harold Pascal, *The Marijuana Maze* (Canfield, Ohio: Alba House Communications, 1976), p. 64.
417. Thomas Weisman, *Drug Abuse And Drug Counseling* (New York: Jason Aronson, 1972), p. 140.
418. I.R. Rosengard, "Marijuana," *Science Digest*, April 1978, p. 74.
419. National Institute on Drug Abuse, *Marijuana and Health, 6th Annual Report to the U.S. Congress*, 1976, p. 23.
420. Madeline H. Engel, *The Drug Scene* (Rochelle Park, New Jersey: Hayden Book Company, Inc., 1974), p. 29.
421. Robert L. Dupont, "Marihuana: Our Next Step," February 4, 1977, (Washington, D.C.: Psychiatric Institute Foundation), pp. 19-20.
422. E.R. Bloomquist, *Marijuana* (Beverly Hills: Glencoe Press, The Macmillan Company, 1968), p. 197. © Copyright, Edward R. Bloomquist, 1968.
423. Weldon L. Witters and Patricia Jones-Witters, *Drugs & Sex* (New York: Macmillan Publishing Co. Inc., 1975), p. 142. Copyright © 1975, Weldon L. Witters and Patricia Jones-Witters.
424. Weldon L. Witters and Patricia Jones-Witters, *Drugs & Sex* (New York: Macmillan Publishing Co., Inc., 1975), p. 142, citing National Commission on Marihuana and Drug Abuse, *Second and Final Report* 22 March 1973 (Washington, D.C.: U.S. Government Printing Office), pages pp. 63-67. Copyright © 1975, Weldon L. Witters and Patricia Jones-Witters.
425. From THE DRUG SCENE by Donald B. Louria. Copyright © 1968 by Donald B. Louria. Used with permission of McGraw-Hill Book Company.
426. George K. Russell, *Marihuana Today* rev. ed. (New York: The Myrin Institute, Inc. for Adult Education, 1976), p. 20.
427. U.S., Congress, Senate, Committee On The Judiciary, *Marihuana-Hashish Epidemic And Its Impact On United States Security, Hearings Before The Subcommittee To Investigate The Administration Of The Internal Security Act And Other Internal Security Laws*. 93 Cong., 2d sess., 1974, p. 301.

428. Gabriel G. Nahas, *Keep Off the Grass* (New York: Reader's Digest Press, 1976), p. 85.
429. U.S., Congress, House, First Report by the Select Committee on Crime, *Marihuana*, H.R. 91-978, 91st Cong., 2d sess., 1970, p. 10.
430. I.R. Rosengard, "Marijuana," *Science Digest*, April 1978, p. 76.
431. U.S., Congress, Senate, Committee On The Judiciary, *Marihuana-Hashish Epidemic And Its Impact On United States Security, Hearings Before The Subcommittee To Investigate The Administration Of The Internal Security Act And Other Internal Security Laws*. 93 Cong., 2d sess., 1974, p. 33.
432. From THE MARIJUANA SMOKERS, by Erich Goode, © 1970 by Basic Books, Inc., Publishers, New York.
433. National Institute on Drug Abuse, *Marijuana and Health, 6th Annual Report to the U.S. Congress*, 1976, p. 24.
434. David H. Karney, "Flying with 'Mary Jane,'" *U.S. Army Aviation Digest*, March 1977.
435. Hardin B. Jones and Helen C. Jones, *Sensual Drugs* (Cambridge, England: Cambridge University Press, 1977), p. 284.
436. Hardin B. Jones and Helen C. Jones, *Sensual Drugs* (Cambridge, England: Cambridge University Press, 1977), p. 284, citing L.C. Kier, "A simple method for the determination of the smoking of marijuana," *Alcohol, Drugs, and Traffic Safety: Proceedings of the 6th International Conference on Alcohol, Drugs, and Traffic Safety, Toronto, September 8-13, 1974* (Toronto: Addiction Research Foundation of Ontario, 1975).
437. U.S., Congress, House, First Report by the Select Committee on Crime, *Marihuana*, H.R. 91-978, 91st Cong., 2d sess., 1970, p. 8.
438. Paul R. Robbins, *Marijuana: A Short Course* (Boston: Branden Press, Inc., 1976), p. 44, citing "Cannabis and Alcohol: Effects on simulated car driving and psychological tests. In Cannabis and its Derivatives," *Pharmacology and Experimental Psychology* (eds. W.D.M. Paton and J. Crown, n.d.).
439. The Official Report Of The National Commission on Marihuana And Drug Abuse, *Marihuana: A Signal Of Misunderstanding*, with a foreword from Raymond P. Shafer, Chairman (New York: The New American Library, Inc., 1972), p. 98.
440. U.S., Congress, House, First Report by the Select Committee on Crime, *Marihuana*, H.R. 91-978, 91st Cong., 2d sess., 1970, p. 10.
441. U.S. Department of Health, Education and Welfare, HEW NEWS, March 10, 1977.
442. Nils Bejerot, *Addiction and Society* (Springfield, Illinois Charles C. Thomas, 1970), p. 57. Courtesy of Charles C. Thomas, Publisher.
443. "Marijuana—Good Or Bad?" *Farmers' Almanac*, vol. 159, 1976.
444. L.E. Hollister, "Status Report on Clinical Pharmacology of Marijuana," *Marijuana: Chemistry, Pharmacology and Patterns of Social Use* (New York: Annals of the New York Academy of Sciences, vol. 191, 1971), pp. 132-142.
445. U.S., Congress, House, First Report by the Select Committee on Crime, *Marihuana*, H.R. 91-978, 91st Cong., 2d sess., 1970, p. 10.
446. Paul R. Robbins, *Marijuana: A Short Course* (Boston: Branden Press, Inc., 1976), p. 45, citing "Chronic marijuana use and psychosocial adaptation," *American Journal of Psychiatry* 130 (1973): 132-140. Copyright © 1973, the American Psychiatric Association. Reprinted by permission.
447. Weldon L. Witters and Patricia Jones-Witters, *Drugs & Sex* (New York: Macmillan Publishing Co., Inc., 1975), p. 142, citing, H. Moskowitz, "A Comparison of the effects of marihuana and alcohol in tissue function," *Current Research in Marihuana* (New York: Academic Press, 1972), Copyright © 1975, Weldon L. Witters and Patricia Jones-Witters.
448. Roy H. Hart, letter to Assemblyman Vincent Nicolosi, April 15, 1977.
449. E.R. Bloomquist, *Marijuana* (Beverly Hills: Glencoe Press, The Macmillan Company, 1968), p. 198. © Copyright, Edward R. Bloomquist, 1968.
450. Rena Hamelfarb, "Undeniable Evidence of Danger and Damage," in *Marijuana: Teenage Killer*, ed. Norman Hill (New York: Webster's Red Seal Publications, Inc., 1971), p. 67. Copyright © 1971 by Webster's Red Seal Publications, Inc.
451. U.S., Congress, House, First Report by the Select Committee on Crime, *Marihuana*, H.R. 91-978, 91st Cong., 2d sess., 1970, p. 10.
452. Harold Pascal, *The Marijuana Maze* (Canfield, Ohio: Alba House Communications, 1976), p. 22.
453. U.S., Congress, House, First Report by the Select Committee on Crime, *Marihuana*, H.R. 91-978, 91st Cong., 2d sess., 1970, p. 9.
454. Western Electric Company, *Drug Facts* (pamphlet).
455. Steve Letzler, "Problems Executives Must Anticipate With The Growth of MARIJUANA Smoking," *Executive Health* (P.O. Box 589, Rancho Santa Fe, California 92067), October, 1977.
456. U.S. Department of Health, Education and Welfare, HEW NEWS, March 10, 1977.
457. E.R. Bloomquist, *Marijuana* (Beverly Hills: Glencoe Press, The Macmillan Company, 1968), p. 81. © Copyright, Edward R. Bloomquist, 1968.
458. E.R. Bloomquist,*af25Marijuana* (Beverly Hills: Glencoe Press, The Macmillan Company, 1968), p. 12. © Copyright, Edward R. Bloomquist, 1968.
459. Dr. D. Harvey Powelson (as told to Ted Torkelson and Leon Cornforth), "Our Most Dangerous Drug," Selections from *Listen* (Washington, D.C.: Narcotics Education, Inc., n.d.).
460. "Riding high: Drugs harder to detect than drink," *Long Island Sunday Press*, 2 May 1976, sec. 5, p.1.
461. Jack D. Blaine et al., "Marihuana Smoking and Simulated Flying Performance," in *Pharmacology of Marihuana*, vol. 1., eds. M.C. Braude and S. Szara (New York: Raven Press, 1976), p. 446.
462. David H. Karney, "Flying With 'Mary Jane,'" *U.S. Army Aviation Digest*, March 1977.
463. David H. Karney, "Flying with 'Mary Jane,'" *U.S. Army Aviation Digest*, March 1977.
464. Roy H. Hart, letter to Assemblyman Vincent Nicolosi, April 15, 1977.
465. David H. Karney, "Flying With 'Mary Jane,'" *U.S. Army Aviation Digest*, March 1977.
466. David H. Karney, "Flying With 'Mary Jane,'" *U.S. Army Aviation Digest*, March 1977.
467. David H. Karney, "Flying With 'Mary Jane,'" *U.S. Army Aviation Digest*, March 1977.
468. David H. Karney, "Flying With 'Mary Jane,'" *U.S. Army Aviation Digest*, March 1977.
469. David H. Karney, "Flying With 'Mary Jane,'" *U.S. Army Aviation Digest*, March 1977.
470. E.R. Bloomquist, *Marijuana* (Beverly Hills: Glencoe Press, The Macmillan Company, 1968), p. 113. © Copyright, Edward R. Bloomquist, 1968.
471. U.S., Congress, Senate, Committee On The Judiciary, *Marihuana-Hashish Epidemic And Its Impact On United States Security, Hearings Before The Subcommittee To Investigate The Administration Of The Internal Security Act And Other Internal Security Laws. 93 Cong., 2d sess*, 1974, p. 298.
472. A.G. de Keyzer, "Cannabis: World-Wide Destroyer Of National Energy," in *Marijuana: Teenage Killer*, ed. Norman Hill (New York: Webster's Red Seal Publications, Inc., 1971), p. 156. Copyright © 1971 by Webster's Red Seal Publications, Inc.
473. Gabriel G. Nahas, *Marihuana: Deceptive Weed* (New York: Raven Press, 1973, p. 44.
474. U.S., Congress, Senate, Committee On The Judiciary, *Marihuana-Hashish Epidemic And Its Impact On United States Security, Hearings Before The Subcommittee To Investigate The Administration Of The Internal Security Act and Other Internal Security Laws, Part 2*. 94 Cong., 1st sess., 1975, pp. 431-432.
475. A.G. de Keyzer, "Cannabis: World-Wide Destroyer Of National Energy," in *Marijuana: Teenage Killer*, ed. Norman Hill (New York: Webster's Red Seal Publications, Inc., 1971), p. 156. Copyright © by Webster's Red Seal Publications, Inc.
476. From MARIJUANA AND YOUR CHILD by Jules Saltman. Copyright © 1970 by Jules Saltman. Used by permission of Grosset & Dunlap, Inc.
477. From MARIJUANA AND YOUR CHILD by Jules Saltman. Copyright © 1970 by Jules Saltman. Used by permission of

Grosset & Dunlap, Inc.
478. U.S., Congress, Senate, Committee On The Judiciary, *Marihuana-Hashish Epidemic And Its Impact On United States Security, Hearings Before The Subcommittee To Investigate The Administration Of The Internal Security Act And Other Internal Security Laws.* 93 Cong., 2d sess, 1974, p. 271.
479. *Journal of the American Medical Association* 210 (October 13, 1969): 299-302, cited by Dr. Roy H. Hart, in *A Psychiatrist Looks at Medicine* (Hicksville, N.Y.: Exposition Press, Inc., 1972), p. 35. Copyright 1969, American Medical Assoc.
480. Ronald Bruce, ed., *The Pot Report* (New York: Universal-Award House, Inc.; Award Books, 1971), p. 76.
481. "Train Crash Hearing Is Told Of Marijuana," *The New York Times,* 18 March 1977, p. A12. © 1977 by The New York Times Company. Reprinted by permission.
482. William S. Dalton, et al., "Effects of marijuana combined with secobarbital," *Clinical Pharmacology and Therapeutics* 18 (3): 298-304. © by the C.B. Mosby Company, St. Louis, Mo. U.S.A.
483. I.R. Rosengard, "Marijuana," *Science Digest,* April, 1978, p. 75.
484. Leo E. Hollister, "Human Pharmacology of Marihuana (Cannabis) in *Drug Dependence* eds. Robert T. Harris, William M. McIsaac, and Charles R. Schuster, Jr. (Austin, Texas: University of Texas Press, 1970), p. 75. Copyright 1970 by the University of Texas Press. All rights reserved.
485. W.D.M. Paton and R.G. Pertwee, "The Actions of Cannabis in Man," in *Marijuana: Chemistry, Pharmacology, Metabolism and Clinical Effects,* ed. Raphael Mechoulam (New York: Academic Press, Inc., 1973), p. 317.
486. C.A. Tassinari et al., "The Neuropsychiatric Syndrome of Delta-9-Tetrahydrocannabinol and Cannabis Intoxication in Naive Subjects: A Clinical and Polygraphic Study during Wakefulness and Sleep," in *Pharmacology of Marihuana,* vol. 1., eds. M.C. Braude and S. Szara (New York: Raven Press, 1976), pp. 370-371.
487. U.S., Congress, Senate, Committee On The Judiciary, *Marihuana-Hashish Epidemic And Its Impact On United States Security, Hearings Before The Subcommittee To Investigate The Administration Of The Internal Security Act And Other Internal Security Laws.* 93 Cong., 2d sess., 1974, p. 179.
488. Jack N. Mendelson, A. Michael Rossi, and Roger E. Meyer, eds., *Marihuana: A Psychological and Physiological Inquiry* (New York: Plenum Press, 1974), p. 2, citing R.E. Meyer et al., "Administration of marihuana to heavy and casual marihuana users," *A.J. Psychiat.* 128 (1971): 198-204. Copyright 1971, the American Psychiatric Association. Reprinted by permission.
489. Tharp, Paul, "Cannabis Conference: The Latest Word from Science," *The Village Voice,* February 9, 1976.
490. Gabriel G. Nahas, *Keep Off the Grass* (New York: Reader's Digest Press, 1976), pp. 64-65.
491. Paul R. Robbins, *Marijuana: A Short Course (Boston: Branden Press, Inc., 1976), p.44, citing "Marijuana, memory and perception,"* American Journal of Psychiatry 128 (1971): 194-197. Copyright 1971, the American Psychiatric Association. Reprinted by permission.
492. U.S., Congress, House, First Report by the Select Committee on Crime, *Marihuana,* H.R. 91-978, 91st Cong., 2d sess., 1970, p. 11.
493. W.D.M. Paton and R.G. Pertwee, "The Actions of Cannabis in Man," in *Marijuana: Chemistry, Pharmacology, Metabolism and Clinical Effects,* ed. Raphael Mechoulam (New York: Academic Press, Inc., 1973), p. 306.
494. Gurbaksh S. Chopra and Balwant S. Jandu, "Psychoclinical Effects Of Long-Term Marijuana Use in 275 Indian Chronic Users. A Comparative Assessment of Effects In Indian and USA Users," *Chronic Cannabis Use* (New York: Annals of the New York Academy of Sciences, vol. 282, 1976), p. 105.
495. Stanley F. Yolles, "The Psychiatrist Looks At Drug Abuse," in *Drug Abuse In Industry,* eds. Pasquale A. Carone and Leonard W. Krinsky (Springfield, Illinois: Charles C. Thomas, 1973), p. 71. Courtesy of Charles C. Thomas, Publisher.
496. Stanley F. Yolles, "The Psychiatrist Looks at Drug Abuse," in *Drug Abuse In Industry,* eds. Pasquale A. Carone And Leonard W. Krinsky (Springfield, Illinois: Charles C. Thomas, 1973, p. 72. Courtesy of Charles C. Thomas, Publisher.
497. E.R. Bloomquist, *Marijuana* (Beverly Hills: Glencoe Press, The Macmillan Company, 1968), pp. 72-73. © Copyright, Edward R. Bloomquist, 1968.
498. L.E. Hollister, "Status Report on Clinical Pharmacology of Marijuana," *Marijuana: Chemistry, Pharmacology, and Patterns of Social Use,* (New York: Annals of the New York Academy of Sciences, vol. 191, 1971), pp. 132-142.
499. Excerpt from "Marijuana: More Dangerous Than You Know," by Dr. Harvey Powelson, *The Reader's Digest,* December 1974.
500. Ian Campbell, "The Amotivational Syndrome And Cannabis Use With Emphasis On The Canadian Scene," *Chronic Cannabis Use* (New York: Annals of the New York Academy of Sciences, vol. 282, 1976, p. 34.
501. Ronald Bruce, ed., *The Pot Report* (New York: Universal-Award House, Inc.; Award Books, 1971), p. 73.
502. Paul R. Robbins, *Marijuana: A Short Course* (Boston: Branden Press, Inc., 1976), p. 40.
503. Hardin B. Jones, "Problems Executives Must Anticipate With The Growth of Marijuana Smoking," *Executive Health* (P.O. Box 589 Rancho Santa Fe, California 92067), October, 1977.
504. From THE DRUG SCENE by Donald B. Louria. Copyright © 1968 by Donald B. Louria. Used with permission of McGraw-Hill Book Company.
505. *Journal of the American Medical Association* 215 (March 22, 1971): 1988, cited by Dr. Roy H. Hart, *A Psychiatrist Looks At Medicine* (Hicksville, N.Y.: Exposition Press, Inc., 1972), p. 35. Copyright © 1971, American Medical Association.
506. A.M.G. Campbell et al., "Cerebral Atrophy in Young Cannabis Smokers," *Lancet,* 7736 (1971): 1219-1224.
507. Hardin B. Jones and Helen C. Jones, *Sensual Drugs* (Cambridge, England: Cambridge University Press, 1977), p. 251.
508. The Official Report Of The National Commission on Marihuana And Drug Abuse, *Marihuana: A Signal Of Misunderstanding,* with a foreword from Raymond P. Shafer, Chairman (New York: The New American Library, Inc., 1972), p. 75.
509. Doris H. Milman, Letters, *The New York Times,* 2 June 1977. © 1977 by The New York Times Company. Reprinted by permission.
510. The Official Report Of The National Commission on Marihuana And Drug Abuse, *Marihuana: A Signal of Misunderstanding,* with a foreword from Raymond P. Shafer, Chairman (New York: The New American Library, Inc., 1972), p. 108.
511. Franz Winkler, *About Marijuana* (New York: The Myrin Institute, Inc., 1970).
512. "New Evidence on Marijuana," *The Phyllis Schlafly Report,* vol. 8, no. 10, section 1, May 1975, p. 1.
513. Franz Winkler, *About Marijuana* (New York: The Myrin Institute, Inc., 1970).
514. U.S., Congress, Senate, Committee On The Judiciary, *Marihuana-Hashish Epidemic And Its Impact On United States Security, Hearings Before The Subcommittee To Investigate The Administration Of The Internal Security Act And Other Internal Security Laws,* Introduction by Senator James O. Eastland. 93 Cong., 2d sess., 1974, p. XI.
515. Kenneth McKenna, "Marijuana Kills," in *Marijuana: Teenage Killer,* ed. Norman Hill (New York: Webster's Red Seal Publications, Inc., 1971), p. 40. Copyright © 1971 by Webster's Red Seal Publications, Inc.
516. E.R. Bloomquist, *Marijuana* (Beverly Hills: Glencoe Press, The Macmillan Company, 1968), p. 186. © Copyright, Edward R. Bloomquist, 1968.
517. Stanley F. Yolles, "Facts and Fallacies on Student Use of Drugs," Geigy Medical Symposium, 9 October 1969, Kansas City, Missouri, p. 25.
518. U.S., Congress, House, First Report by the Select Committee on Crime, *Marihuana,* H.R. 91-978, 91st Cong., 2d sess., 1970, p. 12.
519. From MARIJUANA AND YOUR CHILD by Jules Saltman. Copyright © 1970 by Jules Saltman. Used by permission of Grosset & Dunlap, Inc.
520. From MARIJUANA AND YOUR CHILD by Jules Saltman. Copyright © 1970 by Jules Saltman. Used by permission of Grosset & Dunlap, Inc.

521. Thomas Weisman, *Drug Abuse and Drug Counseling* (New York: Jason Aronson, 1972), p. 149.
522. Franz Winkler, *About Marijuana* (New York: The Myrin Institute, Inc., 1970).
523. From MARIJUANA AND YOUR CHILD by Jules Saltman. Copyright © 1970 by Jules Saltman. Used by permission of Grosset & Dunlap, Inc.
524. From THE MARIJUANA SMOKERS, by Erich Goode, © 1970 by Basic Books, Inc., Publishers, New York.
525. U.S., Congress, Senate, Committee On The Judiciary, *Marihuana-Hashish Epidemic And Its Impact On United States Security, Hearings Before The Subcommittee To Investigate The Administration Of The Internal Security Act And Other Internal Security Laws.* 93 Cong., 2d sess., 1974, p. 152.
526. Reprinted with the permission of the American Medical Association, from HEALTH ASPECTS OF MARIHUANA USE, a report of the AMA Council on Scientific Affairs, December 6, 1977.
527. National Institute on Drug Abuse, *Marijuana and Health, 6th Annual Report to the U.S. Congress*, 1976, p. 21.
528. E.R. Bloomquist, *Marijuana* (Beverly Hills: Glencoe Press, The Macmillan Company, 1968), p. 187. © Copyright, Edward R. Bloomquist, 1968.
529. Paul R. Robbins, *Marijuana: A Short Course* (Boston: Branden Press, Inc., 1976), p. 47, citing "A social psychology of marijuana use: Longitudinal studies of high school and college youth," *Journal of Personality and Social Psychology* 26 (1973):15.
530. Copyright © 1971, Los Angeles Times, Reprinted with permission.
531. U.S., Congress, Senate, Committee On The Judiciary, *Marihuana-Hashish Epidemic And Its Impact On United States Security, Hearings Before The Subcommittee To Investigate The Administration Of The Internal Security Act And Other Internal Seccurity Laws.* 93 Cong., 2d sess., 1974, p. 184.
532. U.S., Congress, Senate, Committee On The Judiciary, *Marihuana-Hashish Epidemic And Its Impact On United States Security, Hearings Before The Subcommittee To Investigate The Administration Of The Internal Security Act And Other Internal Security Laws.* 93 Cong., 2d sess., 1974, p. 258.
533. "Drop In Heroin Addiction Tied To Legal Marijuana," *The New York Times*, 14 February 1972, p. 24C. © 1972 by The New York Times Company. Reprinted by permission.
534. Harold Pasal, *The Marijuana Maze* (Canfield, Ohio: Alba House Communications, 1976), pp. 73-74, citing "Adverse Reactions to Marijuana," *New England Journal of Medicine* 282 (1970): 997-1000. Reprinted By Permission From The New England Journal Of Medicine.
535. Paul R. Robbins, *Marijuana: A Short Course* (Boston: Branden Press, Inc., 1976), p. 43, citing "A Comment on the 'Amotivational Syndrome' in marijuana smokers," *American Journal of Psychiatry* 130 (1973): 1319-1322. Copyright 1973, the American Psychiatric Association. Reprinted by permission.
536. A.M.G. Campbell et al., "Cerebral Atrophy in Young Cannabis Smokers," *Lancet* 7736 (1971): 1219-1224.
537. Dr. Hardin B. Jones, "Sex, Marijuana, and the Unborn Child," Selections from *Listen* volume 30 (Washington D.C.: Narcotics Education, Inc., n.d.).
538. From MARIJUANA AND YOUR CHILD by Jules Saltman. Copyright © 1970 by Jules Saltman. Used by permission of Grosset & Dunlap, Inc.
539. E.R. Bloomquist, *Marijuana* (Beverly Hills: Glencoe Press, The Macmillan Company, 1968), pp. 92-93. © Copyright, Edward R. Bloomquist, 1968.
540. Jess R. Lord, *Marijuana and Personality Change* (Lexington, Massachusetts: D.C. Heath and Company: Lexington Books, 1971), p. 102.
541. U.S., Congress, Senate, Committee On The Judiciary, *Marihuana-Hashish Epidemic And Its Impact On United States Security, Hearings Before The Subcommittee To Investigate The Administration Of The Internal Security Act and Other Internal Security Laws.* 93 Cong., 2d sess., 1974, pp. 192-193.
542. The Official Report of the National Commission on Marihuana And Drug Abuse, *Marihuana: A Signal of Misunderstanding*, with a foreword from Raymond P. Shafer, Chairman (New York: The New American Library, Inc., 1972), pp. 85-86.
543. U.S., Congress, House, First Report by the Select Committee on Crime, *Marihuana*, H.R. 91-978, 91st Cong., 2d sess., 1970, p. 7.
544. Dr. D. Harvey Powelson (as told to Ted Torkelson and Leon Cornforth), "Our Most Dangerous Drug," Selections from *Listen* (Washington, D.C.: Narcotics Education, Inc., n.d.).
545. Jack H. Mendelson et al., "The Effects of Marihuana Use on Human Operant Behavior: Individual Data," in *Pharmacology of Marihuana*, vol. 2, eds. M.C. Braude and S. Szara (New York: Raven Press, 1976), p. 643.
546. Stuart L. Hills, "Marijuana, Morality, and The Law," *Crime And Delinquency*, January 1970, p. 61.
547. Sidney Cohen, in *Drugs: For & Against*, Harold Hart, ed. (New York: Hart Publishing Company, Inc., 1970), p. 14.
548. The Official Report Of The National Commission on Marihuana And Drug Abuse, *Marihuana: A Signal Of Misunderstanding*, with a foreword from Raymond P. Shafer, Chairman (New York: The New American Library, Inc., 1972), p. 107.
549. Erich Goode, "Sex and Marijuana," *Sexual Behavior*, May 1972, p. 49.
550. U.S., Congress, Senate, Committee On The Judiciary, *Marihuana-Hashish Epidemic And Its Impact On United States Security, Hearings Before The Subcommittee To Investigate The Administration Of The Internal Security Act And Other Internal Security Laws.* 93 Cong., 2d sess. 1974, p. 235.
551. Jess R. Lord, *Marijuana and Personality Change* (Lexington, Massachusetts: D.C. Heath and Company, Lexington Books, 1971), p. 100.
552. National Institute on Drug Abuse, *Marijuana and Health, 6th Annual Report to the U.S. Congress*, 1976, pp. 13-14.
553. Paul R. Robbins, *Marijuana: A Short Course* (Boston: Branden Press, 1976), p. 27, citing "Cannabis: Review of behavioral effects in animals," *Psychological Bulletin*, 81 (1974): 401-417.
554. L.E. Hollister, "Status Report on Clinical Pharmacology of Marijuana," *Marijuana: Chemistry, Pharmacology and Patterns of Social Use* (New York: Annals of the New York Academy of Sciences, vol. 191, 1971), pp. 132-142.
555. Franz Winkler, *About Marijuana* (New York: The Myrin Institute, Inc., 1970).
556. Ronald Bruce, ed., *The Pot Report* (New York: Universal-Award House, Inc.; Award Books, 1971), pp. 69-70, citing C.T. Tart, "Marijuana Intoxication, common experiences," *Nature* 222 (1970): 701-704.
557. Tharp, Paul, "Cannabis Conference: The Latest Word From Science," *The Village Voice*, February 9, 1976.
558. Madeline H. Engel, *The Drug Scene*, (Rochelle Park, New Jersey: Hayden Book Company, Inc., 1974), p. 30.
559. Hardin B. Jones, "What the Practicing Physician Should Know About Marijuana," *Private Practice*, January 1976, pp. 34-40.
560. Erich Goode, "Sex and Marijuana," *Sexual Behavior*, May 1972, p. 47.
561. E.R. Bloomquist, *Marijuana* (Beverly Hills: Glencoe Press, The Macmillan Company, 1968), p. 184. © Copyright, Edward R. Bloomquist, 1968.
562. Dr. Hardin B. Jones, "What Marijuana Really Does," Selections from *Listen* volume 30 (Washington, D.C.: Narcotics Education, Inc., n.d.).
563. A Michael Rossi et al., "Mood States," in *The Use Of Marihuana: A Psychological and Physiological Inquiry*, eds. Jack H. Mendelson, A. Michael Rossi and Roger E. Meyer (New York: Plenum Press, 1974), p. 127, citing E.S. Robbins et al., "College student drug use," *Am. J. Psychiat.* 126 (1970): 1743-1751. Copyright 1970, the American Psychiatric Association. Reprinted by permission.
564. Ronald Bruce, ed., *The Pot Report* (New York: Universal-Award House, Inc.; Award Books, 1971), p. 76.
565. Excerpt from THE SEEKERS by Jess Stearn. Copyright © 1968, 1969 by Jess Stearn. Used by permission of Doubleday & Company, Inc.

566. Nils Bejerot, *Addiction: An Artificially Induced Drive* (Springfield, Illinois: Charles C. Thomas, 1972), p. 23. Courtesy of Charles C. Thomas, Publisher.
567. From THE DRUG SCENE by Donald B. Louria. Copyright © 1968 by Donald B. Louria. Used with permission of McGraw-Hill Book Company.
568. Roy H. Hart, "A Psychiatric Classification of Cannabis Intoxication," *J. Amer. Acad. Psychiat. Neurol.* vol. 1, no. 4 (1976): 88-89.
569. Dr. Hardin B. Jones, "What Marijuana Really Does," Selections from *Listen*, volume 30 (Washington, D.C.: Narcotics Education Inc. n.d.).
570. "The Perils of 'Pot' Start Showing Up," *U.S. News & World Report*, June 10, 1974, p. 58.
571. National Institute on Drug Abuse, *Marijuana and Health, 6th Annual Report to the U.S. Congress*, 1976, p. 13.
572. E.R. Bloomquist, *Marijuana* (Beverly Hills: Glencoe Press, The Macmillan Company, 1968), p. 93. © Copyright, Edward R. Bloomquist, 1968.
573. Excerpt from "Marijuana: More Dangerous Than You Know" by Dr. Harvey Powelson, *The Readers Digest*, December 1974.
574. E.R. Bloomquist, *Marijuana* (Beverly Hills: Glencoe Press, The Macmillan Company, 1968), p. 169. © Copyright, Edward R. Bloomquist, 1968.
575. I.R. Rosengard, "Marijuana," *Science Digest*, April 1978, p. 71.
576. Reprinted with the permission of the American Medical Association, from HEALTH ASPECTS OF MARIHUANA USE, a report of the AMA Council on Scientific Affairs, December 6, 1977.
577. W.D.M. Paton and R.G. Pertwee, "The Actions of Cannabis in Man," in *Marijuana: Chemistry, Pharmacology, Metabolism and Clinical Effects*, ed. Raphael Mechoulam (New York: Academic Press, Inc., 1973), p. 312.
578. Nils Bejerot, *Addiction: An Artificially Induced Drive* (Springfield, Illinois: Charles C. Thomas, 1972), p. 23, citing H. Edery, "Cannabis—Pharmacology," International Symposium on Drug Addiction, Jerusalem, 1970. Courtesy of Charles C. Thomas, Publisher.
579. Reprinted with the permission of the American Medical Association, from HEALTH ASPECTS OF MARIHUANA USE, a report of the AMA Council on Scientific Affairs, December 6, 1977.
580. Jess R. Lord, *Marijuana and Personality Change* (Lexington, Massachusetts: D.C. Heath and Company. Lexington Books, 1971), p. 100.
581. Dr. Hardin B. Jones, "What Marijuana Really Does," Selections from *Listen* volume 30 (Washington, D.C.: Narcotics Education, Inc., n.d.).
582. Gabriel G. Nahas, *Marihuana: Deceptive Weed* (New York: Raven Press, 1973), p. 236, citing H.S. Kaplan, "Psychosis Associated with marijuana," *N.Y. State J. Med.* 71 (1971): 433-435.
583. U.S., Congress, House, First Report by the Select Committee on Crime, *Marihuana*, H.R. 91-978, 91st Cong., 2d sess., 1970, p. 9.
584. Hardin B. Jones, "What the Practicing Physician Should Know About Marijuana," *Private Practice*, January 1976, pp. 34-40.
585. Jess R. Lord, *Marijuana and Personality Change* (Lexington, Massachusetts: D.C. Heath and Company, Lexington Books, 1971), pp. 100-101.
586. Kenneth McKenna, "Marijuana Kills," in *Marijuana: Teenage Killer*, ed. Norman Hill (New York: Webster's Red Seal Publications, Inc., 1971), p. 20. Copyright © 1971 by Webster's Red Seal Publications, Inc.
587. Gurbakhsh S. Chopra and Balwant S. Jandu, "Psycho-clinical Effects Of Long-Term Marijuana Use in 275 Indian Chronic Users. A Comparative Assessment of Effects In Indian and USA Users," *Chronic Cannabis Use* (New York: Annals of the New York Academy of Sciences, vol. 282, 1976), p. 101.
588. Roy H. Hart, "A Psychiatric Classification of Cannabis Intoxication," *J. Amer. Acad. Psychiat. Neurol. vol. 1, no. 4 (1976): 94.*
589. E.R. Bloomquist, *Marijuana* (Beverly Hills: Glencoe Press, The Macmillan Company, 1968), pp. 200-201. © Copyright, Edward R. Bloomquist, 1968.
590. I.R. Rosengard, "Marijuana," *Science Digest*, May 1978, p. 69.
591. Thomas Weisman, *Drug Abuse and Drug Counseling* (New York: Jason Aronson, 1972), p. 143.
592. Doris H. Milman, "The role of marihuana in patterns of drug abuse by adolescents," *The Journal of Pediatrics* vol. 74, no. 2. (February 1969): 283-290.
593. Kenneth McKenna, "Marijuana Kills," in *Marijuana: Teenage Killer*, ed. Norman Hill (New York: Webster's Red Seal Publications, Inc., 1971), p. 20. Copyright © by Webster's Red Seal Publications, Inc.
594. Martin H. Keeler, "Adverse Reaction to Marijuana," in *Drug Awareness: Key documents on LSD, marijuana, and the drug culture*, eds. Richard E. Horman and Allan M. Fox (New York: Avon Books, 1970), p. 399.
595. Excerpt from THE SEEKERS by Jess Stearn. Copyright © 1968, 1969 by Jess Stearn. Used by permission of Doubleday & Company, Inc.
596. I.R. Rosengard, "Marijuana," *Science Digest*, April 1978, p. 72.
597. I.R. Rosengard, "Marijuana," *Science Digest*, May 1978, p. 69.
598. W.D.M. Paton and R.G. Pertwee, "The Actions of Cannabis in Man," in *Marijuana: Chemistry, Pharmacology, Metabolism and Clinical Effects*, ed. Raphael Mechoulam (New York: Academic Press, Inc., 1973), p. 312, citing M.H. Keeler, *Amer. J. Psychiat.* 124 (1967): 674. Copyright 1967, the American Psychiatric Association. Reprinted by permission; and J.A. Talbott and J.W. Teague, *J.Amer.Med.Assoc.* 210 (1969): 299.
599. E.R. Bloomquist, *Marijuana* (Beverly Hills: Glencoe Press, The Macmillan Company, 1968), p. 73. © Copyright, Edward R. Bloomquist, 1968.
600. Leo E. Hollister, "Human Pharmacology of Marihuana (Cannabis)," in *Drug Dependence* eds. Robert T. Harris, William M. McIsaac, and Charles R. Schuster, Jr. (Austin, Texas: University of Texas Press, 1970), p. 77. Copyright © 1970 by the University of Texas Press. All rights reserved.
601. Hardin B. Jones and Helen C. Jones, *Sensual Drugs* (Cambridge, England: Cambridge University Press, 1977), p. 221-222, citing F.T. Melges et al., "Temporal disorganization and delusional-like ideation: Processes induced by hashish and alcohol," *Arch. Gen. Psychiatry* 30 (1974): 855-861.
602. Jess R. Lord, *Marijuana and Personality Change* (Lexington, Massachusetts: D.C. Heath and Company, Lexington Books, 1971), p. 100.
603. U.S., Congress, House, First Report by the Select Committee on Crime, *Marihuana*, H.R. 91-978, 91st Cong., 2d sess., 1970, p. 6.
604. National Institute on Drug Abuse, *Marijuana and Health, 6th Annual Report to the U.S. Congress*, 1976, p. 21.
605. Gabriel G. Nahas, *Keep Off the Grass* (New York: Reader's Digest Press, 1976), p. 150.
606. U.S., Congress, Senate, Committee On The Judiciary, *Marihuana-Hashish Epidemic And Its Impact On United States Security, Hearings Before The Subcommittee To Investigate The Administration Of The Internal Security Act And Other Internal Security Laws*. 93 Cong., 2d sess. 1974, p. 192.
607. From THE MARIJUANA SMOKERS, by Erich Goode, © 1970 by Basic Books, Inc., Publishers, New York.
608. Thomas Weisman,*af17Drug Abuse and Drug Counseling* (New York: Jason Aronson, 1972), p. 143.
609. Alexander R.K. Mitchell, *Drugs: The Parent's Dilemma* (London, England: Priory Press Limited, 1972), p. 44.
610. Max Rafferty, in *Drugs: For & Against*, Harold Hart, ed. (New York: Hart Publishing Company, Inc., 1970), p. 38.
611. From MARIJUANA AND YOUR CHILD by Jules Saltman. Copyright © 1970 by Jules Saltman. Used by permission of Grosset & Dunlap, Inc.
612. From THE DRUG SCENE by Donald B. Louria. Copyright © 1968 by Donald B. Louria. Used with permission of McGraw-Hill Book Company.

613. I.R. Rosengard, "Marijuana," *Science Digest*, May 1978, p. 69.
614. I.R. Rosengard, "Marijuana," *Science Digest*, May 1978, p. 69.
615. Roy H. Hart, "A Psychiatric Classification of Cannabis Intoxication," *J. Amer. Acad. Psychiat. Neurol.* vol. 1, no. 4 (1976): 91-92.
616. I.R. Rosengard, "Marijuana," *Science Digest*, April 1978, p. 71.
617. Excerpt from THE SEEKERS by Jess Stearn. Copyright © 1968, 1969 by Jess Stearn. Used by permission of Doubleday & Company, Inc.
618. Alexander R.K. Mitchell, *Drugs: The Parent's Dilemma* (London, England: Priory Press Limited, 1972), p. 45.
619. From THE DRUG SCENE by Donald B. Louria. Copyright 1968 by Donald B. Louria. Used with permission of McGraw-Hill Book Company.
620. W.D.M. Paton and R.G. Pertwee, "The Actions of Cannabis in Man," in *Marijuana: Chemistry, Pharmacology, Metabolism and Clinical Effects*, ed. Raphael Mechoulam (New York: Academic Press, Inc., 1973), p. 311.
621. George K. Russell, *Marihuana Today* rev. ed. (New York: The Myrin Institute Inc. for Adult Education, 1976), p. 17, citing H. Isbell et al., "Effects of Delta-9-Tetrahydrocannabinol in Man," *Psychopharmacologia* 14 (1967): 115-123.
622. W.D.M. Paton and R.G. Pertwee, "The Actions of Cannabis in Man," in *Marijuana: Chemistry, Pharmacology, Metabolism and Clinical Effects*, ed. Raphael Mechoulam (New York: Academic Press, Inc., 1973), p. 312, citing I.C. Chopra and R.W. Chopra, *Bull. Narcotics* 9 (1957): 4.
623. Gabriel G. Nahas, *Marihuana: Deceptive Weed* (New York: Raven Press, 1973), p. 242, citing D.J. Spencer, "Cannabis-Induced Psychosis," *W. Indian Med. J.* 19 (1970): 228-230.
624. Gabriel G. Nahas, *Marihuana: Deceptive Weed* (New York: Raven Press, 1973), p. 237.
625. Harold Pascal, *The Marijuana Maze* (Canfield, Ohio: Alba House Communications, 1976), p. 71, citing "Cannabis Induced Psychosis," *West Indian Medical Journal* 19 (1970): 228-230.
626. National Institute on Drug Abuse, *Marijuana and Health, 6th Annual Report to the U.S. Congress*, 1976, p. 22.
627. Gabriel G. Nahas, *Marihuana: Deceptive Weed* (New York: Raven Press, 1973), p. 237.
628. I.R. Rosengard, "Marijuana," *Science Digest*, May 1978, p. 69.
629. I.R. Rosengard, "Marijuana," *Science Digest*, May 1978, p. 68.
630. Rena Hamelfarb, "Undeniable Evidence of Danger and Damage," in *Marijuana: Teenage Killer*, ed. Norman Hill (New York: Webster's Red Seal Publications, Inc., 1971), p. 69. Copyright © 1971 by Webster's Red Seal Publications, Inc.
631. I.R. Rosengard, "Marijuana," *Science Digest*, April 1978, p. 72.
632. Ronald Bruce, ed., *The Pot Report* (New York, Universal-Award House, Inc.; Award Books, 1971), p. 86, citing S.M. Mirin et al., "Casual vs. heavy use of marijuana, a redefinition of the marijuana problem," paper presented to American Psychiatric Association Meeting, May 1970.
633. U.S., Congress, House, First Report by the Select Committee on Crime, *Marihuana*, H.R. 91-978, 91st Cong., 2d sess., 1970, p. 112.
634. "The Perils of 'Pot' Start Showing Up," *U.S. NEWS & WORLD REPORT*, June 10, 1974, p. 58.
635. Excerpt from THE SEEKERS by Jess Stearn. Copyright © 1968, 1969 by Jess Stearn. Used by permission of Doubleday & Company, Inc.
636. The Official Report Of The National Commission on Marihuana And Drug Abuse, *Marihuana: A Signal Of Misunderstanding*, with a foreword from Raymond P. Shafer, Chairman (New York: The New American Library, Inc., 1972), p. 81.
637. Gabriel G. Nahas, "Medical Aspects of Marihuana Use," Testimony before the U.S. House of Representatives Select Committee on Narcotics Abuse, March 16, 1977, p. 18.
638. John Kaplan *Marijuana—The New Prohibition* (New York: Thomas Y. Crowell Company, 1970; Apollo Edition, 1975), pp. 161-162, citing David P. Ausubel, *Drug Addiction*.
639. From THE MARIJUANA SMOKERS, by Erich Goode, © 1970 by Basic Books, Inc., Publishers, New York.
640. The New York State Office of Drug Abuse Services.
641. U.S., Congress, Senate, Committee On The Judiciary, *Marihuana-Hashish Epidemic And Its Impact On United States Security, Hearings Before The Subcommittee To Investigate The Administration Of The Internal Security Act And Other Internal Security Laws*. 93 Cong., 2d sess., 1974, p. 178.
642. The Official Report Of The National Commission on Marihuana And Drug Abuse, *Marihuana: A Signal Of Misunderstanding*, with a foreword from Raymond P. Shafer, Chairman (New York: The New American Library, Inc., 1972), p. 81.
643. Rena Hamelfarb, "Undeniable Evidence of Danger and Damage," in *Marijuana: Teenage Killer*, ed. Norman Hill (New York: Webster's Red Seal Publications, Inc., 1971), p. 60. Copyright 1971 by Webster's Red Seal Publications, Inc.
644. Roy H. Hart, "A Psychiatric Classification of Cannabis Intoxication," *J. Amer. Acad. Psychiat. Neurol.* vol. 1, no. 4 (1976): 94.
645. From MARIJUANA AND YOUR CHILD by Jules Saltman. Copyright © 1970 by Jules Saltman. Used by permission of Grosset & Dunlap, Inc.
646. U.S., Congress, Senate, Committee On The Judiciary, *Marihuana-Hashish Epidemic And Its Impact On United States Security, Hearings Before The Subcommittee To Investigate The Administration Of The Internal Security Act And Other Internal Security Laws*. 93 Cong., 2d sess., 1974, p. 80.
647. U.S., Congress, Senate, Committee On The Judiciary, *Marihuana-Hashish Epidemic And Its Impact On United States Security, Herings Before The Subcommittee To Investigate The Administration Of The Internal Security Act And Other Internal Security Laws*, Introduction by Senator James O. Eastland. 93 Cong., 2d sess., 1974, p. XVI.
648. Paul R. Robbins, *Marijuana: A Short Course* (Boston: Branden Press, 1976), p. 28, citing "The subjective dimensions of the drug experience," *Journal of Psychedelic Drugs* 5 (1972): 37-44.
649. I.R. Rosengard, "Marijuana," *Science Digest*, May 1978, p. 68.
650. Gabriel G. Nahas, "Medical Aspects of Marihuana Use," Testimony before the U.S. House of Representatives Select Committee on Narcotics Abuse, March 16, 1977, pp. 16-17.
651. Gordon T. Pryor, "Acute and Subacute Behavioral and Pharmacological Interactions of delta-9-Tetrahydrocannabinol with Other Drugs," in *Pharmacology of Marijuana*, vol. 2., eds. M.C. Braude and S. Szara (New York: Raven Press, 1976), p. 553.
652. Excerpt from THE SEEKERS by Jess Stearn. Copyright © 1968, 1969 by Jess Stearn. Used by permission of Doubleday & Company, Inc.
653. Dr. D. Harvey Powelson (as told to Ted Torkelson and Leon Cornforth), "Our Most Dangerous Drug," Selections from *Listen* (Washington, D.C.: Narcotics Education, Inc., n.d.).
654. From MARIJUANA AND YOUR CHILD by Jules Saltman. Copyright © 1970 by Jules Saltman. Used by permission of Grosset & Dunlap, Inc.
655. Gabriel G. Nahas, "Is Marijuana Really All That Bad," Selections from *Listen* (Washington, D.C.: Narcotics Education, Inc., 1977).
656. Kenneth McKenna, "Marijuana Kills," in *Marijuana: Teenage Killer*, ed. Norman Hill (New York: Webster's Red Seal Publications, Inc., 1971), p. 32. Copyright © 1971 by Webster's Red Seal Publications, Inc.
657. Kenneth McKenna, "Marijuana Kills," in *Marijuana: Teenage Killer*, ed. Norman Hill (New York: Webster's Red Seal Publications, Inc., 1971), p. 32. Copyright 1971 by Webster's Red Seal Publications, Inc.
658. Anne Kaufman, "Seducer of the Young," in *Marijuana: Teenage Killer*, ed. Norman Hill (New York: Webster's Red Seal Publications, Inc., 1971), p. 97. Copyright © 1971 by Webster's Red Seal Publications, Inc.
659. Weldon L. Witters and Patricia Jones-Witters, *Drugs & Sex* (New York: Macmillan Publishing Co. Inc., 1975), p. 143, citing J.E. Manno et al., "Comparative effects of smoking marihuana or placebo on human motor and mental

performance," *Clinical Pharmacol. Ther.* 11(1970): 808-815. Copyright © 1975, Weldon L. Witters and Patricia Jones Witters.
660. Allen Geller and Maxwell Boas, *The Drug Beat* (Chicago: Cowles Book Company, Inc., 1969), p. 89.
661. Marvin Moser, "First Report: Scarsdale Drug Abuse Committee," 20 November 1969.
662. Excerpt from THE SEEKERS by Jess Stearn. Copyright © 1968, 1969 by Jess Stearn. Used by permission of Doubleday & Company, Inc.
663. Edward Bloomquist, in *Drugs: For & Against*, Harold Hart, ed. (New York: Hart Publishing Company, Inc., 1970), p. 164, citing *Psychology Today*, May 1970, p. 52.
664. U.S., Congress, Senate, Committee On The Judiciary, *Marihuana-Hashish Epidemic And Its Impact On United States Security, Hearings Before The Subcommittee To Investigate The Administration Of The Internal Security Act And Other Internal Security Laws.* 93 Cong., 2d sess., 1974, p. 29.
665. U.S., Congress, House, First Report by the Select Committee on Crime, *Marihuana*, H.R. 91-978, 91st Cong., 2d sess., 1970, p. 58.
666. Daniel Glasser, James Inciardi, and Dean V. Babst, "Later Heroin Use by Marijuana-Using, Heroin-Using, and Non-Drug-Using Adolescent Offenders in New York City," *NACC Reprints*, vol. 3, no. 4 (New York State: Narcotic Addiction Control Commission, n.d.), pp. 1-5.
667. Allen Geller and Maxwell Boas, *The Drug Beat* (Chicago: Cowles Book Company, Inc., 1969), pp. 92-93.
668. U.S., Congress, Senate, Committee On The Judiciary, *Marihuana-Hashish Epidemic And Its Impact On United States Security, Hearings Before The Subcommittee To Investigate The Administration Of The Internal Security Act And Other Internal Security Laws.* 93 Cong., 2d sess., 1974, p. 38.
669. U.S., Congress, House, First Report by the Select Committee on Crime, *Marihuana*, H.R. 91-978, 91st Cong., 2d sess., 1970, pp. 58-59.
670. Dr. Hardin B. Jones, "What Marijuana Really Does," Selections from *Listen* volume 30 (Washington, D.C.: Narcotics Education, Inc., n.d.).
671. U.S., Congress, Senate, Committee On The Judiciary *Marihuana-Hashish Epidemic And Its Impact On United States Security, Hearings Before The Subcommittee To Investigate The Administration Of The Internal Security Act And Other Internal Security Laws.* 93 Cong., 2d sess., 1974, p. 260.
672. The Official Report Of The National Commission on Marihuana And Drug Abuse, *Marihuana: A Signal Of Misunderstanding*, with a foreword from Raymond P. Shafer, Chairman (New York: The New American Library, Inc., 1972), p. 54.
673. The Official Report Of The National Commission on Marihuana And Drug Abuse, *Marihuana: A Signal Of Misunderstanding*, with a foreword from Raymond P. Shafer, Chairman (New York: The New American Library, Inc., 1972), p. 101.
674. U.S., Congress, House, First Report by the Select Committee on Crime, *Marihuana*, H.R. 91-978, 91st Cong., 2d sess., 1970, p. 33.
675. Dr. Hardin B. Jones, "What Marijuana Really Does," Selections from *Listen* volume 30 (Washington, D.C.: Narcotics Education, Inc., n.d.).
676. Gabriel G. Nahas, "Is Marijuana Really All That Bad," Selections from *Listen* (Washington, D.C.: Narcotics Education, Inc., 1977).
677. Nils Bejerot, *Addiction: An Artificially Induced Drive* (Springfield, Illinois: Charles C. Thomas, 1972), p. 22. Courtesy of Charles C. Thomas, Publisher.
678. Alan Brown and Arthur Stickgold, "Self-Diagnosed Marijuana Flashbacks," *Clinical Research* 22(3): 316A (1974).
679. Excerpt from "Marijuana: More Dangerous Than You Know," by Dr. Harvey Powelson, *The Reader's Digest*, December 1974.
680. E.R. Bloomquist, *Marijuana* (Beverly Hills: Glencoe Press, The Macmillan Company, 1968), p. 201. © Copyright, Edward R. Bloomquist, 1968.
681. Gabriel G. Nahas, *Marihuana: Deceptive Weed* (New York: Raven Press, 1973), p. 240.
682. C.A. Tassinari et al., "The Neuropsychiatric Syndrome of delta-9-Tetrahydrocannabinol and Cannabis Intoxication in Naive Subjects: A Clinical and Polygraphic Study during Wakefulness and Sleep," in *Pharmacology of Marihuana*, vol. 1, eds. M.C. Braude and S. Szara (New York: Raven Press, 1976), p. 361.
683. W.D.M. Paton, R.G. Pertwee, and Elizabeth Tylden, "Clinical Aspects of Cannabis Action," in *Marijuana: Chemistry, Pharmacology, Metabolism and Clinical Effects*, ed. Raphael Mechoulam (New York: Academic Press, Inc., 1973), p. 342, citing M.H. Keeler, *Amer. J. Psychiat.* 125 (1968): 386. Copyright © 1968, The American Psychiatric Association. Reprinted by permission.
684. From MARIJUANA AND YOUR CHILD by Jules Saltman. Copyright © 1970 by Jules Saltman. Used by permission of Grosset & Dunlap, Inc.
685. Harold Pascal, *The Marijuana Maze* (Canfield, Ohio: Alba House Communications, 1976), p. 18.
686. U.S., Congress, Senate, Committee On The Judiciary, *Marihuana-Hashish Epidemic And Its Impact On United States Security, Hearings Before The Subcommittee To Investigate The Administration Of The Internal Security Act And Other Internal Security Laws, Part 2.* 93 Cong., 2d sess., 1974, p. 443.
687. "Medical Counterpoint," January 1971, cited by Dr. Roy H. Hart, in *A Psychiatrist Looks At Medicine* (Hicksville, N.Y.: Exposition Press, Inc., 1972), p. 36.
688. Excerpt from "Marijuana: More Dangerous Than You Know" by Dr. Harvey Powelson, *The Readers Digest*, December 1974.
689. Gabriel G. Nahas, *Marihuana: Deceptive Weed* (New York: Raven Press, 1973), pp. 77-78.
690. U.S., Congress, Senate, Committee On The Judiciary, *Marihuana-Hashish Epidemic And Its Impact On United States Security, Hearings Before The Subcommittee To Investigate The Administration Of The Internal Security Act And Other Internal Security Laws*, Introduction by Senator James O. Eastland. 93 Cong., 2d sess., 1974, p.v.
691. Hardin B. Jones and Helen C. Jones, *Sensual Drugs* (Cambridge, England: Cambridge University Press, 1977), p. 267, citing U.S. National Commission on Marihuana and Drug Abuse, *Marihuana: A Signal of Misunderstanding* (Washington, D.C.: Government Printing Office, 1972).
692. Morton A Stenchever, "Observations on the Cytogenetic Effects of Marijuana," in *Marijuana and Health Hazards*, ed. Jared R. Tinklenberg (New York: Academic Press, Inc., 1975), pp. 28-29.
693. U.S., Congress, Senate, Committee On The Judiciary, *Marihuana-Hashish Epidemic And Its Impact On United States Security, Hearings Before The Subcommittee To Investigate The Administration Of The Internal Security Act And Other Internal Security Laws. Part 2.* 93 Cong., 2d sess., 1974, p. 436.
694. Gabriel G. Nahas, "Medical Aspects of Marihuana Use," Testimony before the U.S. House of Representatives Select Committee on Narcotics Abuse, March 16, 1977, pp. 27-28.
695. George K. Russell, "Critique of Dr. Norman E. Zinberg's Article on Marihuana in Psychology Today," [Written testimony submitted to the March 14-17, 1977 hearings of the House Select Committee on Narcotics Abuse (Rep. Lester L. Woff, Chairman)].
696. Max Rafferty, in *Drugs: For & Against*, Harold Hart, ed. (New York: Hart Publishing Company, Inc., 1970), pp. 37-38.
697. U.S., Congress, Senate, Committee On The Judiciary, *Marihuana-Hashish Epidemic And Its Impact On United States Security, Hearings Before The Subcommittee To Investigate The Administration Of The Internal Security Act And Other Internal Security Laws*, Introduction by Senator James O. Eastland. 93 Cong., 2d sess., 1974, p.v.
698. "New Data on Marijuana Points To Bad Effects," *Long Island, New York, Newsday*, 6 October 1974, p. 12.
699. Gabriel G. Nahas, *Keep Off The Grass* (New York: Reader's Digest Press, 1976), p. 87.
700. Gabriel G. Nahas, *Keep Off the Grass* (New York: Reader's Digest Press, 1976), p. 25.

701. William A. Rusher, "Current 'Pot' Debate Clouds Real Issue," *Human Events*, 9 December 1974, p. 12.
702. New York State Narcotic Addiction Control Commission, *The Attack on Narcotic Addiction and Drug Abuse*. (Winter 1970), p. 11.
703. U.S., Congress, Senate, Committee On The Judiciary, *Marihuana-Hashish Epidemic And Its Impact On United States Security: The Continuing Escalation, Hearings Before The Subcommittee To Investigate The Administration Of The Internal Security Act And Other Internal Security Laws. Part 2*. 94 Cong., 1st sess., 1975, p. VII.
704. "The Perils Of 'Pot' Start Showing Up," *U.S. News & World Report*, June 10, 1974, p. 58.
705. David V. Forrest et al., "Elimination of the reverse Heisenberg (HO) effect by closed circuit television," *American Journal of Psychiatry*, vol. 134, no. 1, p. 92. Copyright 1977, the American Psychiatric Association. Reprinted by permission.
706. Hardin B. Jones, "Problems Executives Must Anticipate With The Growth of Marijuana Smoking," *Executive Health* (P.O. Box 589, Rancho Santa Fe, California 92067), October, 1977.
707. Eric Pace, "Cardinal Cooke Urges Help, Not Jail, In Marijuana Cases," *The New York Times*, 28 May 1977. © 1977 by The New York Times Company. Reprinted by permission.
708. Kenneth McKenna, "Marijuana Kills," in *Marijuana Teenage Killer*, ed. Norman Hill (New York: Webster's Red Seal Publications, Inc., 1971), p. 18. Copyright © 1971 by Webster's Red Seal Publications, Inc.
709. Harold Pascal, *The Marijuana Maze* (Canfield, Ohio: Alba House Communications, 1976), p. 24.
710. E.R. Bloomquist, *Marijuana* (Beverly Hills: Glencoe Press, The Macmillan Company, 1968), p. 187. © Copyright, Edward R. Bloomquist, 1968.
711. Gabriel G. Nahas, *Keep Off The Grass* (New York: Reader's Digest Press, 1976), citing Foreword by Andre F. Cournand, p.x.
712. Madeline H. Engel, *The Drug Scene* (Rochelle Park, New Jersey: Hayden Book Company, Inc., 1974), pp. 35-36.
713. Robert L. Dupont, "Marihuana: Our Next Step," February 4, 1977, (Washington, D.C.: Psychiatric Institute Foundation), p. 17.
714. New Evidence on Marijuana," *The Phyllis Schlafly Report*, vol. 8, no. 10, section 1, May 1975, p. 1.
715. U.S., Congress, Senate, Committee On The Judiciary, *Marihuana-Hashish Epidemic And Its Impact On United States Security, Hearings Before The Subcommittee To Investigate The Administration Of The Internal Security Act And Other Internal Security Laws*, 93 Cong., 2d sess., 1974, p. 4.
716. I.R. Rosengard, "Marijuana," *Science Digest*, May 1972, p. 72.
717. Excerpt from "Marijuana: More Dangerous Than You Know" by Dr. Harvey Powelson, *The Readers Digest*, December 1974.
718. Robert L. Dupont, "Marihuana: Our Next Step," February 4, 1977, (Washington, D.C.: Psychiatric Institute Foundation), pp. 17-18.
719. Excerpt from THE SEEKERS by Jess Stearn. Copyright © 1968, 1969 by Jess Stearn. Used by permission of Doubleday & Company, Inc.
720. Gabriel G. Nahas, "Is Marijuana Really All That Bad," Selections from *Listen* (Washington, D.C.: Narcotics Education, Inc., 1977).
721. U.S., Congress, Senate, Committee On The Judiciary, *Marihuana-Hashish Epidemic And Its Impact On United States Security, Hearings Before The Sumbcommittee To Investigate The Administration Of The Internal Security Act And Other Internal Security Laws, Part. 2*. 93 Cong., 2d sess., 1974, p. 463.
722. Hardin B. Jones and Helen C. Jones, *Sensual Drugs* (Cambridge, England: Cambridge University Press, 1977), pp. 216-217.
723. U.S., Congress, Senate, Committee On The Judiciary, *Marihuana-Hashish Epidemic And Its Impact On United States Security, Hearings Before The Subcommittee To Investigate The Administration Of The Internal Security Act And Other Internal Security Laws*. 93 Cong., 2d sess., 1974, p. 186.
724. Gabriel G. Nahas, *Keep Off the Grass* (New York: Reader's Digest Press, 1976), p. 27.
725. U.S., Congress, Senate, Committee On The Judiciary, *Marihuana-Hashish Epidemic And Its Impact On United States Security, Hearings Before The Subcommittee To Investigate The Administration Of The Internal Security Act And Other Internal Security Laws*. 93 Cong., 2d sess., 1974, p. 235.
726. Nicholas A. Pace, "About the Damage Marijuana Can Do," Letters, *The New York Times*, 16 May 1977. © 1977 by The New York Times Company. Reprinted by permission.
727. U.S., Congress, Senate, Committee On The Judiciary, *Marihuana-Hashish Epidemic And Its Impact On United States Security: The Continuing Escalation, Hearings Before The Subcommittee To Investigate The Administration Of The Internal Secrity Act And Other Internal Security Laws. Part 2*. 94 Cong., 1st sess., 1975, p. V.
728. E.R. Bloomquist, *Marijuana* (Beverly Hills: Glencoe Press, The Macmillan Company, 1968), p. 107. © Copyright, Edward R. Bloomquist, 1968.
729. E.R. Bloomquist, *Marijuana* (Beverly Hills: Glencoe Press, The Macmillan Company, 1968), pp. 139-141. © Copyright, Edward R. Bloomquist, 1968.
730. U.S., Congress, Senate, Committee On The Judiciary, *Marihuana-Hashish Epidemic And Its Impact On United States Security, Hearings Before The Subcommittee To Investigate The Administration Of The Internal Security Act And Other Internal Security Laws, Part 2*. 93 Cong., 2d sess., 1974, p. 464.
731. Leo F. Hollister, "Human Pharmacology of Marihuana (Cannabis)," in *Drug Dependence* eds. Robert T. Harris, William M. McIsaac, and Charles R. Schuster, Jr. (Austin, Texas: UNIVERSITY OF Texas Press, 1970), p. 78. Copyright © 1970 by the University of Texas Press. All rights reserved.
732. E.R. Bloomquist, *Marijuana* (Beverly Hills: Glencoe Press, The Macmillan Company, 1968), pp. 134-135. © Copyright, Edward R. Bloomquist, 1968.
733. U.S., Congress, Senate, Committee On The Judiciary, *Marihuana-Hashish Epidemic And Its Impact On United States Security, Hearings Before The Subcommittee To Investigate The Administration Of The Internal Security Laws, Introduction by Senator James O. Eastland*. 93 Cong., 2d sess., 1974, pp. XII-XIII.
734. The Official Report Of The National Commission on Marihuana And drug Abuse, *Marihuana: A Signal of Misunderstanding*, with a foreword from Raymond P. Shafer, Chairman (New York: The New American Library, Inc., 1972), p. 88.
735. Excerpt from THE SEEKERS by Jess Stearn. Copyright © 1968, 1969 by Jess Stearn. Used by permission of Doubleday & Company, Inc.
736. Hardin B. Jones and Helen C. Jones, *Sensual Drugs* (Cambridge, England: Cambridge University Press, 1977), pp. 293-294.
737. Harold M. Schmeck, Jr., "Ford Aide Backs Marijuana Curbs," *The New York Times*, 20 November 1974. © 1974 by The New York Times Company. Reprinted by permission.
738. Michael P. Rosenthal, "Amelioration of Marihuana Laws," in *Drug Dependence* eds. Robert T. Harris, William M. McIsaac, and Charles R. Schuster, Jr. (Austin, Texas: University of Texas Press, 1970), p. 297. Copyright © 1970 by the University of Texas Press. All rights reserved.
739. Allen Geller and Maxwell Boas, *The Drug Beat* (Chicago: Cowles Book Company, Inc., 1969), p. 95.
740. Kenneth McKenna, "Marijuana Kills," in *Marijuana: Teenage Killer*, ed. Norman Hill (New York: Webster's Red Seal Publications, Inc., 1971), pp. 33-34. Copyright © 1971 by Webster's Red Seal Publications, Inc.
741. Madeline H. Engel, *The Drug Scene*. (Rochelle Park, New Jersey: Hayden Book Company, Inc., 1974), p. 30.
742. Kenneth McKenna, "Marijuana Kills," in *Marijuana: Teenage Killer*, ed. Norman Hill (New York: Webster's Red Seal Publications, Inc., 1971), p. 18. Copyright © 1971 by Webster's Red Seal Publications, Inc.
743. *The New York Times*, 16 May 1977, © 1977 by The New York Times Company. Reprinted by permission.

744. U.S., Congress, Senate, Committee On The Judiciary, *Marihuana-Hashish Epidemic And Its Impact On United States Security, Hearings Before The Subcommittee To Investigate The Administration Of The Internal Security Act And Other Internal Security Laws*. 93 Cong., 2d sess., 1974, p. 193.
745. "Donny & Marie Osmond Tell: Why We're Opposed to Pot," *The NATIONAL ENQUIRER*, p. 42.
746. Edward Bloomquist, in *Drugs: For & Against*, Harold Hart, ed. (New York: Hart Publishing Company, Inc., 1970), p. 161.
747. The Official Report Of The National Commission on Marihuana And Drug Abuse, *Marihuana: A Signal of Misunderstanding*, with a foreword from Raymond P. Shafer, Chairman (New York: The New American Library, Inc.: 1972), p. 80.
748. U.S., Congress, Senate, Committee On The Judiciary, *Marihuana-Hashish Epidemic And Its Impact On United States Security, Hearings Before The Subcommittee To Investigate The Administration Of The Internal Security Act And Other Internal Security Laws*, 93 Cong., 2d sess., 1974, p. 35.
749. Stanley F. Yolles, "Men, Money and Marihuana," paper presented at a joint meeting of the Queens County Medical Society and Queens County Psychiatric Society, Forest Hills, New York, 26 May 1970, pp. 19-20.
750. Gabriel G. Nahas, "Is Marijuana Really All That Bad," Selections from *Listen* (Washington, D.C.: Narcotics Education, Inc., 1977).
751. Rena Hamelfarb, "Undeniable Evidence of Danger and Damage," in *Marijuana: Teenage Killer*, ed. Norman Hill (New York: Webster's Red Seal Publications, Inc., 1971), pp. 69-70. Copyright © 1971 by Webster's Red Seal Publications, Inc.
752. Gabriel G. Nahas, *Keep Off The Grass* (New York: Reader's Digest Press, 1976), pp. 35-36.
753. Hardin B. Jones and Helen C. Jones, *Sensual Drugs* (Cambridge, England: Cambridge University Press, 1977), p. 287.
754. E.R. Bloomquist, *Marijuana* (Beverly Hills: Glencoe Press, The Macmillan Company, 1968), p. 205. © Copyright, Edward R. Bloomquist, 1968, citing P. Wolff, *Marihuana in Latin America: The Threat It Constitutes*.
755. E.R. Bloomquist, *Marijuana* (Beverly Hills: Glencoe Press, The Macmillan Company, 1968), p. 108. © Copyright, Edward R. Bloomquist, 1968.
756. U.S., Congress, Senate, Committee On The Judiciary, *Marihuana-Hashish Epidemic And Its Impact On United States Security, Hearings Before The Subcommittee To Investigate The Administration Of The Internal Security Act And Other Internal Security Laws*, Introduction by Senator James O. Eastland, 93 Cong., 2d sess., 1974, p. XVII.
757. Gabriel G. Nahas, *Keep Off the Grass* (New York: Reader's Digest Press, 1976), p. 4.
758. Dr. Peter Bourne, White House Special Assistant for Health Issues.